maternal behavior in

MAMMALS

maternal behavior in

MAMMALS

Harriet L. Rheingold, *editor, National Institute of Mental Health*

JOHN WILEY & SONS, INC., NEW YORK • LONDON

59.845

contributors

MARGARET ALTMANN
Department of Psychology
University of Colorado

VICTOR H. DENENBERG
Department of Psychology
Purdue University

IRVEN DEVORE
Center for Advanced Study
in the Behavorial Sciences
Stanford, California

ERNST W. HANSEN
Primate Laboratory
University of Wisconsin
(now at Institute of Animal)
Behavior, Rutgers University)

HARRY F. HARLOW
Primate Laboratory
University of Wisconsin

MARGARET K. HARLOW
Primate Laboratory
University of Wisconsin

LEONARD HERSHER
College of Medicine
State University of New York,
Syracuse

PHYLLIS JAY
Center for Advanced Study
in the Behavioral Sciences
Stanford, California

JOHN A. KING
Department of Zoology
Michigan State University

DANIEL S. LEHRMAN
Institute of Animal Behavior
Rutgers University

A. ULRIC MOORE

Behavior Farm Laboratory
Cornell University

HARRIET L. RHEINGOLD

Laboratory of Psychology
National Institute of
Mental Health

JULIUS B. RICHMOND

College of Medicine
State University of New York
Syracuse

JAY S. ROSENBLATT

Institute of Animal Behavior
Rutgers University

SHERMAN ROSS

American Psychological
Association
Washington, D. C.

PAUL B. SAWIN

Hamilton Station
Roscoe B. Jackson
Memorial Laboratory

T. C. SCHNEIRLA

Department of Animal Behavior
The American Museum of
Natural History

ETHEL TOBACH

College of Medicine
New York University

M. X. ZARROW

Department of Biological
Sciences
Purdue University

contents

vii

introduction

Harriet L. Rheingold

This book is a collection of studies on maternal behavior in infrahuman mammals. Each study is the current research report of an investigator of maternal behavior and thus the book provides a record of recent work and thought. The mammals range from mouse to baboon; the investigators come from the disciplines of genetics, physiology, psychology, zoology, anthropology, and medicine; and the methods of study differ, varying from naturalistic observation in the field to experimental manipulation in the laboratory. Different as the studies are, however, the main topic is behavior.

The study of maternal care in mammals has lagged behind the study of other kinds of social behavior. Less space is devoted to it in textbooks of comparative psychology than, for example, to dominant-subordinate relationships or to courting and mating. Until the last decade much of the work was limited to experimental studies of retrieving (for example, Wiesner and Sheard, 1933), nest building (Sturman-Hulbe and Stone, 1929) and grid crossing to the young (for example, Nissen, 1930; Warden, 1931) in the rat, and to narrative accounts of mother-infant behavior in the rhesus monkey (for example, Tinkle-

Geraldine C. Keene and Bruce Berman assisted me in my task as editor; their efforts are gratefully acknowledged.

1

paugh and Hartman, 1932) and chimpanzee (Yerkes and Tomilin, 1935). Life history accounts by zoologists, in contrast, have always included information on mother-young behavior (for example, Darling 1937; Murie 1944), although not in the detail to be found in such recent accounts as Bartholomew's (1952) on the northern elephant seal, Eibl-Eibesfeldt's (1953) on the hamster, and Koford's (1957) on the vicuña. Mention, too, must be made of the extensive literature of isolated observations in the *Journal of Mammalogy*, wildlife journals, and publications of natural history museums. Still, the last decade has seen an increasing amount of interest in the subject. Today, as this book attests, maternal behavior has become the major topic of a number of investigations.

Maternal behavior occupies a central position in the lives of the mother and offspring, in the social organization of the species, and in the preservation of the species. For the mother, parturition, an event of considerable biologic importance, signals maturity, and her behavior is profoundly modified by the presence of the young. For the offspring, the behavior of the mother is crucial not only for life itself but for its own subsequent adjustment to the environment into which it is born. In this environment other members of its species are prominent elements; the extent to which it has contact with them and the nature of this contact are mediated by the behavior of its caretaker. Furthermore, maternal behavior, intimately related to the state of maturity of the young at birth, constitutes a trait possessing adaptive value for the preservation of the species. It is, however, the effect of maternal behavior upon the behavior of the young which concerns most of the investigators in this book.

Maternal behavior during the animal's infancy may be viewed as the main source of environmental events affecting the behavior of the young. It is a source from which arises the major set of variables labeled early experience. Cutting across this set are such related variables as the sensory and motor capacities of the infant at birth and the number of siblings in the litter. There is not yet sufficient knowledge about the interaction of these variables to permit the statement of general principles. Still, it is possible to enumerate some of the factors in maternal behavior which may qualify as early experience variables.

The mother and her behavior determine in large part the physical and social environment of the young. To maternal behavior can be attributed the site where the young is born and lives, its movements away from the site, and hence the physical objects it will encounter.

To it also can be attributed the number and character of other members of the species present at the time of parturition and subsequently throughout infancy and childhood, of fathers, other males or females, juveniles, or other infants. Thus maternal behavior determines the nature of the social group into which the infant is born and the kinds of contact he has with its members.

Closely associated with the effect of maternal behavior upon the social experience of the young is the specificity of the mother-infant relationship. In some species, the relationship is close and enduring; in others, the relationship is less specific and adoption is frequent, as in many rodents (Kahmann and Frisch, 1952), or the rule, as in the bat (Davis, Herried, and Short, 1962). Specificity of a mother-infant relationship implies recognition of the one by the other and raises interesting questions about the stimuli upon which recognition is based. So far more attention has been directed toward maternal recognition of the young (for example, Beach and Jaynes, 1956) than toward infant recognition of the mother.

Maternal behavior may be viewed also as the chief agent in modifying the behavior of the young, that is, as the chief agent responsible for its learning. The mother by her response to the separate acts of the young may be said to shape its behavior, maintain the acts in its repertoire, or extinguish them. These acts may be directed to physical objects in the environment, to her, to littermates, or to other members of the group. No anthropomorphic intent to instruct need be invoked to demonstrate how maternal behavior can permit, increase, or prevent, for example, the infant's social experience with other members of the species, including his peers.

The variables constituting maternal behavior, then, warrant analysis as a source of environmental events which affect the behavior of the young and are thus capable of influencing his behavior as an adult, as a member of a social group, and as a member of a species.

Each in his own way, the investigators in this book have dealt with the variables comprising maternal care. Placed side by side their efforts can do more than inform; they can throw into relief similarities and differences in maternal behavior among different species. One sees also that in terms of maternal care no simple ordering of the mammals by species or families is possible. Even the broad division into precocial and altricial—terms first used to classify birds on the degree of maturity of the young at birth—breaks down; within one order, Rodentia, both forms may be found, the guinea pig being much more advanced at birth than the mouse or rat, and even within one family, Muridae, one species *(Acomys cahirinus)* may be precocial and the others not (Dieterlen, 1962). Apparent similarities must be judiciously weighed against differences before generalizations from one species to another can be made. How much more caution should be exercised before generalizing from genus to genus and from order to order!

It is hoped that still other advantages may result from bringing these studies together. New problems may be revealed when the questions raised by one investigator about the behavior of the animal he has studied are seen as appropriate for other animals. Questions not yet asked may occur to others. Methods of study also can be examined for their effectiveness, and work on new species may be stimulated. Many of our small native mammals, for example, await study. Their nocturnal habits, shyness, and hidden lairs present difficulties for the field observer, but new techniques for recording the subterranean movements of animals will prove helpful (for example, Johanningsmeier and Goodnight, 1962; Cochran and Lord, 1963).

These studies may also be useful in suggesting similarities and differences in maternal care between man and the other mammals. The study of animal behavior does not need to be justified by the knowledge it may yield about the behavior of man. Still, the study of infrahuman maternal behavior by its distance and contrasts can give greater objectivity to the study of human maternal behavior. The study of maternal care in man will be advanced when he is studied as one of the mammals.

Man's omission from this book is a considered decision. In one way, too much has been written about maternal care in man to find space here; in another way, too little lends itself to clear and definite statement. In particular, its pathological aberrations have received more attention than its normal manifestations. Furthermore, what is known about its normal course stems more from retrospective accounts and questionnaires than from observation, measurement, and experiment. Greater progress will be made when investigators pay less attention to what the human caretaker says he thinks and feels about his offspring and more attention to what he does in caring for the infant and child.

The most important consequence of this book may well be its contribution to the formulation of general principles about the genesis of social behavior, the formation of the family, and the organization of social groups. In Darling's words . . . "sociality has its roots in the physiological and psychological processes of reproduction" (1937, p. 69). Knowledge of the state of the organism at birth, the composition of the group into which he is born, his experiences with the members of that group, including his peers, offers the possibility of predicting the organism's later social behavior. A clear portrayal of how some of these variables function may be seen in the behavior of the moose and the elk (Altmann, Chapter 7), the moose mother and offspring forming a small unit living apart from others of its kind for a long period of time, the elk mother and offspring returning to the herd very soon after parturition.

The term "maternal behavior" has proved somewhat troublesome. Although in mammals it is the biologic mother that is most attentive to the young, "maternal" has been used in the title of this book in its generic sense and is not meant to exclude any other member of the species which has commerce with the young. Parental care, used by Kendeigh (1952) and Lehrman (1961) for birds, was considered as an alternative. But among mammals care is given the young not only by the mother and father but often by other members of the group, males as well as females, juveniles as well as adults. Then, under the conditions of many of the studies reported here, all but the mother and her offspring were excluded. Maternal care, a term so common that it has crept into this introduction, was rejected for the title because of its implications of solicitude for the needs of the offspring and its anthropomorphic overtones. Furthermore, it causes one to stumble over those activities of the caretaker which separate the young from her, her withdrawing from them and inflicting pain on them. Maternal behavior was chosen, then, to mean the behavior of the mother and her surrogates in the presence of the young.

Each contributor to this book has struggled, as must every student of maternal behavior, with the necessity of studying the behavior of two different organisms at once, the caretaker and the cared-for. (And sometimes the cared-for are a litter of twelve.) Not only does each stimulate the behavior of the other so that it is difficult to study the one without endlessly qualifying conclusions by reference to the other, but the young, increasing rapidly in size and activity, are continually contributing new stimuli to which the caretaker must respond. This difficulty, inherent in naturalistic observation, can be solved by experimental manipulation of the structure and behavior of a member of the pair, the mother or the young.

Once we focus on the young, we discover that they also contribute new ideas for the study of maternal behavior. The first is provided by the competence of the infrahuman mammalian infant, especially in contrast to the human infant. The infant rat, although blind and deaf, can crawl under its mother's body, position itself, locate a nipple, and suckle by itself; the newborn ungulate can walk in a matter of hours. Beyond this competence is a persistence of effort which insures the attention of the caretaker and even, as Harlow et al. (Chapter 8) show, makes mothers out of most unpromising material. A consideration of the means by which the young shape the behavior of the caretaker opens up new areas for investigation. Furthermore, the attractiveness of the young of many species to the other members of the group besides the mother must be reckoned with. Thus Rowell (1961) observed juvenile hamsters retrieving infant hamsters and Beniest-Noirot (1958) reported the presence of several "maternal" activities in virgin female, adult bachelor male, and immature mice. The response of adult langur monkeys (Jay, Chapter 9) and baboons (DeVore, Chapter 10) permits no doubt concerning the attractiveness of the infant. One might speculate that this attractiveness possesses biologic utility, guaranteeing that the young will be cared for. It may be as instructive to consider that at least some measure of maternal care, in the broad sense in which it is here conceived, may be classed as manipulatory responses to a small, interesting, active, and responsive object. Touching, licking, holding, carrying, grooming, and play easily fall into this class. And, since the young may sometimes be seen to avoid or protest these manipulations, even at the hand of the mother, the idea that some maternal behavior may satisfy the needs of the caretaker rather than of the cared-for can be entertained.

The purpose of this introduction has been to provide a setting for the research reports and not to anticipate their contents. Although much of it has been speculative, it should orient the reader to the nature and significance of the investigators' findings and, more generally, to the importance of maternal behavior as a subject for study.

References

Bartholomew, G. A., Jr. (1952), Reproductive and social behavior of the northern elephant seal. *Univ. Calif. Publ. Zoöl.,* **47** (15), 369–472.

Beach, F. A., and J. Jaynes (1956), Studies of maternal retrieving in rats. I: Recognition of young. *J. Mammal.,* **37**, 177–180.

Beniest-Noirot, Eliane (1958), Analyse du comportement dit maternel chez la souris. *Monographies Françaises de Psychologie,* I, Paris: Centre National de la Recherche Scientifique.

Cochran, W. W., and R. D. Lord, Jr. (1963), A radio-tracking system for wild animals. *J. Wildlife Mgmt.,* **27**, 9–24.

Darling, F. F. (1937), *A Herd of Red Deer,* London: Oxford University Press.

Davis, R. B., C. F. Herreid II, and H. L. Short (1962), Mexican free-tailed bats in Texas. *Ecol. Monogr.,* **32**, 311–346.

Dieterlen, F. (1962), Geburt und Geburtshilfe bei der Stachelmaus, *Acomys cahirinus*. Z. *Tierpsychol.*, **19**, 191–222.

Eibl-Eibesfeldt, I. (1953), Zur Ethologie des Hamsters (*Cricetus cricetus L.*). Z. *Tierpsychol.*, **10** (2) 204–254.

Johanningsmeier, A. G., and C. J. Goodnight (1962), Use of iodine-131 to measure movements of small animals. *Science*, **138**, 147–148.

Kahmann, H., and O. v. Frisch (1952), Über die Beziehungen von Muttertier und Nestling bei kleinen Saügetiern. *Experientia*, **8**, 221–223.

Kendeigh, S. C. (1952), Parental care and its evolution in birds, *Illinois biol. Monogr.*, **22**, Nos. 1–3.

Koford, C. B. (1957), The vicuña and the puma. *Ecol. Monogr.*, **27**, 153–219.

Lehrman, D. S. (1961), Hormonal regulation of parental behavior in birds and infrahuman mammals. In W. C. Young (Ed.), *Sex and Internal Secretions*, 3rd ed., Baltimore: Williams and Wilkins. Pp. 1268–1382.

Murie, A. (1944), *The Wolves of Mount McKinley*, Washington: United States Government Printing Office, (Fauna of the National Parks of the United States, Fauna Series No. 5).

Nissen, H. W. (1930), A study of maternal behavior in the white rat by means of the obstruction method. *J. genet. Psychol.*, **37**, 377–393.

Rowell, Thelma E. (1961), Maternal behaviour in non-maternal Golden hamsters (*Mesocricetus auratus*). *Animal Behaviour*, **9**, 11–15.

Sturman-Hulbe, Mary, and C. P. Stone (1929), Maternal behavior in the albino rat. *J. comp. Psychol.*, **9**, 203–237.

Tinklepaugh, O. L., and C. G. Hartman (1932), Behavior and maternal care of the newborn monkey (*Macaca mulatta—*"M. rhesus"). *J. genet. Psychol.*, **40**, 257–286.

Warden, C. J. (1931), *Animal Motivation: Experimental Studies on the Albino Rat*, New York: Columbia University Press.

Wiesner B. P., and Norah M. Sheard (1933), *Maternal Behaviour in the Rat*, Edinburgh: Oliver and Boyd.

Yerkes, R. M., and M. I. Tomilin (1935), Mother-infant relations in chimpanzee. *J. comp. Psychol.*, **20**, 321–359.

Introduction   7

1

maternal behavior of the
LABORATORY RAT

Jay S. Rosenblatt and Daniel S. Lehrman

Maternal behavior is, for many reasons, a particularly interesting aspect of the naturally occurring social behavior of an animal species. It occurs cyclically, when the animal is in a particular physiological condition, thus posing many problems concerning the physiological regulation of behavior. It is different in different species, thus posing various problems of the relationships between genetic species differences and species differences in behavior. It constantly changes in ways which are correlated with changes in the needs of the developing young, thus posing problems of the regulation of developmental changes in behavior. It occurs in primiparous as well as in experienced animals, thus posing problems related to the ontogeny of "unlearned" behavior patterns.

Despite the fact that the rat is the animal most widely used in laboratories of experimental psychology, there is relatively little information available on various aspects of the normal social behavior of this species, including its maternal behavior. Maternal behavior has been

The preparation of this paper was assisted by Research Grant MH-03398 to JSR and by Research Center Award MH-K6-16621 to DSL, both from the National Institute of Mental Health. We gratefully acknowledge the assistance of Mrs. Lorraine Roth, Mrs. Pearl Knobe Weinstein, and Mr. Carl Erickson in the collection of the data.

shown to be a major behavioral pattern of the mature female, occurring regularly four or five times a year in a colony functioning under optimal ecological conditions. Sociopsychological conditions in a colony strongly influence the reproductive physiology of the female and the organization of maternal behavior. Crowding of individuals of a colony and the consequent increase in the nature and frequency of antagonistic contacts between the animals sharply reduce the ability of females to carry young to term and to care for those that are delivered (Calhoun, 1962). Thus some information is available about the social and ecological setting of rat behavior, but since the pioneering work of Sturman-Hulbe and Stone (1929) and Wiesner and Sheard (1933), little progress has been made toward an understanding of the organization of the maternal behavior of the rat, and of its biological basis (Eibl-Eibesfeldt, 1958; Munn, 1950).

Our approach to the analysis of the problems of maternal behavior is a developmental one. The processes underlying the organization of the behavior of an animal at any developmental age, or at any stage of a cyclically-varying pattern, appear to us to be best illuminated by analyzing the ways in which that age (or stage) has arisen from preceding ones, and the ways in which that age (or stage) influences or gives rise to succeeding ones. The relationships among those processes and influences which persist through several stages, those continuous through the life of the animal, and those specific to different stages, are often complex. Their analysis involves the simultaneous consideration of events at different biological and psychological levels. These may include physiological events which are themselves organized at different levels (for example, central nervous regulation, local sensitivities and reactions, regulation of endocrine secretion, specific effects of hormones, and so on), and psychological processes of varying complexity, ranging from reactions to simple forms of stimulation to behavior patterns characterizing interindividual (that is, social) situations (Schneirla, 1949).

A number of patterns of animal behavior has been investigated and discussed in ways which reveal the extent to which the consideration of developmental changes facilitates insight into the structure and dynamics of a pattern. Some examples are: cyclic variation in army-ant colony behavior (Schneirla, 1938); development of mammalian sexual behavior (Rosenblatt and Aronson, 1958a; Rosenblatt and Aronson, 1958b; Young, 1961; Young, 1962); reproductive behavior cycles in birds (Hinde, 1962; Lehrman, 1959; Lehrman, 1961); suckling in kittens (Rosenblatt, Turkewitz, and Schneirla, 1962).

Even when a behavior pattern does not vary cyclically in the life of the animal or when it is not practicable to analyze its early ontogeny, detailed consideration of the pattern of events and interactions giving rise to the behavior provides a developmental conception of its origin and course during each occurrence. A good example is the particularly vivid impression of the dynamics of the regulation of a feeding episode in the blowfly which is provided by the work of Dethier (1962).

The purpose of this chapter is to describe the maternal behavior of the laboratory rat, and to discuss various aspects of this behavior which are now under investigation in our laboratory. We shall first describe the pattern of maternal behavior in relation to the behavioral development of the young; following this, we shall summarize a number of experimental studies of the regulation of this behavior; finally, we shall discuss the problem of physiological control of maternal behavior and the prospects for future research.

Development of maternal behavior

BEHAVIOR BEFORE PARTURITION

The most noticeable behavioral changes occurring during pregnancy are in the self-licking behavior of the female. The following summary of these changes is based upon observations made by Mrs. Lorraine Roth in our laboratory.

Self licking in the nonpregnant female. Nonpregnant females, and pregnant females near the beginning of pregnancy, lick the fur on the various parts of their bodies in an order that is fairly predictable. Such an animal normally starts a licking episode by alternately licking her forepaws and brushing them over her head and face. After a number of such "washing" actions, she begins to lick the anterior regions of her fur, starting first at one shoulder and the upper back on that side; she then shifts to the other shoulder and works her way around to the back again. Leaving this region, she rapidly licks along one side of her body, including the nipple line of that side, as she moves her nose toward the genital area. When she reaches this area, she licks the ano-genital region and the entire ventral pelvic area between her hind legs. The female usually spends less time licking this general region of her body than other body regions, but by the end of a licking episode she has cleaned the entire anogenital area, a short length of her tail and its base, her hind legs and the lower abdominal region. Finally she completes the cleaning episode by licking her forepaws once again.

Changes in self licking during pregnancy. The female's pattern of self licking gradually changes during the last week of pregnancy. We have studied the change in licking behavior by observing 17 pregnant females in their last 9 days of pregnancy and, for purposes of comparison, 12 nonpregnant estrous cycling females for an identical period. The animals were observed for 30 minutes each day, at times randomly distributed over the night phase of the diurnal light cycle. The occurrence, duration, and sequences of the various items of licking behavior were recorded on an Esterline-Angus 20-pen process recorder, the pens of which were activated by the keys of a 20-key Aronson keyboard (Clark, Aronson, and Gordon, 1954).

Figure 1 shows the mean amount of time spent licking each of five regions of the female's body during the observation sessions on the last 9 days of pregnancy. (The ordinates of Figs. 1 and 2 are based on 3-day moving averages.)

It will be seen that the amount of licking of the pelvic region, the nipple line, and the genital area grew gradually during the week before parturition, whereas the licking of the forepaws and sides declined substantially during the same period.

The shift in distribution of licking on the body surface is displayed more clearly in Fig. 2, where the total amount of time per observation session spent licking three "critical body regions" (pelvic region, nipple line, and anogenital area) is shown for pregnant and for nonpregnant females (upper graph), and compared with the licking of three non-critical body regions (forepaws, back, and sides) by the same animals (lower graph). These graphs make it clear that the amount of time spent by the pregnant female in licking those body areas, in which substantial changes occur during pregnancy, increases drastically during the week preceding parturition, and the licking of other areas decreases equally strikingly, whereas the distribution of licking by nonpregnant animals shows little or no change.

Although the preparturient rat concentrates her licking more and more on the pelvic, mammary, and anogenital region as parturition approaches, there is no change in the general arrangement of events during a licking episode; she continues to start licking at the anterior end of her body, progressing gradually to the posterior end. This changes sharply at the beginning of parturition. At each wave of abdominal contraction, the female turns immediately to her anogenital region and licks it directly without passing through the usual anterior-posterior sequence of body licking. As parturition advances, the genital

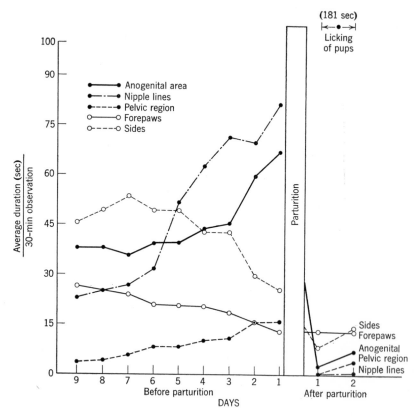

FIG. 1. *Self licking from midpregnancy to 2 days postpartum. Each curve represents the number of seconds of licking (per 30-minute observation period) devoted to each of the body regions. (N = 17.)*

region increasingly becomes the principal site of licking activity, involving first the fur around the vaginal orifice, wetted by birth fluids, then the protruding birth membranes, and eventually the fetus.

It is clear that parturition marks the culmination of organic changes underlying the shift in licking behavior during the last week of pregnancy.

The presence of the pups at the end of parturition, and the changed physiological status of the mother as a result of parturition, represent a new situation; the licking behavior of the female at this time reflects the changes brought about by the recently completed events at birth. Figures 1 and 2 show that the amount of self-licking activity declines dramatically immediately after the postpartum cleaning of the mother's fur. This overall reduction in licking reflects a decline in the amount of licking of every area of the body, except the forepaws, the licking of which is associated with the mother's licking of her young, to which we now turn our attention.

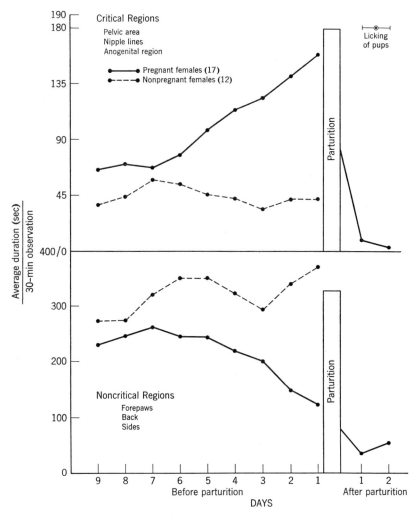

FIG. 2. *Comparison of changes in distribution of self licking in pregnant females, and in nonpregnant (control) females observed for an equivalent period. The curves are smoothed by using 3-day moving averages; each point represents the mean of the score for that day, the preceding day, and the following day (if any).*

Maternal Behavior of the Laboratory Rat   13

After parturition, most of the mother's licking behavior is directed to her newborn young. The female licks the pups in the nest before and during nursing, after retrieving them, and at frequent intervals at other times; only after licking the pups does the female turn to her own body and lick it briefly. In our observations, she typically licked the pups while rotating them with her forepaws, usually in such a way as to bring the pup's anogenital area under her tongue. Licking of this area stimulates urination and defecation by the pup, functions which they are at first unable to perform independently. Most of the mother's licking activity becomes concentrated on the pup's lower abdominal region (including the anogenital area). Figure 3 shows the average amount of time spent by the mother, per observation session during the first two days postpartum, in licking each of the main regions of the pup's body, arranged on this graph from anterior to posterior. The dominance of maternal licking of the genitalia and lower abdomen is obvious.

In summary, the self-licking behavior of the pregnant female rat

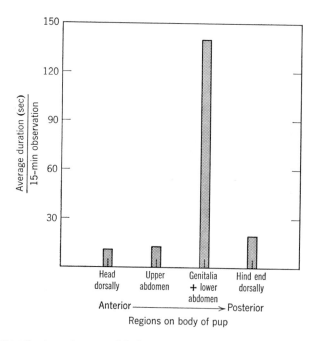

FIG. 3. *Distribution of maternal licking among the various regions of the pup's body on the first 2 days after birth. The ordinate is mean seconds of licking per 15-minute observation session. (N = 14.)*

gradually becomes concentrated on those tissues which are most directly involved in her pregnancy, and which change most strikingly during the period before parturition. This change gradually concentrates her licking behavior in the genital region. This region, and the emerging young, become an even sharper focus of licking activity at the time of parturition; after the postparturitional cleaning of her fur, the licking behavior of the mother becomes concentrated on the young, and particularly on their lower abdominal and anogenital regions.

PARTURITION

The first signs of impending parturition are seen in the female's growing lethargy and in her markedly reduced responsiveness to the cage surroundings, starting around the 19th day of pregnancy. During the 3 to 4 days that remain before parturition, she spends an increasing amount of time in one corner of the cage. At this site, the female builds a small mat of hay, pulling nest material to her body from nearby; the nestlike structure serves as a resting place until parturition. The corner serves both as the site of parturition, where the female delivers her young and where parturition fluids are spread, and as the site of the litter nest where the young are later gathered and nursed (see Fig. 5).

The events of parturition in the rat follow a pattern very similar to that described and analyzed for the cat by Schneirla, Rosenblatt, and Tobach (Chapter 4). The sequence of behavioral items in the rat is roughly similar to that described in the cat; moreover, the relation of parturitive behavior to stimuli arising from the organic processes of delivery (for example, abdominal contractions) and from the products of birth (for example, birth fluids, fetuses) is similar in both species.

The birth of a single rat fetus may be divided into four phases. These phases are, in the order of events from the beginning of the birth of one pup to the start of the birth of a second pup, the *contraction* phase, the *delivery* phase, the *post-delivery* phase, and the *interval between deliveries*. The phases are characterized by different behavior of the female in response to the sequence in stimuli arising from the organic events of delivery and the products of delivery.

Birth begins with the onset of periodic waves of weak contractions of the abdominal muscle layer, starting at the female's shoulders and moving posteriorly along her body. Accompanying these contractions are a series of peristaltic waves, representing contractions of the uterine horns, which may be seen midbody. This is the *contraction phase* of birth, during which the female characteristically lies in the nest with

Maternal Behavior of the Laboratory Rat   15

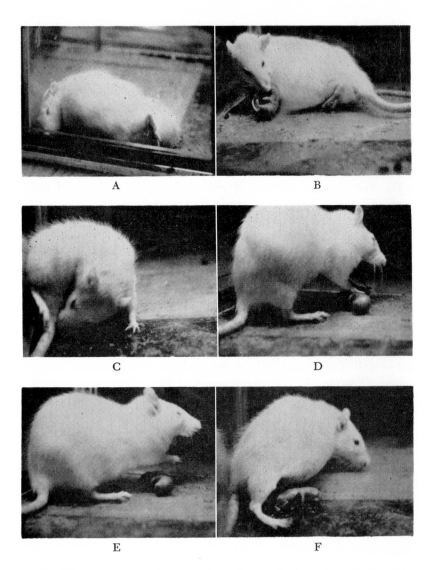

A   B

C   D

E   F

her hind legs stretched backwards and raised, the soles visible (Fig. 4A); her body is pressed against the floor while her head and forelegs may be drawn against her body, or sometimes extended forward.

Gradually, in the hour before delivery of the first fetus, the interval between spasms shortens and the contractions become more forceful. These events mark the beginning of the second phase of birth, the *delivery phase*. The female rises from the nest and begins actively to

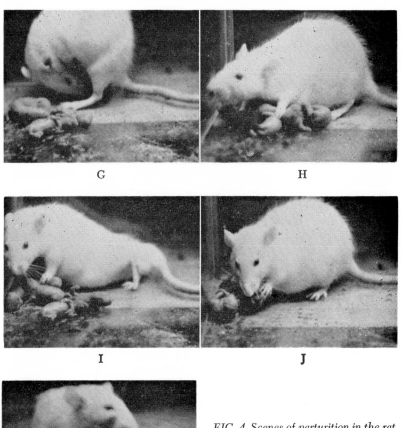

G   H

I   J

FIG. 4. Scenes of parturition in the rat. A female is shown performing the various acts of delivery and care of newly born pups in each of the phases of parturition.

K

assist in expulsion of the fetus by stretching her body full length, arching her back downward and pushing her hind legs against the floor, while contracting the lower part of her body (Fig. 4B, H, I). Often her mouth is opened as though yawning, and her head and neck are extended forward. Both movements are expressive of the effort she is exerting in expulsion of the fetus. Passage of the fetus into the lower birth canal is presumably facilitated when the female pushes her body forward with her forelegs, shifts her weight anteriorly, flattens her belly against the floor and drags her body and raised hind legs forward.

As the fetus enters the lower birth canal and begins to emerge through the vaginal orifice, stretching movements are abruptly interrupted by the female. She rapidly assumes a "head between the heels position" (Fig. 4C, G) sitting with her weight resting on her lower back, to one side, with her hind legs spread widely, thus expanding the size of the vaginal orifice. With her mouth at the opening of the birth canal, she pulls at tufts of hair, bites, and licks the region of the opening, thus widening it further, and at the same time she begins to lick the slightly protruding fetal membranes. The fetal membranes are often broken by the female in the course of her licking and birth fluids then spread over the female's genital area, hindlegs, mouth and forepaws, and on the floor of the nest site. The fetus emerges shortly afterward, expelled by a final series of forceful contractions, aided by the female, who grasps the fetus in her mouth and pulls it forward (Fig. 4G). The female usually assumes this sitting position during expulsion of the first fetus. During subsequent deliveries, the stretching movement of the female and the birth contractions are evidently sufficient, perhaps as a result of the previous widening of the vaginal opening, to expel the fetus and placenta without a period during which the fetus becomes lodged in the lower birth canal. In these instances the female sits *after* the fetus is expelled. Such a situation is shown in Fig. 4I, where the 6th fetus is about to be delivered by the female who is in a characteristic stretch posture. Should a female encounter difficulty in delivering a fetus, as indicated by a prolonged contraction phase, then the sitting position is often seen at the delivery of the second or later fetuses.

The appearance of the fetus, followed usually within a few seconds by the expulsion of the placenta, marks the beginning of the *post-delivery phase* of birth. The female pulls the fetus forward from the vaginal opening between her hind legs using her mouth and forepaws, meanwhile licking and rotating it as she assumes a crouching posture (Fig. 4G). Then she turns to the placenta that has trailed after the fetus and begins to lick and eat it. The placenta is lifted in her forepaws (Fig. 4D, E) and chewed. In the process of chewing the placenta, the female places her forepaws on the pup to hold it in position as she stretches the umbilical cord into a thin thread which she proceeds to chew after the placenta has been consumed. The fetus is often seen dangling from the female's mouth as the last strand of the cord is ingested and before the cord is severed by chewing.

The female now turns her attention to the pup and with rapid sweeps of her tongue over its body surface she tears the closely adhering thin membrane. The pup is freed to move its limbs, tearing the membrane further, but the female completes the cleaning of the pup by deftly grasping an edge of the membrane and pulling it until it is separated from the pup, after which she consumes the membrane. A period of vigorous licking follows, during which the female at first licks the newly born pup's head, body, and limbs; gradually her licking is concentrated at the pup's anogenital region, for licking this area stimulates the pup to urinate and defecate. This area becomes for the female at this time, and in the subsequent days, an area of special attractiveness (see Fig. 3).

After the pup is cleaned, the female turns her attention to licking regions of her own body and objects in the vicinity where birth fluids were spread during delivery, for example, nest material and the previously born young (Fig. 4F, J, K). These activities initiate the *interval between births*. This phase is often brief or absent. Abdominal contractions, signalling the beginning of birth of the next pup, often begin again shortly after delivery. When the start of the next birth is delayed, the female licks the fetuses from previous births, retrieves pups to her by stretching herself toward them and lifting them into the nest, gathers nest material into a nest and grooms herself for long periods during which she licks all areas that have been in contact with the birth fluids. She rests in the nest at times with her pups close by, and it is during this interval that the pups begin to crawl to her body and nuzzle in the mammary regions. Nursing rarely occurs in this interval, however, as the female is soon involved in the birth of the next fetus.

Following the last birth, the *interval between births* is in effect a prolonged period that passes gradually into the period of maternal care proper. Parturitive activities continue for a while after the last delivery before the female settles to rest in the nest with her pups. She continues to lick the newborn with head and tongue motions that sweep over the entire litter. She retrieves pups that have strayed from the nest. She begins to repair the nest, carrying to it the material she scattered by her movements during parturition and adding any material that she finds in the vicinity of the nest site. When the nest is completed the female enters it and lies with her pups. During this rest period, the newborn pups have the first opportunity to begin suckling from the female.

The female's behavior during parturition is centered on the processes of delivery and the products of birth, namely, the fetuses, placenta, and birth fluids, but many elements of maternal behavior, seen later during the period of lactation, make their first appearance during parturition. Retrieving and licking of the young, and many features of nursing behavior, now appear for the first time.

Above all, the parturition serves as the occasion of the first contact between the mother and her young, and this occurs under highly favorable conditions for the establishment of a behavioral bond between them.

GROWTH, MAINTENANCE, AND DECLINE OF MATERNAL BEHAVIOR

The mother's behavior toward her young throughout the suckling period and in the period of weaning is closely adjusted to the behavioral capacities of the young at the different stages of their physical development.

The neonates' urgent need for food, warmth, and sheltering is matched by the rapid appearance in the immediately postpartum female of nursing, retrieving, and nest-building behavior. Most behavioral capacities of the neonate are as yet undeveloped and limited to simple sensorimotor coordination. The mother must therefore play the most active role in the interactions between mother and young. Feeding of the young begins by the end of the first hour, principally through the initiative of the female, although the suckling young are also active. Even before the onset of nursing, the female rebuilds the scattered parturition nest into a compact litter nest which assures warmth and provides protection for the litter. Shortly afterwards she retrieves the pups that may have been scattered during the terminal phase of parturition and gathers them together under her body.

Routine maternal care is established before the end of the first week. During this period, the young continue to be mainly passive. Their suckling activities do exert a significant effect on the female, but their effect on her behavior is mainly through the attractive olfactory, gustatory, and tactual stimulation which they offer.

The contribution of the pups to the character of the mother-young relationship gradually increases toward the end of the second week as they gradually improve in thermoregulation, and as their locomotor abilities and perceptual capacities rapidly develop. These developments enable the young to make more varied and individual behavioral adjustments to the female and to littermates, and to a widening range of stimuli in the cage environment. Consequently, the relationship between mother and young gradually changes in various ways; these changes can be seen in the changing pattern of nursing, retrieving, and nest-building behavior of the female. In the following sections these developments will be traced from the early suckling period through the period of weaning, with a view to understanding the behavioral adjustments which the female makes to changes in the behavior of the young. This will provide a background for interpreting the results of our studies in which the relationship between mother and young was experimentally altered in comparison to the situation that normally obtains in the litter.

Nursing-suckling development. The nursing-suckling relation between mother and young may be divided as in the cat (Rosenblatt, Turkewitz, and Schneirla, 1962) into three developmental phases, according to the nature of the behavioral interaction by which feeding is initiated in the litter. In the first, or neonatal, phase the female plays a major role in initiating a feeding by approaching the young in the nest. She picks them up, licks them and in various ways stimulates them to activity while hovering over them with her mammary region easily available for nipple attachment. Upon arousal, the young begin to nuzzle in the female's fur, and after locating a nipple, they grasp with the mouth and suck.

In this phase of the feeding relation, which gradually comes to an end at the 12th to 14th day, the pups show substantial improvement both in their readiness to react to the approach of the female, by crawling to her for feeding, and in their ability to locate a nipple, attach to it, and suck.

The second phase of the mother-young feeding relationship begins with the appearance of short excursions outside the nest by individual pups. In the course of these excursions, which carry the pup further and further from the nest, usually along one or another wall of the cage, the pup frequently encounters the female and on these occasions feeding may be initiated at a distance from the nest, apart from the main body of the litter. The female facilitates nipple attachment by remaining in place as the pup crawls to her and by making her mammary regions available as the pup begins to nuzzle in her fur. She remains in nursing position throughout the suckling of the pup; frequently a second pup that has wandered from the nest may join the first in nursing. As the young improve in their locomotory ability and widen their perceptual orientation in the cage, they increasingly leave the nest and this mode of initiating feeding gradually replaces that of the previous period.

The third phase of the feeding relationship is more variable in duration than the preceding two phases. It starts around the 16th day and continues until the completion of weaning in the 3rd or 4th week after parturition. Toward the end of the 3rd week suckling declines as the pups begin to take food from other sources. The availability of food thus partly determines the rate at which weaning of the young proceeds and independent feeding develops.

Feeding is initiated almost entirely by the young during the third phase of nursing-suckling behavior. They follow the female as she wanders about the cage, crouch under her and nuzzle at her mammary region. At times when she remains still for a moment, the pups attach and suckle. Under these circumstances the female may permit the young to suck for a brief period while she remains standing, or she may lie down and nurse the young for a longer period. On the other hand, as weaning proceeds, the female more and more frequently evades the feeding approaches of the young by turning away from the pups when they approach her or by lowering her body and pressing her mammary region against the floor, or by standing against a wall with her nipple region out of the reach of the pups. In any case the efforts of the young to suckle fail as access to the mammary region is prevented by these actions of the female. The young turn to other sources of food in the vicinity.

Retrieving behavior. Retrieving arises at parturition and declines between the 12th and 16th day after parturition. The first reactions appear in the interval between deliveries when the female picks up and carries to the general zone of parturition the newly born fetuses that rolled to, or were delivered at, a distance from it. At the end of parturition the pups are gathered together in the nest, largely through the retrieving activity of the female.

After parturition, retrieving appears regularly in response to the general stimulus of a pup located outside the nest. However, a female's attachment to the nest site is an important condition for the appearance of retrieving reactions. This becomes evident when the female's attachment to the nest is disturbed as a result of changes in ecological conditions surrounding the nest: increases in either temperature or light; disturbance due to air currents; disturbance as a result of crowded social conditions which fail to provide the seclusion necessary for the female's stable attachment to a nest. The female abandons her nest and establishes a new nest site when the surrounding ecological conditions are disturbing to her. Under these circumstances pups are retrieved from the old to the new nest. Where a female cannot establish and maintain a stable nest site, carrying of pups is often stimulated in excess but the female fails to deposit her young at any one nest site. The young are therefore deposited at many different places, to their detriment, for often they are left to die there without the benefits of maternal care.

Starting from its appearance at parturition, the female's retrieving behavior gradually changes until it declines and disappears, to reappear with the advent of a new litter. The characteristics of the young play an important part in the mother's retrieving behavior. Changes in the young are closely related to the development, and the eventual disappearance, of this behavior.

For a short time after parturition females readily retrieve to the nest a wide variety of objects having stimulus characteristics that vary greatly from the olfactory, visual, thermal, and tactual properties of newly born young. They retrieve, for example, a recently weaned pup, alien to the female, that is covered with white fur, has a different odor from that of newborn, and moves rapidly about the cage. After a few days, a pup of this age is more likely to be attacked or ignored by the same females.

Before the end of the first week, however, the retrieving behavior of the mother occurs in response to more specific characteristics of the young pups. For example, mothers become able to discriminate their own young from alien pups of the same age on the basis of olfactory stimuli alone. They start retrieving their own young in a shorter time than they do alien pups; when presented with their own as well as alien young, they usually retrieve their own pups before starting to retrieve alien pups (Beach and Jaynes, 1956a; 1956b; 1956c).

Retrieving improves rapidly during the first four days as the female gains practice. She initiates retrieving more promptly, and resumes it more quickly after depositing a pup in the nest. Her ability to locate a pup that has strayed from the nest improves, and she thus takes a more direct route from the nest to the pup and back again.

By the end of the second week, the situation in the litter has changed considerably, primarily because of the behavioral development of the pups. They no longer huddle together as a litter in the nest; they begin to crawl out of the nest, and their excursions often carry them to distant regions of the cage where they remain for long periods. At these places, their behavioral interactions with the female are more varied than previously. Upon the approach of the female, the pup becomes active and often the behavior of the pup engages the female in an interchange such as nursing, which precludes the appearance of retrieving. The pup sometimes crawls back to the nest at the approach of the female, but just as often it may evade the retrieving efforts of the female and crawl away from the nest.

The developmental changes in the young therefore have two kinds of effect, which partially merge with each other. Not only do the pups present new patterns of stimuli to the female, but their own changing behavioral capacities alter the interactions between them and their mother. At first, the young are immobile and capable only of simple responses to the female; she thus reacts mainly to those stimulus properties of her young which are independent of their behavior. After the second week, encounters between the female and her young are increasingly of a social nature, in which the variety of social responses of the young toward the female call forth a correspondingly wide range of social behavior on her part, directed toward the pups. Under these conditions retrieving responses rapidly decline as an important component of maternal behavior.

Nest-building behavior. Nest-building behavior, resulting in an organized nest, arises shortly before parturition and continues for the first 2 weeks of litter care, then declines and disappears. Before the appearance of the first nest the female displays nest-building activity sporadically for short periods, carrying nest material to first one and then another region of the cage. She does not produce a recognizable nest until 2 or 3 days before parturition, when she gradually becomes more lethargic and immobile. She begins to spend most of her time resting in one corner of the cage, and it is in this corner that she builds her first nest.

The female constructs the first nest around her body by reaching out with her mouth and pulling nest material from the vicinity of the nest site against her body. The resulting nest resembles a mat, similar to that which is often constructed by nonpregnant females and by pregnant females in the early period of pregnancy. This method of constructing a nest continues to be the chief nest-building behavior during parturition. The nest thus produced is quite different in appearance from that which the female builds after the young are born. Although this preparturition nest is almost invariably located in a corner of the cage (as is what we shall call the "litter nest"), it usually has only low walls or none at all. In addition the nest is without an inner clearing; in its place is a thin mat of nest material (Fig. 5). Because it is constructed from inside, the outer shape of the nest is highly variable.

Parturition takes place at the preparturition nest site and this site serves too as the place where the female gathers her young after parturition and where she eventually builds the litter nest. Starting at its birth, the litter serves to focus the female's nest-building activity at the nest site, much as her own body provided a focus for her preparturition nest-building activity.

The postpartum female builds a nest by carrying and pushing nest material to the nest site, using methods that vary according to the nature of the available nest material (Eibl-Eibesfeldt, 1955; Sturman-Hulbe and Stone, 1929). As a pile of nest material accumulates at the nest site, covering the litter almost completely, the female spends less time carrying nest material to the nest and more time at the nest working on the nest material to shape it from the outside. At intervals the female tunnels into the nest and there she forms the inner enclosure into a dome-shaped structure. The tunnel used by the female to gain entrance into the nest is usually located along one wall of the nest site. It serves as a route for entering the nest with a minimum of disturbance to its structure.

Nest-building behavior and the form of the nest undergo little change during the first week as the pups continue to huddle together as a litter at the nest site (Fig. 5). The shape of the nest begins to change toward the middle of the second week as the litter increases in weight and in size and as the pups become more active within the nest (Fig. 5). The area of the inner enclosure widens from day to day, the walls of the nest are reduced in height, and are formed by a ridge of nest material that stretches in an arc from one side wall to the neighboring wall of the cage corner. The female confines her nest-building activity to adding nest material to the periphery of the nest, thereby marking the nest site as an area different from the remainder of the cage.

By the end of the second or the beginning of the third week, the original nest site is barely distinguishable from the other areas of the cage as a clearing on the floor of the cage in which several pups may be seen huddling together (Fig. 5). In the main, however, the single nest site has disappeared and several clearings may be seen occupied by small groups of young. The female may occasionally be seen carrying nesting material, but she is likely to push or toss the material to the center of the cage while clearing a path for walking or an area for resting.

Throughout the period of nest building a close correspondence exists between the behavior of the pups, as a litter, and the nest-building behavior of the female. While the pups remain huddling at the nest site the female constructs a compact nest around them. As they develop in size and become more active, the nest constructed by the female

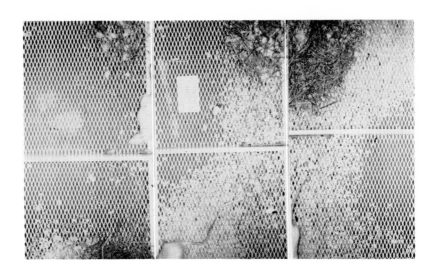

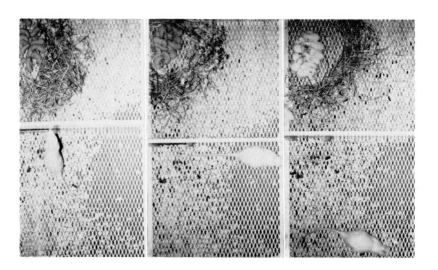

FIG. 5. The appearance of a typical nest one day before parturition and at intervals after parturition. The nest was destroyed and nest-building tests were carried

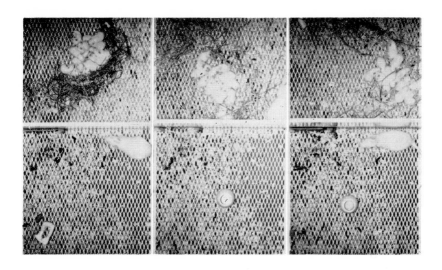

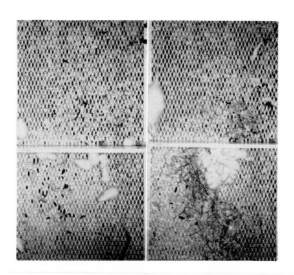

out each day. A shift in the nest site from the upper right to the upper left corner occurred between the 1st and the 4th day.

Maternal Behavior of the Laboratory Rat   27

changes accordingly. When the young become capable of wandering throughout the cage, their attachment to the nest site weakens and they no longer huddle together as a litter at the nest site. Instead they form small huddling groups that settle at temporary sites and remain together only for a brief period. Behavioral interactions between mother and young at this time, in contrast to the earlier period, occur at any of these sites and throughout the area of the entire cage.

Experimental studies of maternal behavior

Our observations, and those of previous workers, provide a picture of a changing pattern of mother-young relationship, in which the behavior of the mother at each stage of development seems appropriate to the changing characteristics of the young. Such observations reveal interesting and consistent changes in the maternal behavior of the female rat, but they do not permit confident conclusions about the causal factors influencing them. The behavior of the mother may change as the young get older simply as a result of internal physiological changes occurring in the mother at parturition and continuing independently during the next few weeks; it may change because the changing young offer new stimuli, eliciting changed behavior of which the mother is capable regardless of her physiological condition; it may change because the young stimulate changes in the mother's physiological condition, making her capable of different kinds of behavior; or it may change because of the complex and interacting influences of all these factors (Lehrman, 1961).

The studies to be described here represent the beginning stages of an attempt to analyze the sources of developmental changes in the maternal behavior of the rat.

ABSENCE OF MATERNAL BEHAVIOR BEFORE PARTURITION

Although nursing and retrieving behavior are, of course, not normally seen until after some young have been born, it is conceivable that the female is prepared to nurse and retrieve young before the start of parturition. Such behavior has occasionally been observed during the last week of pregnancy (Wiesner and Sheard, 1933). As a preliminary to studies of the development of maternal behavior after parturition, we have tested females in the last half of pregnancy for the presence of the various components of the maternal behavior pattern.

The method of testing was as follows. *Nursing:* Five foster pups ranging from 5 to 10 days of age were placed in the female's nest and observed for 30 minutes, in order to see whether the mother attempted to nurse them in that time. *Retrieving:* Following the nursing test, the five young were set down in a corner of the cage diagonally opposite from the nest. If no retrieving occurred, the test was terminated after 3 minutes; if any young were retrieved during the 3-minute period, the test was extended to 5 minutes. *Nest building:* Following the retrieving test, the existing nest was removed, and the female was allowed access to a nest-material dispenser for the next 50 minutes. Twenty-three hours later, the nest produced by the female with the nesting material gathered during this 50-minute period was examined and rated.

Seventeen primiparous pregnant females were tested for nursing, retrieving, and nest building on alternate days starting at the 11th day before parturition and continuing up to the day of delivery. In more than 100 tests carried out during this period, nursing behavior and retrieving were not once observed. The reactions of near-term females to the 5- to 10-day-old pups consisted mainly of brief olfactory investigation. The pregnant females were not notably different in their reaction to huddling pups in the nest or to the approach of crawling pups than were virgin females or females that had returned to a nonmaternal condition after weaning their young.

A few females built nests starting several days before parturition. Although all the females picked up and carried nesting material, most of them did not actually build a nest until just before parturition.

It is apparent from these data that the onset of maternal behavior and of the maternal condition in the female coincide with the appearance of young. To what extent, then, is the onset of maternal behavior dependent upon postpartum contact with young? This point will be discussed later. We must first turn to an analysis of the changes in maternal behavior after parturition.

GROWTH OF THE MATERNAL BEHAVIOR CYCLE AFTER PARTURITION

Variations in maternal behavior in females rearing their own young. As we have pointed out, observation of the behavior of the mother toward her litter cannot reveal whether the cyclic changes in maternal behavior result from changes in her condition or whether they represent behavioral reactions to developmental changes in the young. One way to estimate the extent to which changes in the condition of the mother are involved is to subject mothers who are rearing their own litters to daily tests of maternal responses to a standard stimulus situation. The stimulus situations used for this study were the same as those described previously: a 30-minute test of nursing toward five 5- to 10-day-old foster pups in the nest; then a 3-minute test of retrieving using the same young, placed in the corner diagonally opposite from the nest; finally, a test of nest building by allowing the female to collect nesting material for 50 minutes and then rating the nest built by her during the next 23 hours. The mother's own young were removed from the cage before the beginning of the nursing test, and replaced in the nest at the end of the 50-minute period of access to nesting material.

These mothers were thus living continuously with their own young, but were daily tested with young whose age did not change during the four weeks following parturition. Nine females have been tested so far, with the results shown in Fig. 6.

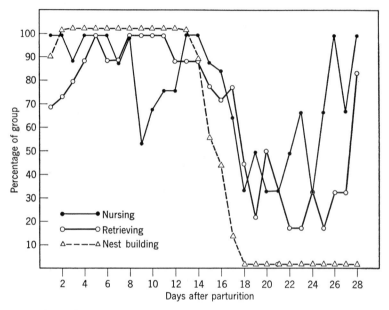

FIG. 6. The cycle of maternal behavior in the female rat rearing its own young from the 1st to the 28th day after parturition. Graphs show the percentage of the group of mothers that nursed and retrieved standard test young and built nests each day. (N = 9.)

It will be seen that all three of the main components of maternal behavior were present on the day of parturition in nearly all the mothers. The following 2 weeks may be called the period of maternal behavior proper, since during this period nearly all the females continued to display all the components of maternal behavior. During the third week, maternal reaction gradually but unmistakably declined, although the test conditions remained constant.

Nest building disappeared first, starting at about the 13th day; nursing and retrieving responses began to decline on the 14th day. By the 18th day of parturition fewer than 40% of the females nursed or retrieved the test young.

Nest building disappeared by the 18th day, and there was no retrieving on the 21st day; on the other hand, the number of nursing females did not fall below one-third of the total.

Nursing and retrieving behavior, but not nest building, reappeared during the 4th week. By the end of this week, almost all the females were showing these responses.

It appears from these observations that the maternal reactions of female rats to 5- to 10-day-old young follow a course which is remarkably similar to that observed in their reactions to their own young in the litter. In both situations nursing, retrieving, and nest-building behavior arise almost simultaneously at parturition and are maintained for the next two weeks. The beginning of a decline in maternal behavior in the litter at around the 13th day was followed within a few days by a similar disappearance of maternal responses in the tests with the standard young.

Observations of mothers and young in the litter situation indicate that the behavioral changes in the mother during the weeks following parturition are appropriate to the behavioral development of the young. It is now apparent that these changes in the mother's behavior reflect, at least in part, changes in her own condition, rather than merely being behavioral responses to the changing characteristics of the young.

Effects of young on the maternal behavior cycle. The question remains whether the presence of the young is necessary for the development of the postparturitional changes in the maternal condition of the mother, or whether, on the other hand, the changes demonstrated by the preceding observations occur as a function of time since parturition, regardless of the presence of the young. We have investigated this question by removing the young from the mother for various periods at parturition, and at various times after parturition, and then testing the mother for maternal response to our standard stimulus—5- to 10-day-old young—for comparison with the responses, to such pups, of mothers who were kept continuously with their own young.

(a) Interruption of mother-young interaction at parturition. A group of six primiparous females were observed during parturition and the fetuses were removed from the cage by the experimenter, one by one,

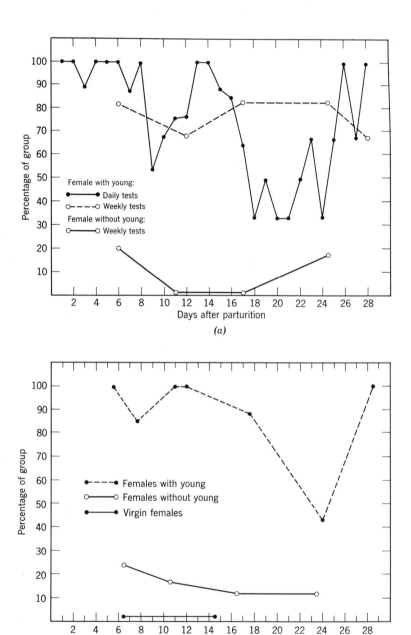

(a)

(b)

Maternal Behavior in Mammals

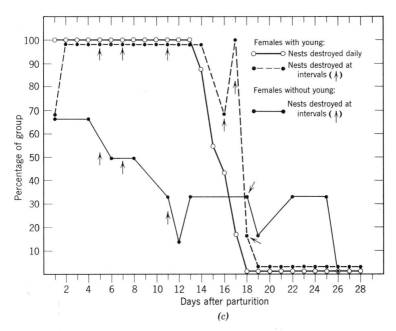

FIG. 7. Maternal responses to standard test young of females whose young were removed at birth compared with those of females whose young remained with them. (a) Nursing: some animals tested daily (N = 9), others tested weekly (N = 6, for each group). (b) Retrieving: virgin females (N = 6) given two tests one week apart shown for comparison. (c) Nest building.

as they were delivered. The females were allowed to remain without young in the cage in which parturition had taken place. At weekly intervals for the next 4 weeks, they were given tests of nursing and retrieving using 5- to 10-day-old young as stimuli. Nest building was scored daily but the nests were removed only at approximately weekly intervals.

The results are summarized in Fig. 7, which shows that removal of the young at birth effectively prevents the appearance of the cycle of maternal behavior which is normally observed during the 4 weeks following parturition. Attempts to nurse the young appeared only rarely (Fig. 7a); retrieving was similarly affected, although comparison with the results of retrieving tests on virgin females reveals some residual effects of parturition on retrieving behavior (Fig. 7b); nest building was also drastically reduced by comparison with that seen in females allowed to rear their young (Fig. 7c).

Although these data show that the cycle of maternal behavior does not appear in the absence of the young during the week following

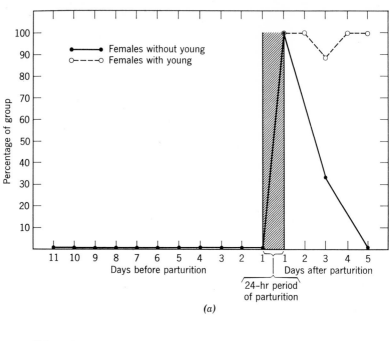

(a)

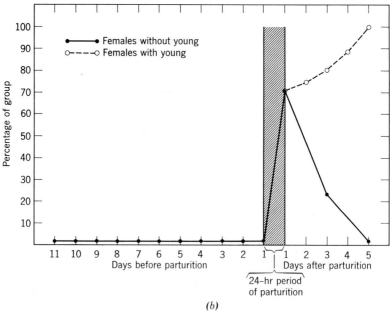

(b)

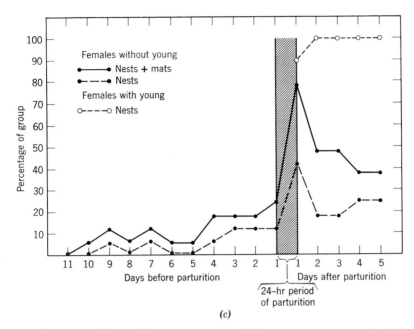

FIG. 8. *Maternal behavior before parturition and after postpartum removal of the young (N = 17). Behavior of mothers whose young were left with them (N = 9) shown for comparison. (a) Nursing. (b) Retrieving. (c) Nest building.*

parturition, the reader will recall that all the elements of maternal behavior were already present at parturition. To determine how this behavior wanes in the absence of the young during the first week following parturition, the following experiment was undertaken.

Seventeen primiparous females were kept under observation during parturition, and the fetuses were removed shortly after they emerged from the birth canal. Females were allowed to clean the pups and to eat the placentas before removal of the young, but further contact between mother and young was prevented. After parturition, the females were left alone in their cages until tests of nursing, retrieving, and nest-building behavior were started several days later. Nine of the females were tested for nursing and retrieving responses to 5- to 10-day-old young at the beginning of the third day, approximately 60 hours after parturition; the remaining eight animals were tested at the beginning of the 5th day, about 108 hours after parturition. Nest building could be rated daily by noting the condition of the nest.

The results are shown in Fig. 8. For each of the three types of behavior represented, there are two curves: one showing the maternal responses, at various times after parturition, of females whose own young had been removed at parturition; the other showing the maternal responses, in the same test situation, of mother rats whose own young had remained with them since parturition.

It is apparent that the mother's capability for maternal response wanes rapidly after parturition in the absence of the young, in marked contrast to the situation in mothers kept with their young. It may be noted that the nest-building behavior (Fig. 8c) did not decline quite as far as did nursing (Fig. 8a) and retrieving (Fig. 8b).

These results indicate that, even though developments during pregnancy and at parturition may suffice for the onset of maternal behavior at parturition, the normal postparturitional development of maternal responses depends upon stimulation from the litter.

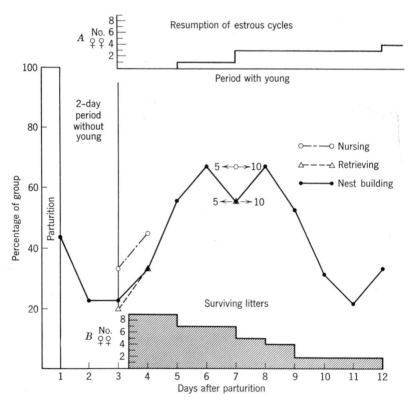

FIG. 9. *Maternal behavior toward standard test pups of females whose young were removed at parturition. Testing delayed until 60 hours postpartum; then pups left with females for rearing. Records of nursing, retrieving, nest building, resumption of estrous cycling (insert A) and survival of litters (insert B) are shown.*

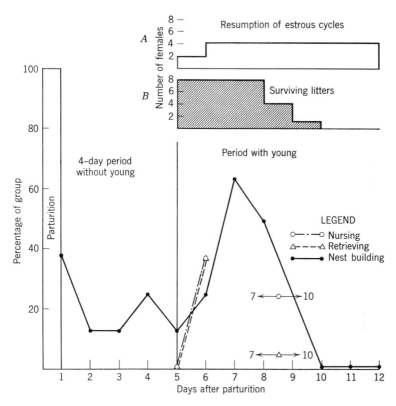

FIG. 10. *Maternal behavior when testing and the reintroduction of pups were delayed until 108 hours postpartum.*

(b) *Maternal behavior following postparturition separation from the young.* We have just described tests of maternal behavior toward 5- to 10-day-old young by females whose own young had been removed at parturition and who had then been left without young for 2 or 4 days. The stimulus pups were then left with the females until 12 days after parturition (that is, for 9 or 7 days).

Nest-building behavior was rated daily. In addition, standard tests of nursing and retrieving were carried out, with 5- to 10-day-old stimulus young, one day after the introduction of the foster pups, and then at irregular intervals until 10 days postparturition (Figs. 9 and 10). In addition, records were kept of the survival and weight gain of the pups in order to determine whether the females were lactating and whether maternal behavior was occurring effectively. As an additional measure of the female's physiological condition, vaginal smears were taken daily. Regular estrous cycling is normally inhibited in nursing females until the fourth week after parturition, but cycling is resumed shortly after parturition if litters are removed at birth, or if litter size falls below three suckling pups (Rothchild, 1960).

The results, as shown in Figs. 9 and 10, are quite striking. Comparison of these figures with Fig. 2 shows that separation from the young for 2 or 4 days following parturition sharply reduces maternal responses to the standard test pups. Furthermore, after the period of initial separation, continuous association with actively suckling young is unable to induce the development of maternal behavior to a level comparable with that occurring in mothers who have associated with young since parturition. Nest-building behavior, which could be rated daily, showed a similar course. After an initial increase when the young were introduced into the cage, which was maintained for a few days, the behavior fell to the low level characteristic of females without young.

It may be noted that the number of females showing nursing and retrieving responses was lower after 4 days of postpartum isolation from young than in the group isolated for only 2 days.

Records of litter survival among the mothers of these two groups confirm the general impression that, despite the occasional display of maternal responses, these females were not functioning as effective mothers. By the 5th day after the young were placed with the mothers, all members of the litters given to the females which had been without young for four days postpartum had died, and fewer than half of those given to the females without young for two days postpartum were still surviving.

The premature appearance of estrous cycling in many of these females also indicated a failure by the newly introduced young to cause the reinstatement of the maternal condition which had declined during the period since parturition. Again, resumption of estrous cycles occurred more quickly and in more animals the longer the period of postpartum separation from young.

The conclusion from the data on litter survival and on estrous cycling reiterates that from the behavioral data. Separation from the young for a period after parturition not only causes the decay of the maternal condition present at parturition, but leaves the mothers largely incapable of developing effective mothering when given new young. Furthermore, this effect is greater the longer the lapse of time since parturition.

(c) *Effects of brief separation from the young during later periods.* The experiments just described indicate that separation from young, beginning at parturition, causes a drastic decline in the mother's ability to show maternal responses. As a first step in analyzing the problem of the maintenance of the female's maternal condition during the weeks following parturition, we wish to know whether separation from the young at various times later during the litter period would have similar effects on her behavior. Experiments on this problem are now in a preliminary stage, but some of the results are sufficiently interesting to warrant brief mention here.

Four groups of mother rats, numbering five to eight individuals, were allowed to rear their own young to 0, 3, 9, or 14 days of age. The young were then removed, and the females left alone for 4 days. At the end of the 4-day solitary isolation period, the females were tested for nursing and retrieving responses to 5- to 10-day-old pups.

Even with these small groups, the results are quite striking. When the separation occurs at birth, none of the mothers shows nursing or retrieving responses to the stimulus pups four days later, indicating (as we have already seen) the total decline of parental responses. When separation from the young for the same period is carried out later during the litter period, nursing responses were shown by 60 to 75% of the mothers, and retrieving responses by 40 to 75% (Fig. 11).

It will be recalled that in an earlier experiment mothers were kept isolated from young for 4 days starting at parturition, tested for maternal response to 5- to 10-day-old young at the end of this four-day period, then left with stimulus pups to rear, and periodically tested for maternal response to new standard (5- to 10-day-old) stimulus pups during the rest of the litter period (Fig. 10). In the present experiment, in contrast, we have repeated this procedure with those mothers for whom the four-day period of separation from young started after 3, 9, or 14 days of postparturition association with their young. Further results of the maternal behavior tests during this post-separation rearing period are shown in Fig. 11, where nest building, nursing, and retrieving responses (all to standard stimulus young) are shown as a function of time after the 4-day separation period.

It is clear from Figs. 10 and 11 that when young are removed for a 4-day period at various times in their rearing period, replacement of the young causes substantial recovery of the mother's maternal condition. In contrast, the loss of maternal behavior in mothers deprived of their young for a similar period at parturition seems not to be reversible by stimulation from young.

In summary, these data indicate that removal of the young after maternal behavior is well established interferes less with the mainten-

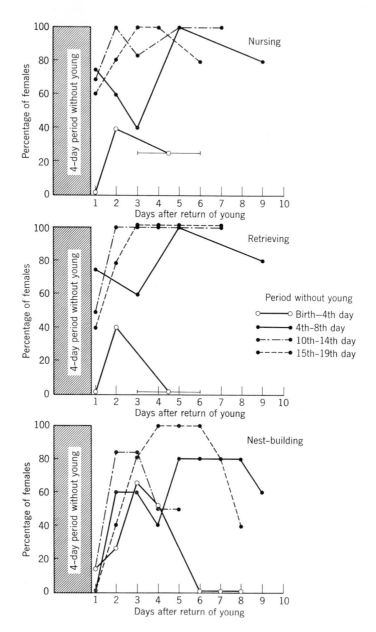

FIG. 11. *Effect of 4-day period without the young, starting at various times after parturition, upon maternal responses to standard test pups.*

ance of nursing and retrieving than does removal of the young for the same period at the onset of maternal behavior just after parturition.

Decline of maternal behavior. The decline of maternal behavior is a normal event in the reproductive cycle. Previous studies (Wiesner and Sheard, 1933) have indicated that the decline of maternal behavior may be delayed by replacing the growing litter with new pups that are less than 10 days of age. This suggests that the characteristics of the young play a role in the decline of maternal condition, just as they do in its development. The following experiment is the beginning of an attempt to explore this process.

Effect of permanent removal of the young. Two groups of ten females each were used for this experiment. The litters were permanently removed from the mothers of the first group on the 9th day after parturition, and of the second group on the 14th day. All mothers were then tested at 2-day intervals for maternal response to 5- to 10-day-old young. The tests were conducted on alternate days for half the animals of each group, so that there are data for each day, but no animal was tested more often than once in 2 days. Nest building was rated daily.

When the young were removed 9 days after parturition, maternal responses declined earlier and to lower levels than in the case of mothers who kept their young, although the difference was small by the 19 to 20th day after parturition (Fig. 12*a*). By contrast, removal of the young on the 14th day, when the decline in maternal responsiveness had already begun, did not speed up this decline (Fig 12*b*). In fact, at least for retrieving responses, removal of the young actually slowed down the decline in maternal responsiveness.

The results strongly suggest that the decline of maternal behavior in the normal litter situation is the result not only of reduction of stimulation for maternal behavior as the young get older, but also of positive interference with the mother's maternal condition by some behavioral or other characteristics of the growing young.

Discussion

MATERNAL BEHAVIOR IN RELATION TO THE DEVELOPMENT OF THE YOUNG

Maternal response and maternal condition. The reader must be reminded that all the experimental data reported in this chapter are based on observations of the maternal responses of female rats to a standard stimulus situation consisting of a litter of 5- to 10-day old foster pups. In those studies in which the experimental animals were being maintained with their own young, or with foster young of various

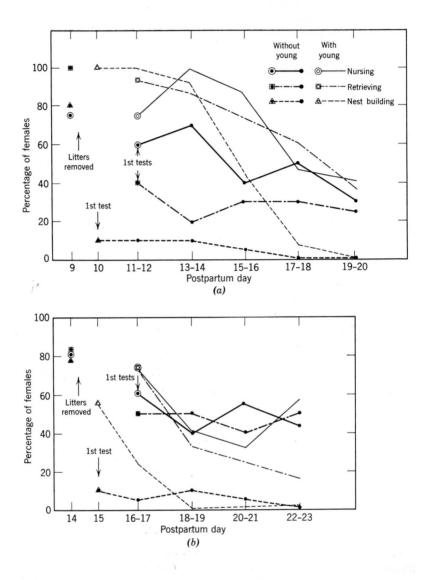

FIG. 12. *Decline of maternal responsiveness to standard stimulus pups after permanent removal of the mother's litter compared with decline of maternal responsiveness in mothers kept with their own young.* (a) *Litters removed at 9th day postpartum.* (b) *Litters removed at 14th day postpartum.*

42   *Maternal Behavior in Mammals*

ages, the data reported here were obtained by testing mothers with the standard stimulus pups during brief periods when their litters had been removed from the cage. This means that all the variations reported here in the maternal responsiveness of the females, whether occurring in the course of the normal maternal cycle or as a result of our experimental manipulations, reflect changes in the mothers' internal condition of readiness to perform these maternal responses. This is a point of considerable importance, since the variations in maternal behavior which are observed during the normal cycle of litter care represent combined effects of the development and decline of the mother's maternal condition, and of the change in stimulus conditions resulting from the physical and behavioral development of the young. Our use of standard stimulus animals under a wide variety of maternal living conditions represents a first step toward an analysis of the interaction between changing maternal condition and changing litter situation in the development of the mother-young relationship.

Since maternal responsiveness to the standard stimulus pups remained high during the postpartum weeks if the mother was allowed to remain with her young, whereas it declined rapidly if she was isolated from them, it is clear that the presence of the litter induces changes in the mother's physiological condition of readiness to perform maternal responses, which we call "maternal condition." Rowell (1960) has shown in the golden hamster that there is a definable range of maternal responses which the female will make to young, varying with her maternal condition. What maternal responses actually appear, however, depends largely upon the age of the pups with which she is tested. We have not yet explored this parameter in our work with rats, but incidental observations make it quite clear that young of different ages induce different behavioral responses from the same mothers. We intend to pursue this problem further.

Our reason for stressing this point is that we believe it to be of the utmost importance to distinguish, conceptually and experimentally, between the litter as a source of stimulation inducing physiological changes in the mother's maternal condition and the litter as a source of stimulation for eliciting maternal responses (Beach, 1951). The appearance of these responses is, of course, in turn dependent on the mother's current condition. Such a distinction is essential, if we are to appreciate the contributions of the characteristics of the mother, the characteristics of the young, and the emergent character of the mother-young relationship, as the basis for the development of the maternal behavior cycle (Lehrman, 1959; Lehrman, 1961; Schneirla and Rosenblatt, 1961).

Parturition: a pivotal event. Parturition is a crucial period for the development of the maternal condition. All the elements of maternal responsiveness first appear at around this time. The shift from self licking to licking of the young, the increase in nest-building behavior and the change in its character, the appearance of retrieving responses, and the occurrence of the first nursing responses, all coming when the helpless and practically immobile young appear on the scene, encourage the establishment of the nursing-suckling relationship between mother and young. If this relationship becomes established, the maternal responsiveness of the female increases and is maintained throughout the litter period. If the young do *not* stimulate the mother just after parturition, her readiness to perform maternal responses declines rapidly and completely. The special nature of the immediately postpartum condition of the female is emphasized by the fact that reintroduction of young after several days of such isolation does not restore the maternal condition to anything like the level which it would have reached if the young had been present continuously since birth. By contrast, when the young are removed for equivalent periods later during the litter period, the decline in maternal responsiveness is not nearly so drastic, and recovery readily follows the reintroduction of the young.

Parturition therefore represents a crucial point of change, or point of inflection, in the relationship between the mother and her (litter) environment. Maternal behavior has made its appearance as the outcome of events during the last few days of pregnancy, culminating in parturition. The processes which gave rise to this maternal behavior do not depend upon the presence of the young. But these processes cannot maintain the mother's maternal condition; the presence of the young is required. Parturition is thus a time of transition in the development of the mother's maternal responses during which the regulation of the physiological processes underlying the development and maintenance of maternal behavior is much more responsive to external stimulation than before or afterwards.

Maintenance and decline of the maternal condition. In addition to contributing to the consolidation of the maternal condition just after parturition, stimulation provided by the litter appears to contribute to the maintenance of this condition during the litter period. If the young are removed *early* in the litter period, before the time when maternal responsiveness normally declines, the maternal responses of the mother disappear more rapidly than they do when she is allowed to remain with her litter. The converse is also true; the period of maternal responsiveness can be extended by replacing older litters with young pups (Wiesner and Sheard, 1933).

If the young are removed *later* in the litter period, at the time when maternal responsiveness is beginning to decline in those mothers who remain with their litters, an apparently anomalous, but very interesting, result is obtained. Maternal responsiveness does not decline more rapidly than in the normal litter situation; indeed, in some respects, maternal behavior persists beyond the time when it would normally decline. This strongly suggests that, when maternal behavior declines in the normal litter situation, it is not only because the growing young fail to provide stimulation which they were earlier providing, but also because they in some way actively oppose the maintenance of the mother's maternal condition.

A logical next step in exploring and verifying this assumption is, of course, to test the effects on the mother's maternal condition of replacing her own young with *older* foster pups. Some preliminary steps which we have made in this direction have given ambiguous results, along with some very interesting observations of the behavior of the young. Contrary to our expectations, substitution of 11-day-old or 19-day-old for 4-day-old young did not clearly accelerate the decline of maternal responsiveness in the succeeding days. However, if 4-day-old young are removed from their mother and replaced by 11-day-old young, the foster mother, during the next few days, retrieves these young more often than their own mother would have done. One result is that such young do not leave the nest to move about actively in its neighborhood until they are some days past the normal age for this development. This means that their behavior, at the age of 15 or 16 days, is in some respects more characteristic of 11- or 12-day-old young than of 15- or 16-day-old young.

This observation suggests that the behavior of the mother, partly dependent upon her maternal condition, influences the behavioral development of the young, just as the behavioral and other characteristics of the young influence her behavioral development during the maternal behavior cycle. One consequence is that the age of the young cannot be regarded as a reliable means of specifying the stimulating conditions for the mother. In our future work, we intend to explore the age of the young as a factor in their ability to stimulate changes in the mother's physiological condition, but paying close attention to the actual behavioral characteristics of the young at different ages in relation to mothers in different physiological conditions.

These observations suggest possible directions for the study of weaning, the normal development of separation between mother and young. Growth changes in the young no doubt involve both the disappearance of some characteristics which were important in stimulating the development of maternal responsiveness, and the appearance of new physical and behavioral characteristics which actively induce a reduction in the mother's physiological readiness to show maternal behavior. Furthermore, this development in the young is probably not entirely autonomous, but depends for some of its characteristics upon influences imposed by the mother's behavior.

PSYCHOBIOLOGY OF THE DEVELOPMENT OF THE MATERNAL BEHAVIOR CYCLE

Since the physiological regulation of maternal behavior has recently been exhaustively reviewed elsewhere (Lehrman, 1961), we shall not here undertake a detailed discussion of it. We would, however, like to call attention to several aspects of psychobiological regulation in the maternal behavior of the rat which are relevant to the material presented in this paper, and which suggest lines for future research.

Change in orientation to the body. Our observations show that the self licking of the female rat changes during the last week or so of pregnancy, when she directs her licking more and more to the nipple line and the genitalia. This shift must reflect changes in tension or in sensitivity of the various body regions induced by the hormonal changes of pregnancy. The marked hyperplasia of the mammary tissue which occurs during pregnancy under the influence of ovarian, pituitary, and placental hormones (Cowie and Folley, 1961) certainly seems to be a logical source of such tension changes, but this still needs to be demonstrated experimentally.

Another probable source of shift in body tension is to be found in the growth of the fetuses and consequent enlargement of the uterus. In addition, we have noted that the fetuses appear to be located perceptibly more posteriorly late in pregnancy than in the earlier days. In many mammals, the approaching end of pregnancy is signaled by a noticeable increase in girth in the pelvic region and by swelling and mucous secretion of the vulva (Slijper, 1960). The increase in salt preference during pregnancy (Barelare and Richter, 1938) also plays a role since the availability of salt decreases genital licking in both pregnant and nonpregnant female rats (Lehrman, 1956; Steinberg and Bindra, 1962).

Since it is well known (see below) that suckling stimulation of the mother's nipples by the young plays a role in the postparturitive stimulation and maintenance of lactation, it seems possible that the concentration of the mother's self licking on her nipples, late in pregnancy, may contribute to the hormonal stimulation of the striking changes which occur in the mammary glands just before and around parturition (Cross, Goodwin, and Silver, 1958). If this can in fact be demonstrated, it would be another example of an interactive relationship between hormone-induced changes in internal condition and the behavior changes influenced by them.

Change in orientation to the cage. The pregnant female sporadically carries nesting material to various parts of the cage. Shortly before parturition, when she becomes lethargic and relatively immobile, she begins to carry the material primarily to the one part of the cage in which she spends most of her time, and it is there that the nest emerges. Its shape depends partly on the fact that the lethargic female pulls material toward her body, rather than carrying it about. Eibl-Eibesfeldt (1955) has shown that the female rat's tendency to build a nest in a particular place in the cage depends primarily upon the fact that that place in the cage has been her regular resting or sleeping place. Her tendency to rest or sleep in one part of the cage is, in turn, a function of some variable combination of the stimulus characteristics of the cage and of her experience of living in it.

The rat's motive for nest building appears to have some relationship to the regulation of her body temperature. Rats do more nest building in colder than in warmer ambient temperatures (Kinder, 1927). Hypophysectomy greatly increases the amount of nest building in both pregnant and nonpregnant rats, apparently by interfering with the thyroid gland's contribution to the regulation of body temperature (Richter, 1937; Richter and Eckert, 1936); hypophysectomized rats choose warmer points in a temperature gradient than do intact rats (Stone and Mason, 1955).

The fact that thyroidectomy increases and thyroid hormone administration decreases nest-building activity is consistent with the idea that this behavior plays a thermoregulatory role. However, the actual temperature preferences of pregnant rats, as compared with those of nonpregnant animals, remain to be investigated, as do thyroid function during pregnancy, the effects of various other hormones on nest building and on body temperature, and particularly the effects of mammary gland changes late in pregnancy upon the distribution of heat loss from the skin on ventral and dorsal surfaces of the body.

Physiological changes at parturition. The attachment to the nest site, developed late in pregnancy, continues through and beyond parturition, and forms the basis for the location of the mother's maternal behavior. During parturition, when the mother, the floor, and the young are all wet with the birth fluids, it is obvious even to casual observation that the mother's licking of herself is continuous with her licking of the young and of the substrate. We have called attention to the abrupt shift from self licking to licking of the young immediately after parturition. That the maternal licking of the young tends to be concentrated in their anogenital region suggests that the sensory characteristics which attract the mother to lick the young have something in common with some of those which oriented her self licking to the genital region late in pregnancy. We still need to determine experimentally whether the pattern of the mother's self licking would change abruptly at parturition, even if she did *not* have an opportunity to lick the young.

In this connection, we should recall that Labriola (1953; see also Wiesner and Sheard, 1933) delivered young rats by Caesarean section and found that the mothers' retrieving and nursing responses were normal 24 hours later. The implication of this experiment is, of course, that the mother's actual experience of parturition is not essential for the establishment of maternal relations with the young. However, since Labriola left the mothers unobserved with their young during the 24-hour period between Caesarean delivery and the first tests of maternal responsiveness, we do not know what interactions occurred between the mother and the pups during this period, what role they may have played in the establishment of her maternal behavior, or whether they were of a kind that would be facilitated by her participation in parturition. Furthermore, the mother's experience during parturition is, in a sense, continuous with the orientation of her self licking to her own anogenital region, which had already developed by the time Labriola's animals were delivered of their pups. Further exploration of the implications of this experiment is obviously of the greatest importance for an understanding of the behavioral transitions which occur at around the time of parturition.

Birch (1956) interfered with the self licking of pregnant rats by placing wide rubber collars around their necks. He reported that most animals so treated failed to attend to their young during parturition and therefore failed to establish maternal behavior. However, Coomans (cited by Eibl-Eibesfeldt, 1958), in a similar study, obtained quite different results. He concluded that any disturbances of maternal behavior in his animals could be attributed solely to mechanical interference with the normal parturitive behavior patterns. Since these authors used different strains of rats, different kinds of collars, and different control procedures, a thorough attempt to reconcile these two studies is now urgently needed.

The elements of maternal behavior appear amid the expulsions of the young, retrieving and nursing movements actually alternating with the movements of labor. The uterine contractions of parturition are stimulated in part by oxytocin secreted by the neurohypophysis (Zarrow, 1961). This hormone also causes contractions of the milk-secreting tubules of the mammary glands, with a consequent increase in pressure of the fluid contained in them (Cross and Harris, 1951; Cross and Harris, 1952), and there is some evidence, for the rabbit, that this kind of increase in intramammary tension plays a role in the motivation of nursing behavior (Cross, 1952). The possibility of this kind of link between the physiological processes of parturition and the physiological basis for the onset of nursing behavior should certainly be investigated further.

Postparturitional maternal development. It has long been known that stimulation provided by the suckling behavior of young mammals induces the secretion by the pituitary glands of the hormones responsible for the maintenance of lactation (Harris, 1958). If young rats are removed from their mothers several days after parturition, milk secretion disappears within a few days, and the milk-secreting tubules disappear shortly thereafter (Selye, 1934). Conversely, the period of active lactation can be extended by replacing growing litters with younger, actively suckling pups (Nicoll and Meites, 1959; Bruce, 1961).

The stimulus for this milk secretion clearly includes mechanical stimulation of the nipples, since irritation of the nipples by local application of turpentine can have the effect of partially maintaining milk secretion after the young are removed (Hooker and Williams, 1940). A number of experiments indicates that the effect of such suckling stimulation is to cause the secretion of oxytocin by the posterior pituitary gland, which causes the ejection of milk by the mammary gland, and to cause the production of prolactin by the anterior hypophysis, which stimulates the manufacture of milk in the mammary gland (Meites and Turner, 1948), although it is not yet certain whether these two effects are causally related to each other or are independent effects of the same stimulus (Benson and Folley, 1957; Rothchild and Quilligan, 1960).

Now we wish to draw attention to a number of interesting parallels between the course of development of lactation as shown by the work just described and the course of development of the mother's maternal condition as shown by the experiments reported in this chapter. The initiation of lactation, and the initial surge of prolactin production, which occur at parturition, do *not* depend upon the presence of the young (Meites and Turner, 1948), but occur spontaneously in response to the physiological changes associated with the termination of pregnancy (Cowie and Folley, 1961). However, if the young are removed at birth, this initial lactation rapidly dies away. If the young are present, and if suckling is established during this period of initial lactation, then lactation and the production of prolactin by the pituitary gland are maintained throughout the litter period (Meites and Turner, 1942; Meites and Turner, 1948). In this connection, it should be noted that parturition involves the sudden loss of the placental hormones with a consequent shift to the dominance of pituitary regulation, which is more subject to neural (and thus stimulus) control.

The parallel with our data on maternal behavior is obvious. Just as with lactation, all three of the principal components of maternal behavior can be elicited at and shortly after parturition, whether or not the mother is kept with her young. Maternal behavior dies away within a few days if the mother does not have her pups, but is maintained if the pups are left with her. Furthermore, the relative inability of older pups, as compared with younger pups, to maintain lactation is consistent with our earlier conclusion that older pups produce stimuli which interfere with the maintenance of maternal condition. Bruce (1961) reports that removal of the young for periods of several days in the middle of a lactation period causes reduction of milk production, but that the mothers readily regain full milk production within a few days after the young are returned to them, a result for lactation similar to that which we obtained for maternal behavior; and we have found that mothers do *not* recover milk production when the separation from the young is for comparable periods just after parturition.

These data certainly suggest that a major area for future exploration lies in the relationships between lactation and maternal behavior. We need coordinated studies of the effects of suckling stimuli and of various hormones on lactation and on the establishment of the nursing-suckling relationship when administered to animals in different physiological condition and with different experience; of the effects on lactation of nonsuckling stimuli from the young; of the role of mammary gland tension in motivating different aspects of maternal behavior; of the relationship between the decline of lactation and the decline of maternal behavior condition, and between the extensions of these events by various stimulating situations; of the relative degree of dependence of the different parts of the maternal behavior pattern on each other and on lactation. Sufficient data are now available to indicate that all of these are promising problems.

THE SUCCESSION OF STAGES AND THE ROLE OF EXPERIENCE

We have presented the maternal behavior cycle of the rat as a developmental series of stages, in which the events occurring at each stage are, in various ways, relevant to the emergence of the next stage. We have suggested a number of ways in which events occurring in an earlier stage can influence the development of a later stage.

Physiological changes occurring in the body of the female rat near the end of pregnancy serve to orient her attention toward those parts of her body which are most relevant to the impending parturition. Simultaneously, the changes in her general activity and probably in her need for temperature regulation serve to limit her behavior to a particular part of the cage and facilitate the building of the nest. Her experience of the cage environment, of course, also plays a role in the development of the nest and in the organization of her activity just before parturition. Parturition itself produces the young and the birth fluids, both of which serve to strengthen her orientation to the young; the drastic change which simultaneously occurs in her own body facilitates the sudden transition from self licking to the licking of the young. The hormonal situation associated with parturition is also responsible for tension changes in the mammary glands, which may play a role in the establishment of the nursing-suckling relationship. The mother's maternal condition, which appears as a consequence of the events leading up to and culminating in parturition, is maintained and developed further as a result of stimulation provided by the young. The behavioral characteristics of the developing young appear, in turn, to depend in part upon the way the mother is acting toward them; conversely, variations in the stimulus characteristics of the young can produce a variety of different response patterns from mothers in the same physiological condition; at the same time, stimulation from the young is changing this physiological condition itself, and thus changing the age-range of young to which the mother will respond and the type of responses of which she is capable. This means that the appropriateness to each other of the behavior of the mother and of the young at different times after parturition is a result both of correlated developmental changes which are in part mutually stimulated, and of the mutual and reciprocal elicitations of behavior by each which is appropriate to the stimuli being provided by the other.

Primiparous rats show perfectly adequate maternal behavior, and it is not to be expected that anything resembling a learning curve can be derived from observations of maternal behavior at successive parturitions. Does this mean that experience plays no role in the development of maternal behavior patterns? Not necessarily. Experience during an early stage may have the effect both of changing the mother's physiological condition so that she is motivated to perform the behavior characteristic of the next stage and of orienting her toward the environment appropriately for the behavior of later stages (Lehrman, 1962).

If this conception is correct, we would expect that animals breeding for the first time would be able to carry out the behavior appropriate to the various stages as they occur. However, if in nonpregnant animals we induced by hormone injection the physiological conditions which motivate the behavior of a particular stage of the maternal behavior cycle, we might expect to find a sharp difference in the frequency and efficiency of such behavior between those animals who had, and those who had not, previously experienced this physiological condition under circumstances in which their immediately preceding experience had oriented them toward the appropriate object of the behavior associated with this motive state. Precisely this set of relationships has been demonstrated in the ring dove (Lehrman, 1959; Lehrman, 1962), and we consider this formulation to point to the most appropriate route toward the analysis of the role of experience.

In this connection, the experiments of Lott (1962) and of Lott and Fuchs (1962), which demonstrated that progesterone and prolactin are not capable of inducing maternal retrieving behavior in virgin rats, must be regarded as only a preliminary approach to the problem of how these hormones are involved in maternal behavior. Prolactin apparently cannot produce maternal behavior in virgin rats. We should now ask, for example, whether it could *maintain* maternal behavior in rats whose young are removed from them ten days postpartum when the mother's behavior is already oriented toward the young and when her physiological condition is in all respects (not merely in the presence of this hormone) conducive to the maintenance of maternal behavior. Bruce (1961) observed that foster pups could induce lactation in parous rats whose own young had been weaned many weeks earlier, but not in virgin rats. Such observations should be extended to compare untreated virgin rats with rats which have been allowed to bear, but not to rear, young (Uyldert, 1946) and with virgin and parous rats subjected to a variety of hormonal pretreatments; and they should include data on the behavior of the females and of the foster pups to determine whether the young actually gain access to the nipples, whether they suck, and whether sucking induces lactation in all these groups of animals.

The analysis of the contributions of various hormones, and of various kinds and amounts of experience, to the development of maternal behavior requires close attention to the details of the normal physiological relationships, and to the succession of physiological and behavioral stages characteristic of the maternal cycle.

The maternal behavior pattern, as it is seen to develop in the normal litter situation, emerges from a set of interlocking causal relationships: between autonomous physiological changes and consequent changes in behavior; between external stimuli, including those arising from the behavior of the young, and endocrine changes; between experience at one stage of development and orientation to the environment at another stage; between the behavioral characteristics of the mother and those of the young at any particular stage; etc. It is not to be expected that we will be able to discover and define "the" hormonal basis of maternal behavior, "the" role of experience in the origin of maternal behavior, "the" relative importance of autonomous and of stimulus-induced changes in physiological and behavioral condition, or "the" neural basis of maternal behavior. Rather, continuous and simultaneous attention to as many behavioral and physiological aspects of this complex pattern as possible may be rewarded by a gradual and continual increase in our understanding of the problems which we have posed and in our ability to pose further problems.

Summary

A developmental approach to the study of maternal behavior in the laboratory rat emphasizes the interrelationships between, on the one hand, the behavioral condition and physiological status of the female and, on the other hand, the effects of stimuli from her body, the cage surroundings, and the young, both on her behavioral responses and on the physiological and behavioral conditions from which these arise. The successive phases of the maternal behavior cycle are related to one another through the development of these interrelationships. Using her responses to 5- to 10-day-old test young, we have studied the changes in the female's behavioral condition during the last week of pregnancy through parturition, and during the period of growth, maintenance, and decline of maternal behavior, extending to 28 days postpartum.

Parturition is a pivotal event in the maternal behavior cycle. Behaviorally it marks the culmination of the changes in the mother's self-licking pattern and the shift in her orientation from her own body to that of the newly born young. Furthermore, the basis of her orientation to the cage space, indicated by her nest-building behavior, changes, coming under the domination of stimuli from the young. Physiologically, parturition represents a drastic and sudden change in the distribution of body tensions, and a shift from the dominance of placental hormones to that of the pituitary gland, which is more subject to neural (that is, stimulus) control. The appearance of the young provides a source of stimulation which is capable of eliciting lactation-inducing pituitary activity at a time when the mother is maximally responsive to such stimulation.

Finally, the young continue to provide stimulation, both by suckling and, presumably, by their other activities, which help to maintain the maternal condition until changes in the young permit or encourage it to decline. The maintenance of the maternal condition and the elicitation of maternal responses partly dependent on the maternal condition must be regarded as partially independent results of stimulation by the young. Our studies indicate that the maternal condition of the female is closely synchronized with the behavioral development of the young, largely because her condition is dependent upon stimulation provided by the young at each phase of the maternal behavior cycle.

We have indicated a number of lines of research for future development arising out of the data reported here and out of the same general considerations that led to the formulation of the studies.

References

Barelare, B., Jr., and C. P. Richter (1938), Increased sodium chloride appetite in pregnant rats. *Amer. J. Physiol.*, **121**, 185–188.

Beach, F. A. (1951), Instinctive behavior: reproductive activities. In S. S. Stevens (Ed.), *Handbook of Experimental Psychology*, New York: Wiley. Pp. 387–434.

Beach, F. A., and J. Jaynes (1956a), Studies of maternal retrieving in rats. I. Recognition of young. *J. Mammal.*, **37**, 177–180.

Beach, F. A., and J. Jaynes (1956b), Studies of maternal retrieving in rats. II. Effects of practice and previous parturitions. *Amer. Nat.*, **90**, 103–109.

Beach, F. A., and J. Jaynes (1956c), Studies of maternal retrieving in rats. III. Sensory cues involved in the lactating female's response to her young. *Behaviour*, **10**, 104–125.

Benson, G. K., and S. J. Folley (1957), The effect of oxytocin on mammary gland involution in the rat. *J. Endocrin.*, **16**, 189–201.

Birch, H. G. (1956), Sources of order in the maternal behavior of animals. *Amer. J. Orthopsychiat.*, **26**, 279–284.

Bruce, Hilda M. (1961), Observations on the suckling stimulus and lactation in the rat. *J. Reprod. Fertil.*, **2**, 17–34.

Calhoun, J. B. (1962), A "behavioral sink." In E. L. Bliss (Ed.), *Roots of Behavior*, New York: Harper. Pp. 295–315.

Clark, Eugenie L., L. R. Aronson, and M. Gordon (1954), Mating behavior patterns in two sympatric species of Xiphophorin fishes: their inheritance and significance in sexual isolation. *Bull. Amer. Mus. nat. Hist.*, **103**, 135–226.

Cowie, A. T., and S. J. Folley (1961), The mammary gland and lactation. In W. C. Young (Ed.), *Sex and Internal Secretions*, 3rd ed., Baltimore: Williams and Wilkins. Pp. 590–642.

Cross, B. A. (1952), Nursing behaviour and the milk ejection reflex in rabbits. *J. Endocrin.*, **8**, xiii–xiv.

Cross, B. A., R. F. W. Goodwin, and I. A. Silver (1958), A histological and functional study of the mammary gland in normal and agalactic sows. *J. Endocrin.*, **17**, 63–74.

Cross, B. A., and G. W. Harris (1951), The neurohypophysis and "let-down" of milk. *J. Physiol.*, **113**, 35P.

Cross, B. A., and G. W. Harris (1952), The role of the neurohypophysis in the milk-ejection reflex. *J. Endocrin.*, **8**, 148–161.

Dethier, V. G. (1962), Neurological aspects of insect behavior. In E. L. Bliss (Ed.), *Roots of Behavior*, New York: Harper. Pp. 24–34.

Eibl-Eibesfeldt, I. (1955), Angeborenes und Erworbenes im Nestbauverhalten der Wanderratte. *Naturwissenschaften*, **42**, 633–634.

Eibl-Eibesfeldt, I. (1958), Das Verhalten der Nagetiere. *Handb. Zool., Berlin*, Bd. 8, Lfg. 12, Teil 10, 1–88.

Harris, G. W. (1958), The central nervous system, neurohypophysis and milk ejection. *Proc. roy. Soc.*, **149**, Ser. B, 336–353.

Hinde, R. A. (1962), The interaction of internal and external factors in the integration of canary reproduction. Paper read at Conference on Sexual Behavior, University of California, August 1962.

Hooker, C. W., and W. L. Williams (1940), Retardation of mammary involution in the mouse by irritation of the nipples. *Yale J. Biol. Med.*, **12**, 559–564.

Kinder, Elaine F. (1927), A study of the nest-building activity of the albino rat. *J. exp. Zool.* **47**, 117–161.

Labriola, J. (1953), Effects of Caesarean delivery upon maternal behavior in rats. *Proc. Soc. exp. Biol., N. Y.*, **83**, 556–557.

Lehrman, D. S. (1956), On the organization of maternal behavior and the problem of instinct. In P. P. Grassé (Ed.), *L'Instinct dans le Comportement des Animaux et de l'Homme*, Paris: Masson & Cie. Pp. 475–520.

Lehrman, D. S. (1959), Hormonal responses to external stimuli in birds. *Ibis*, **101**, 478–496.

Lehrman, D. S. (1961), Hormonal regulation of parental behavior in birds and infrahuman mammals. In W. C. Young (Ed.), *Sex and Internal Secretions*, 3rd ed., Baltimore: Williams and Wilkins. Pp. 1268–1382.

Lehrman, D. S. (1962), Interaction of hormonal and experiential influences on development of behavior. In E. L. Bliss (Ed.), *Roots of Behavior*, New York: Harper. Pp. 142–156.

Lott, D. F. (1962), The role of progesterone in the maternal behavior of rodents. *J. comp. physiol. Psychol.*, **55**, 610–613.

Lott, D. F., and Stephanie S. Fuchs (1962), Failure to induce retrieving by sensitization or the injection of prolactin. *J. comp. physiol. Psychol.*, **55**, 1111–1113.

Meites, J., and C. W. Turner (1942), Studies concerning mechanism controlling initiation of lactation at parturition. IV. Influence of suckling on lactogen content of pituitary of postpartum rabbits. *Endocrinology*, **31**, 340–344.

Meites, J., and C. W. Turner (1948), Studies concerning the induction and maintenance of lactation. II. The normal maintenance and experimental inhibition and augmentation of lactation. *Res. Bull. Mo. agric. Exp. Sta.*, No. 416.

Munn, N. L. (1950), *Handbook of Psychological Research on the Rat*, Boston: Houghton Mifflin.

Nicoll, C. S., and J. Meites (1959), Prolongation of lactation in the rat by litter replacement. *Proc. Soc. exp. Biol., N. Y.*, **101**, 81–82.

Richter, C. P. (1937), Hypophyseal control of behavior. *Cold Spr. Harb. Symp. quant. Biol.*, **5**, 258–268.

Richter, C. P., and J. F. Eckert (1936), Behavior changes produced in the rat by hypophysectomy. *Proc. Ass. Res. nerv. Dis.*, **17**, 561–571.

Rosenblatt, J. S., and L. R. Aronson (1958a), The influence of experience on the behavioural effects of androgen in prepuberally castrated male cats. *Anim. Behav.*, **6**, 171–182.

Rosenblatt, J. S., and L. R. Aronson (1958b), The decline of sexual behavior in male cats after castration with special reference to the role of prior sexual experience. *Behaviour*, **12**, 285–338.

Rosenblatt, J. S., G. Turkewitz, and T. C. Schneirla (1962), Development of suckling and related behavior in neonate kittens. In E. L. Bliss (Ed.), *Roots of Behavior*, New York: Harper. Pp. 198–210.

Rothchild, I. 1960. The corpus luteum-pituitary relationship: the association between the cause of luteotrophin secretion and the cause of follicular quiescence during lactation; the basis for a tentative theory of the corpus luteum-pituitary relationship in the rat. *Endocrinology*, **67**, 9–41.

Rothchild, I., and E. J. Quilligan (1960), The corpus luteum-pituitary relationship: on the reports that oxytocin stimulates the secretion of luteotrophin. *Endocrinology*, **67**, 122–125.

Rowell, Thelma E. (1960), On the retrieving of young and other behaviour in lactating golden hamsters. *Proc. zool. Soc. Lond.*, **135**, 265–282.

Schneirla, T. C. (1938), A theory of army-ant behavior based upon the analysis of activities in a representative species. *J. comp. Psychol.*, **25**, 51–90.

Schneirla, T. C. (1949), Levels in the psychological capacities of animals. In R. W. Sellars, V. J. McGill, and M. Farber (Eds.), *Philosophy for the Future*, New York: Macmillan. Pp. 243–286.

Schneirla, T. C., and J. S. Rosenblatt (1961), Behavioral organization and genesis of the social bond in insects and mammals. *Amer. J. Orthopsychiat.*, **31**, 223–253.

Selye, H. (1934), On the nervous control of lactation. *Amer. J. Physiol.*, **107**, 535–538.

Slijper, E. J. (1960), Die Geburt der Säugetiere. In *Handb. Zool., Berlin*, Bd. 8, Lfg. 25, Teil 9, 1–108.

Steinberg, June, and D. Bindra (1962), Effects of pregnancy and salt-intake on genital licking. *J. comp. physiol. Psychol.*, **55**, 103–106.

Stone, C. P., and W. A. Mason (1955), Effects of hypophysectomy on behavior in rats: III. Thermoregulatory behavior. *J. comp. physiol. Psychol.*, **48**, 456–462.

Sturman-Hulbe, Mary, and C. P. Stone (1929), Maternal behavior in the albino rat. *J. comp. Psychol.*, **9**, 203–237.

Uyldert, Ina E. (1946), A conditioned reflex as a factor influencing the lactation of rats. *Acta brev. neerl. Physiol.*, **14**, 86–89.

Wiesner, B. P., and Norah M. Sheard (1933), *Maternal Behaviour in the Rat*, London: Oliver and Boyd.

Young, W. C. (1961), The hormones and mating behavior. In W. C. Young (Ed.), *Sex and Internal Secretions*, 3rd ed., Baltimore: Williams and Wilkins. Pp. 1173–1239.

Young, W. C. (1962), Patterning of sexual behavior. In E. L. Bliss (Ed.), *Roots of Behavior*, New York: Harper. Pp. 115–122.

Zarrow, M. X. (1961), Gestation. In W. C. Young (Ed.),*Sex and Internal Secretions*, 3rd ed., Baltimore: Williams and Wilkins. Pp. 958–1031.

2

maternal behavior in
PEROMYSCUS

John A. King

This chapter compares the maternal behavior of two subspecies of deermice and, in addition, provides comparative material from other species within the genus *Peromyscus*. Comparisons of behavior can be made at all degrees of genetic diversity, ranging from a difference in a single gene to a difference in chromosomal arrangements. In order to segment this continuum of genetic diversity into manageable and meaningful categories, three levels of comparison can be recognized: (1) genetic, (2) specific, and (3) phyletic. These categories indicate degree of genetic diversity and establish techniques and aims of the comparison rather than hard and fast boundaries. The first two categories include a much smaller proportion of genetic diversity occurring in the animal kingdom than the last (King and Nichols, 1960).

The object of genetic comparisons is to analyze the genetic mechanisms in behavior, which may include the techniques of population genetics, selection, and physiological or ecological genetics of behavior. Genetic level comparisons are made between animals of the same species but which differ by a few, often recognizable, genes, such as

Studies by the author reported in this chapter were supported by research Grants MH-123 and M-5643 from the National Institutes of Health of the United States Public Health Service.

breeds of dogs, inbred lines or mutant strains of mice, and geographical varieties of *Drosophila*. Chapter 3 provides an illustration of this level of comparison using various races of rabbits. The actual number of divergent genes is rarely known, except in comparisons of animals with single gene differences.

Specific or species comparisons refer to the degree of genetic diversity found among animals of closely related species, but may also include comparisons at the subspecies and generic levels. An example of generic comparisons is given by Altmann, using the elk *(Cervus)* and moose *(Alces)* in Chapter 7. Because this chapter illustrates subspecies and species comparisons, the objectives of this level of comparison will be examined in detail. The primary objective of species comparisons is to define homologous patterns of behavior and the effect of evolutionary factors on behavior.

Homologous patterns of behavior occur in two or more species as a result of a common origin in divergent evolution. Usually the frequency or similarity of homologous behavior decreases as the distance of relationship between species increases. Homologous behavior patterns, which must be genetically determined, tend to be conservative traits which are retained among species utilizing different environments. Tracing a homologous pattern of behavior requires an almost continuous sequence of closely related animals. Comparisons of species from any family, order, or class are not suitable, because a closely related species often fails to show a trait common to distantly related species. An interruption in the phylogenetic sequence of a trait indicates either that it is not homologous or that the closely related species lacking it is very exceptional and specialized. Unwarranted generalizations derived from the discovery of a trait which occurs in many different species can be prevented by the search for homologous patterns. For example, maternal defense of young is so common among mammals that one may conclude it is an essential mammalian characteristic which tolerates little variability. It will be seen later that two closely related subspecies of mice differ in this trait. If infant *Macacus mulattus* requires "contact comfort," and the same is demonstrated for *Pan chimpanse*, one should not conclude that it is also necessary for the human infant. Perhaps infant *Macacus cynomolgus* needs "straddling stimulation."

The other principal objective of species comparisons is to assess the effect of natural selection upon behavior. Although homology deals with conservative patterns, this objective often deals with plastic patterns, which are modified through natural selection. Attempt is made to isolate environmental factors responsible for differences in the behavior of two species. Conspicuous environmental factors are more likely to be responsible for behavioral differences between closely related species, which have similar requirements, than between distantly related species. Temperature differences are less likely to be responsible for the differences in nest construction exhibited by hares *(Lepus)* and rabbits *(Oryctolagus)* than for differences between closely related species of mice. Selection not only operates on a particular behavior pattern but also upon other characters which necessitate the acquisition of a compatible behavior trait. The adaptation of a species of mouse to the grasslands may necessitate the use of grass in the nest, although the grass itself is of neutral selective value.

The third type of comparison, phyletic, contains the remainder of genetic diversity occurring in the animal kingdom, from genera through phyla. Usually some limited segment of the animal kingdom, such as the class Mammalia represented in this book, is selected for comparison. Sometimes the scope of phyletic comparisons is larger and an entire phylum or even several phyla may be used, such as comparisons among earthworms, snails, ants, and rats. The scope of these comparisons reveals little about genetic mechanisms or the evolution of behavior. Rather, phyletic comparisons relate general behavioral capacities to various stages in the evolutionary development of physiological processes or anatomical structures. Phyletic comparisons also permit holding certain physiological features constant while the variety of behavior they exhibit is investigated. Comparisons of maternal behavior as illustrated by the various chapters are of interest because all mammals have a common physiological process for the nutrition of their infants. What, if any, behavioral patterns are common to this class and to what extent can the differences in behavior be attributed to variations in the process of supplying the neonate with milk?

The species compared in this chapter are cricetid rodents of the genus *Peromyscus*. About 56 species are recognized and these have diverged into well over 200 subspecies. Table 1 lists those forms mentioned in this chapter. Corresponding to the wide distribution and proliferation of the genus, some representative of the genus occurs in most habitats on the North American continent. Although no single description of the mouse would pertain to all species, the general size and bodily configuration are similar to those of the house mouse, with the conspicuous exception of the large eyes possessed by *Peromyscus* (King, 1961a).

The types of responses exhibited in the maternal care of *Peromyscus* can be described briefly in a naturalistic fashion based on the studies

TABLE 1
Classification of Species and Subspecies of the Genus Peromyscus Described in Text

Subgenus	Species Group	Species	Subspecies
Peromyscus	maniculatus	maniculatus	bairdii
Peromyscus	maniculatus	maniculatus	gracilis
Peromyscus	maniculatus	maniculatus	artemesiae
Peromyscus	maniculatus	maniculatus	nebrascensis
Peromyscus	maniculatus	maniculatus	abietorum
Peromyscus	maniculatus	maniculatus	osgoodi
Peromyscus	maniculatus	maniculatus	gambelli
Peromyscus	maniculatus	polionotus	polionotus
Peromyscus	leucopus	leucopus	noveboracensis
Peromyscus	leucopus	gossypinus	gossypinus
Peromyscus	boylii	boylii	—
Peromyscus	truei	truei	—
Haplomylomys	—	californicus	—
Podomys	—	floridanus	—

After Hall and Kelson, 1959.

cited later. The female locates a site and builds a nest prior to parturition. Gestation ended, she gives birth to her litter, cleans them of the amnion and umbilical cord, and usually eats the afterbirth. The mother then exhibits a daily routine of nursing and cleaning her young. During the nursing period she may move the young to a new nest or retrieve them to her old nest when they are displaced. She usually shows aggression towards strange intruders into the nest. Later, the young are weaned and exposed outside the nest. At any point in this process, the usual pattern may be disrupted and the young abandoned, injured, killed, or eaten. Each of these general patterns produces a number of observable and comparable responses which will be examined.

Only a few of these maternal responses will be found in the following comparisons and, when they appear, the number of species reported on is few indeed. Some observations are obtained from the field and present just a glimpse into the maternal behavior of the mice. Other observations are from careful, but incomplete, laboratory experiments. A number of the experiments reported are original or previously published studies done in the laboratory at the Roscoe B. Jackson Memorial Laboratory. The result of these field and laboratory studies is not a thorough comparative study of maternal behavior in Peromyscus, but an illustration of species level comparisons that may permit formation of hypotheses. The development of behavior in the young will be predominantly affected by homologous patterns in the mother or by her relatively recent adaptations to the selective pressures of her particular environment.

Nests

The nests of *Peromyscus* function as refuges from predators, homes during periods of diurnal inactivity, and nurseries for the young (Blair, 1951; Howard, 1949). Insulation provided by the nesting material conserves the body heat of the small mice. Neonatal mice, lacking pelage and weighing about 2 grams, are partially poikilothermic, but they endure chilling only at the expense of metabolic activity and growth (Adolph, 1948; Morrison and Ryser, 1959). With increasing age, homoiothermy develops and they depend upon the insulation provided by pelage and nests. The nest site and material, and the presence of heat-providing adults, are critical to the survival and development of the blind, nonmotile neonates (King and Connon, 1955).

SITES

Nest sites may be classified as (1) subterranean, (2) arboreal, and (3) surface. Subterranean sites are typically used by mice living in habitats devoid of brush and trees or the debris they create on the surface. *Peromyscus polionotus,* which often lives among the sand dunes of our southeastern coast, digs burrows 2 or 3 feet long in the loose sand (Blair, 1951; Ivy, 1949; Sumner and Karol, 1929). The nature of the soil determines, to some extent, the depth and size of the nest chamber (Hayne, 1936). *P. polionotus* frequently plug their burrows with loose sand and have an escape tunnel leading from the nest. Within the home range, twenty burrows may be used from time to time by the resident individuals (Blair, 1951). The mice also use the burrows of crabs with which they are sometimes associated. Another resident of the sandy soils of Florida is *Peromyscus floridanus,* which builds subterranean nests, often burrowing laterally from the much larger tunnels of the gopher turtle (Blair and Kilby, 1936).

Subterranean nest sites are also used by species of *Peromyscus* living on the prairies and grasslands of the Midwest. *P. maniculatus bairdii* dig their own shallow burrows or use the burrows of ground squirrels and other small mammals (Blair, 1940). Another race of *maniculatus (gambelli)* regularly escaped into gopher, mole, and spider holes, but actual nests were discovered only on the surface amid accumulations of brush and leaves (McCabe and Blanchard, 1950). *P. m. bairdii* readily utilize subterranean nest boxes provided by the investigator (Howard, 1949). *Peromyscus leucopus, P. boylii, P. nasutus,* and other species often live in rocky areas, where they place their nests in crevasses between piles of rocks or on cliffs and rock outcroppings (Drake, 1958; Hoffmeister, 1951; Long, 1961; Quast, 1954; Rainey, 1955).

Many *Peromyscus* nests are at the ground surface under or amid the accumulation of litter, logs, brush, wood, or rock slabs. The abundance of such sites, requiring the minimum amount of excavation, renders them acceptable to most species. *P. m. bairdii* living along sand beaches make their nests under planks and logs lying on the beach (Dice, 1932). *P. leucopus* nests have been found under stone heaps, old logs, trash piles, flat rocks, and wood piles (Burt, 1940; Edwards and Pitts, 1952; Fitch, 1958; Metzger, 1955). This species is also attracted to artificial nest sites placed on the ground (Blair and Kennerly, 1959). Abundant surface nest sites about farm buildings, cabins, or rural dwellings provide the homes for many families of *P. leucopus* and *P. maniculatus* (Hall, 1928; Schorger, 1956).

Hollow palm logs are a favorite site for *P. gossypinus* in Florida (Ivy, 1949), whereas in the lowlands of Tennessee this species nest under logs or brush piles or amid thick moss accumulations on floating logs (Goodpaster and Hoffmeister, 1954). The abandoned nests of woodrats *(Neotoma)* or piles of sticks and leaves brought together by the mice themselves are used by some species. *P. truei, P. californicus,* and *P. leucopus* are frequent inhabitants of this type of surface nest (Fitch, 1958; McCabe and Blanchard, 1950).

Arboreal nests of *Peromyscus* again reflect their ability to exploit any suitable location found in tree hollows, old woodpecker holes, abandoned nests of squirrels or birds. Such sites have been the homes for *P. leucopus* (Barbour, 1951; Burt, 1940; Edwards and Pitts, 1952; Metzger, 1955), *P. gossypinus* (Ivy, 1949; Goodpaster and Hoffmeister, 1954), and *P. maniculatus* (Dice, 1925; Manville, 1949). Unique arboreal nests are made by a closely related genus *(Ochrotomys)*, which has just recently been removed from the genus *Peromyscus* (Hooper, 1958). These nests are globular structures in a tangle of vines or bushes 4 to 50 feet off the ground (Barbour, 1942; Goodpaster and Hoffmeister, 1954; Ivy, 1949). Artificial nest boxes placed on trees are readily occupied by *P. leucopus* (Blair and Kennerly, 1959; Jackson, 1953; Nicholson, 1941).

Tests of nest-site selection have been given to free-living mice by offering them nest boxes on the ground or attached to trees. In Michigan, Nicholson (1941) found that boxes located in trees 3 to 30 feet above ground were used by 86% of a population of 325 *P. leucopus*. The surface boxes were used more frequently in the winter, which agrees with the findings by Blair and Kennerly (1959) in Texas. An artificial population of *P. maniculatus* enclosed in an outdoor pen occupied elevated nest boxes more frequently than surface boxes (Evans, 1957).

MATERIAL

Most of the authors cited refer to the type of nesting material used by *Peromyscus*. The type of material used depends largely on its availability. The inner lining of the nest usually consists of a soft fiber, such as fur, wool, feathers, cotton, paper, palm fiber, thistledown, milkweed silk, moss, or a coarse material, finely chewed and shredded, such as cedar bark, roots, leaves, and stems of various plants. One mouse traveled over 100 feet to obtain thistledown for its nest (Dice, 1932). An investigator may often locate a mouse nest by following trails of cotton fiber left by the mice as they carry it to their nests. The type and texture of the material grade outwardly from the soft, compact lining to the coarse and bulky exterior. Leaves constitute the most common exterior, but Spanish moss, twigs, conifer needles, and small sticks are sometimes added, depending on the materials available.

The amount of nesting material used by *Peromyscus* has been examined experimentally. In a temperature-controlled cabinet, the amount of paper shredded for nests by *P. m. osgoodi* varies inversely with the temperature. Light is also a factor reducing the amount of material shredded by the mice, except at low temperature (Thorne, 1958). The thermoregulatory, hormonal, and parental aspects of nest building in rodents have recently been reviewed by Lehrman (1961).

A comparative study of nest-building behavior in three forms of *Peromyscus (P. floridanus, P. m. bairdii,* and *P. m. gracilis)* has recently been completed in the laboratory (with the assistance of Dianne Maas). Quilting cotton was rolled into small bales of about 20 grams and forced into a 3 inch diameter cup made of ¼ inch wire mesh. The cup was suspended from the top of a plastic cage (12 inches × 12 inches × 6 inches) in the same way the food was presented. The experimental room was kept at a constant temperature of $70° \pm 2°F$. A 12-hour, light-dark cycle was maintained, corresponding to the natural daily cycle. Each day the quantity of cotton removed from the cup by the mice was obtained by weighing the remainder to the nearest 1/10 gram. Cotton used in the nest became fouled and useless as a measure. Tests were run for four successive days. All mice were tested between 3 and 4 months of age. The numbers of mice used were: 26 females, 24 males of *bairdii* and *gracilis,* 8 females and 9 males of *floridanus.*

P. m. gracilis took a mean of 2.8 grams of cotton each day; *P. m. bairdii* took 1.8 grams, and *P. floridanus* took an average of 1.0 grams. The differences among the three groups were significant. Differences in the quantity of cotton used by each sex were not significant, but there were significant differences in day-to-day variability. Males tended to be less variable than females, whose performance may be affected by endocrine factors related to estrus. Although these mice had been raised and bred in the laboratory for several generations, the quantity of nesting material used under the same experimental conditions is related to the geographical distribution of the species. The most northernly distributed, *gracilis*, build larger nests than their southern relatives, *bairdii*, and both of these build larger nests than the southernmost *floridanus*.

NEST COHABITANTS

Although the site of the nest, type, and amount of nesting material are essential to the physical well-being of the neonates, these factors probably have little effect on the behavior of the young, unless they later select nest sites and materials similar to those in which they were raised. On the other hand, the presence of nest cohabitants other than the mother may affect their behavior. A previous litter from the same mother can crowd the neonates, compete with them for the mother's milk, and constantly stimulate them by their activities. The father may also stimulate the neonates as well as share in their care (Horner, 1947). Unrelated mice, such as other females, their litters, juveniles, or other males which occupy the same nest may affect the development of behavior of the young. They can at least acquaint the young with a variety of odors not associated with the mother.

Peromyscus tends to be monogamous during the breeding season, as determined by the most frequently observed sex combinations (Blair, 1951; Howard, 1949). Previous litters of *P. maniculatus*, usually the last two litters of the season, often remain with the parents throughout the winter (Blair, 1958; Howard, 1949). The fall-born mice consequently have a different social environment from the spring-born mice, even when produced by the same mother. The tendency of litters to remain together in the fall has also been observed in *P. leucopus* (Nicholson, 1941). Usually the preceding litter disperses at weaning when a new litter arrives or the mother moves to a different nest (Howard, 1949). In the laboratory, two succeeding litters are often raised successfully together in a small cage.

The father is sometimes associated with the mother and a newborn litter, but frequently he is absent from the nest until the young are near weaning age (Nicholson, 1941). Mothers are aggressive toward strange males and even their mates when they have a litter (King, 1958). Presumed fathers have been found with their litters in *P. leucopus* (Nicholson, 1941) and *P. maniculatus* (Blair, 1958; Howard, 1949), the two most commonly studied species in the field. In the laboratory, the usual practice is to mate pairs and leave them together throughout the birth and development of the young. Some individual females tend to exclude their mates from the nest in the laboratory (Dice, 1929), but the male often occupies the nest with the female and young.

Aside from the parents, other nest occupants are sometimes additional females and occasionally their litters. Exchange of the young between the females occurs and the young suckle the females indiscriminately. Of 185 litters of *P. maniculatus bairdii* observed in the field, Howard (1949) found three cases, or six litters which were raised simultaneously by two females. One pair of lactating females consisted of a mother and her daughter, both with their own litters. Two lactating females of *P. maniculatus* were found together with their litters as well as with one or two males (Blair, 1958; Hansen, 1957). In these nursery aggregations, the litters of the two females may be of different ages (Barbour and Gault, 1953). Unfortunately, the nest life of the young *Peromyscus* in the field is known only for a few species. However, it is clear that even within a species, considerable variation occurs in the social environment of the young.

Parturition

Parturition has been observed only in captive mice and there are few published observations of this process. Pournelle (1952) found that 65% of 26 litters of *P. gossypinus* were born between 6 A.M. and noon in the laboratory, and 15% were born between noon and 6 P.M. The only records of nocturnal parturition were from three litters born in live traps left out overnight. In the laboratory, where the lights were on from 7:30 A.M. to 5:30 P.M., C. R. Terman (unpublished) recorded 98 litters born during the periods of light and 21 litters born during periods of darkness from approximately 50 breeding pairs of *P. m. bairdii*. Of 52 litters, whose hour of birth was more closely recorded, 61% were born between 8 A.M. and noon, 22% between noon and 4:30 P.M. and 17% after 4:30 P.M., mostly during periods of darkness. Parturition in these nocturnally active mice primarily occurs during the day while they are in their nests.

The descriptions of parturition in *Peromyscus* reveal a great deal of variability. In one instance, a parturient *P. m. artemisiae* female squatted, licked her perineum, "pulled the region surrounding the vulva aside with her paws and simultaneously with a contraction of the abdominal muscles, the head of a young mouse appeared" (Svihla, 1932, p. 11). The female then pulled the young out with her teeth, picked it up, and licked it. Immediately after, the placenta appeared and the mother ate it, breaking the umbilical cord in the process of stretching it. Three young were born in an hour and they were nursing within 2 hours. In *P. m. nebrascensis,* Clark (1937) observed six young born in 15 minutes. Birth was aided by the mother pulling the young with her forefeet. The afterbirth was eaten. A different female produced seven young at intervals of 25, 25, 25, 10, 15, and 5 minutes, for a total of 105 minutes. The mother hunched on the floor, put forepaws on each side of vulva, and licked the young as they appeared. She did not use her teeth in the delivery. The afterbirth was eaten immediately after each birth. Five births in *Peromyscus gossypinus* were observed by Pournelle (1952). In one litter, four young were delivered in 36 minutes. The mean time for the delivery of five litters was 55 minutes; 12 of the 19 young were produced in breech deliveries.

In general, the mother assists delivery of the young with forepaws or teeth and by contraction of the abdominal muscles. The placenta is eaten after birth and the young are thoroughly licked. Most deliveries last about an hour. The young are usually gathered into a group around the mother. Breech deliveries are common.

Routine daily care

The environment most likely to affect the growth and behavior of the young is the care the mother gives them from day to day. Experimental manipulation of young *Peromyscus* during their neonatal period has been shown to be a factor in their adult performance in a learning situation (King and Eleftheriou, 1959). Studies on the neonate rat also demonstrated the importance of stimulation during this period (Denenberg et al., 1962; Levine, 1962a; Levine, 1962b). Much of the stimulation neonatal mammals receive is provided by the mother in caring for them.

Quantitative measures of the maternal care in mice are scarce, because observations should extend throughout the day and last for 3 weeks. Automatic recording apparatus can assist, but it usually records only a few of the maternal responses at a time. R. L. Webster, F. M. Hart, and I used an automatic device to record for *Peromyscus* the frequency with which the mothers went to the nest and the duration of time spent inside the nest with their young. These variables were examined under two different lighting conditions. *P. maniculatus bairdii* and *P. m. gracilis*, which had been laboratory bred for a period of approximately 12 years, served as subjects. In the first experiment, 14 *bairdii* matrons and 12 *gracilis* matrons were used. Four virgin females of each subspecies were studied as controls. The second experiment used 10 matrons and 10 virgins of each subspecies.

The mice were housed in a row of six cage units, kept in a room lighted 24 hours a day, with the level of illumination 16 to 23 foot-candles over the cages. A masking noise reduced the effect of periodic sounds outside the experimental room. Each cage unit consisted of a 4 inch cubed nest box connected to a 6 inch × 6 inch × 12 inch plastic cage by a treadle tunnel, which recorded the frequency and duration of the mouse's entrances and exits from the nest box on an Esterline-Angus recorder. Food and water were available in the cage and cotton was provided in the nest box.

The matrons were placed in the apparatus about 3 days before parturition and their behavior recorded for 10 days postpartum. After 10 days, the possible interference of the young mice going through the treadle tunnel made the records suspect. Litter size varied from three to seven with a mode of four. Daily examination of the mice was made from 11 A.M. until noon, during which time the records were not used. The detailed records were reduced to quarter-hour periods for the analysis of (1) total number of minutes in the nest, (2) longest single period in the nest, (3) mean duration of periods in the nest, and (4) frequency of visits to the nest. Analysis of variance for each measure included subspecies and days.

In the first experiment, gracilis spent significantly more time in the nest than did *bairdii* on each of the postpartum days (Fig. 1). *Gracilis* was with the young about 19 to 21 hours of each 23-hour day, and *bairdii* about 1 hour less each day. Although these are gross records, the amount of time with the young is considerable, particularly in comparison with the rabbit, which may spend only 5 minutes per day with their young (Chapter 3).

The duration of periods in the nest was obtained by dividing the total time in the nest by the frequency and is therefore dependent upon these other two measures. Subspecific differences indicated by this measure were more extreme, with *gracilis* spending significantly longer periods in the nest than *bairdii* (Fig. 2). The mean duration in the nest was from 75 to 120 minutes for *gracilis,* and 40 to 80 minutes for *bairdii.* Both subspecies showed a significant decrease in mean duration of periods in the nest over days as the young grew older.

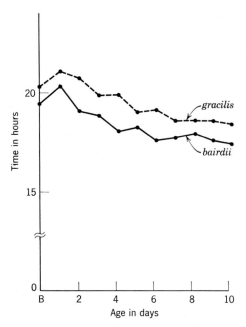

FIG. 1. *Mean number of hours* bairdii *and* gracilis *mothers spent in the nest with their offspring.*

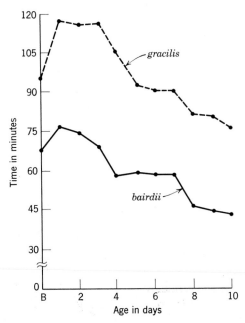

FIG. 2. *Mean number of minutes* bairdii *and* gracilis *mothers spent in nest with their offspring during each visit.*

Since the preceding two measures included many relatively short visits to the nest when nursing was unlikely, the longest uninterrupted period is probably the best estimate of the time actually spent nursing the young. The mean longest period for *gracilis* was 345 minutes, and for *bairdii* 210 minutes, on the first day (Fig. 3). A significant decrease

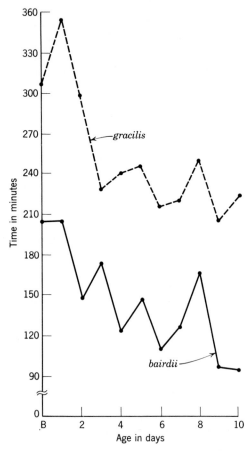

FIG. 3. *Mean number of minutes* bairdii *and* gracilis *mothers spent in the nest with their offspring during longest uninterrupted period.*

in this period throughout the ten days for both subspecies reduced the period to 175 minutes for *gracilis*, and to 75 minutes for *bairdii*, on the ninth day.

A measure of quarter-hour visits to the nest excluding the frequent short bursts of activity is presented in Figure 4. *Bairdii* went in and out of the nest significantly more often than *gracilis,* and there was a tendency to increase the number of these trips with the age of the young.

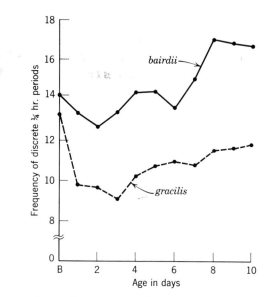

FIG. 4. *Mean number of discrete quarter hour periods* bairdii *and* gracilis *mothers visited their nest each day; visits less than a quarter hour duration were not counted.*

Neither subspecies showed any evidence of periodicity under continuous light in contrast to the normal periodicity shown by these nocturnal mice (Rawson, 1959). Although the number of virgins used was too small for statistical analysis, the virgins differed from the matrons by exhibiting circadian periodicity which is characteristic of mice kept under constant lighting conditions (Rawson, 1959). Maternity obviously interrupts normal periodicity.

The same apparatus and procedures were used in the second experiment. The difference was a change from continuous light to a 12-hour, light-dark cycle. Equal numbers of virgin controls were used and the young mice were weighed daily in order to ascertain the effect of amount of time the mothers were in the nest on the growth of the young.

The total amount of time in the nest was similar to the results from the first experiment: *gracilis* matrons were in the nest about 20 hours and *bairdii* matrons about an hour to 2 hours less each day (Fig. 5). Both subspecies spent less time in the nest as the age of the young increased. Virgins spent significantly less time in the nests than the matrons, averaging about 14 hours per day. Although the *gracilis* virgins consistently spent more time in the nest than the *bairdii* virgins, the difference was not significant. In addition to the difference in maternity, the analysis revealed a highly significant subspecies-maternity-days interaction. This indicates that the matrons of each subspecies diverged from each other over the ten-day period of suckling the young, whereas the virgins of both subspecies remained the same.

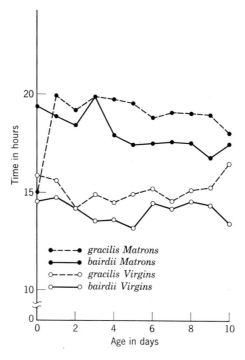

FIG. 5. *Mean number of hours* bairdii *and* gracilis *mothers and virgins spent in nest each day.*

The frequency of discrete periods was not significantly different between subspecies or between maternity and virginity. Measures on duration and longest uninterrupted periods were not completed for the second experiment.

The 12-hour light cycle kept the virgins on regular rhythms of nocturnal activity with no trace of circadian patterns. The matrons also tended to confine their periods outside the nest to the dark 12 hours, but without the regularity of the virgins. Some individuals spent relatively long periods out during light hours.

The results demonstrate that mothers (1) spent the major portion of the day with their neonatal offspring; (2) had their usual periods of activity interrupted; (3) spent less time with the young as the age of the young increased; and that (4) mice as closely related as subspecies differed in the amount of time spent with the young. These experiments failed to reveal any differential effect on the growth of the mice nor did they indicate how much of the time spent with the young was actual nursing time. We would particularly like to know about the various types of behavior displayed by the mother during the lactation period.

Transport of young

FIELD OBSERVATIONS

When a nest is disturbed, the mother frequently will move the young across open space, in full light, and before a human observer—conditions usually avoided by the mice. One *Peromyscus leucopus* mother fled from her nest and scattered the young as they fell off her nipples. She later returned, picked them up, and carried them, one by one, up a canvas-covered wall to another refuge (Hall, 1928). Another mother of the same species removed her young from a disturbed nest in a potato hill and carried them to an adjacent field at intervals of 7 minutes (Smith, 1939). Two communally nesting *P. maniculatus* mothers were captured in their nest and retained in cages while the young were weighed and examined. When released, one mother moved both litters to a nearby nest, where she was later joined by the other mother (Hansen, 1957). Nest box studies have indicated that changing nests and transporting young are a regular occurrence among free-living mice (Howard, 1949; Nicholson, 1941).

POSITION OF HOLDING YOUNG

Huestis (1933) described how *P. maniculatus* mothers manipulated the young into a position where they were grasped on the belly by the teeth and transported with their backs exposed to any obstacles the mother might encounter. The young curved their bodies in toward the mother's head, thus making a compact bundle. This carrying position is common when the young are small and can be manipulated easily into position by the mother. Older mice are often transported by the nape of the neck or by the skin on their backs (King, 1958).

Retrieving is usually an experimentally induced response fashioned after the transport of young under natural conditions. Mothers regularly return their young to the nest after they have been removed by an experimenter and placed apart. This response was used to examine possible subspecific differences (King, 1958). Litters of eight females each of *P. m. bairdii* and *P. m. gracilis* were used. The young were removed from the nest, weighed, tested, and then returned to the corner farthest from the nest box of their foot-square cage. The interval between the time when the young were returned to the cage and the time when the mother retrieved the first, second, and the third young to the nest box was recorded. The test was repeated each day during the first 30 days in the life of the young.

Measures of the initial retrieving latency of the first, second, and third neonate, as well as the accumulated time to retrieve all three, revealed no significant differences between subspecies. The retrieving latency of the first neonate showed a marked decrease during the first 5 days, after which it leveled off at about 0.5 minutes (Fig. 6). The second and third neonates were retrieved immediately after the first was taken to the nest even on the first day. When 15 to 18 days of age, the young became quite active and returned to the nest by themselves or resisted the attempts of the mother to grasp them, thus making the measures inaccurate. The initial decrease in latency for retrieving the first young and expectant waiting for the young at the corner of the cage suggest that mothers learned the young were going to be returned. The absence of subspecies differences in retrieving may indicate that natural selection for this response is about the same for both subspecies.

Retrieving behavior of mothers varied considerably. Most mothers tended to wait for the return of the young and then either began to inspect them or immediately began to retrieve them. Some mothers picked up one young, set it down, and went to another before taking any to the nest. Others manipulated the young between their forefeet and mouth a few seconds before the young were suitably placed in the mouth and retrieved. Still others would grab the young by the nape, rump, or flank and carry or drag them into the nest. On the day of birth, mothers often attempted to build nests over the young at the place of return. This nest building response was not observed after the first day. When all the young were retrieved, the mothers usually came out from the nest and inspected the cage as if they were searching for more young. On the other hand, occasionally a mother would begin to nurse the young in the nest while one or two of the litter were still

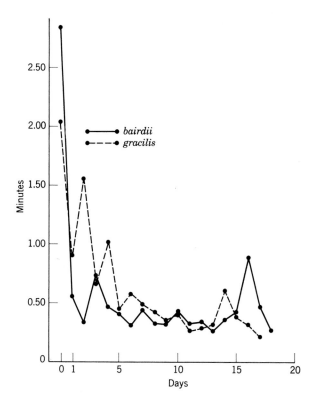

FIG. 6. Mean number of minutes bairdii and gracilis mothers took to retrieve the first young over the first 20 days postpartum. (From King, 1958, p. 181.)

outside. Further variability was noticed in the route taken by the mother to the nest. Some took the young directly to the nest while others circled the cage several times before entering. Despite these irregularities, the mean retrieving time remained quite constant in both subspecies.

The act of retrieving is an interaction between mother and young and changed markedly during the development of the young. The neonates were passive while being manipulated by the mother. As they grew older, they frequently resisted the attempts of the mother to retrieve them. Mothers repulsed by one young went to another, before struggling with those most irritable. At later ages, the young returned to the nest by themselves or came out of the nest after retrieval. The mother persisted in her efforts to keep the young in the nest by retrieving young which were now about one-third of her weight. These vain attempts to retrieve the active young stopped in a few days; at the end of the 30-day test period retrieving in any form had ceased.

NIPPLE CLINGING

Unlike the laboratory rat and mouse, the young of many species of cricetid rodents cling to the mother's nipples when she is frightened from the nest and drag along behind her when she runs. Variations in clinging were observed between subspecies and the nutritional state of the young. Hungry or malnourished young appear to cling more tenaciously than well-fed young; however, this variable has not been examined. The adaptive value of nipple-clinging appears to be the removal of young as well as the mother from a nest disturbed by a predator. Mothers leaving the nest without being startled release the hold of the young by stretching and slowly moving off the nest. Once the disturbed young become attached, she must forcibly pull them off, often with great difficulty. Indeed, the young become so firmly attached to the nipples that the mother and her remaining young can be lifted off the floor of the cage by picking up one of the clinging young.

With the assistance of John Deshaies, tests were made of differences in clinging behavior among subspecies. Eleven litters of each *P. m. bairdii* and *P. m. gracilis* were reduced to four young per litter shortly after birth and examined for clinging from 3 to 20 days of age. The procedure involved picking up the mother by the tail with a pair of 10 inch, rubber-tipped forceps and holding her above the cage for 30 seconds each day. The duration of clinging while the young supported themselves only by their mouths attached to the mother's nipples and the number of young clinging were recorded. This procedure involved several variables not controlled by the experimenter: length of time the young had been suckling prior to the test, behavior of the mother, and ease of capturing the mother by the tail.

The percentage of mice not clinging at the time of the test was significantly lower in *bairdii* than in *gracilis*. The mean percentage of nonclinging *bairdii* from the 4th through the 14th day of age was 40, whereas 74% of young *gracilis* failed to cling (Fig. 7). After the 14th day, the percentage of nonclinging *bairdii* rose to over 70 and remained that high until the 20th day when none of the mice clung. Some young *gracilis*, however, tended to cling throughout the 20 days of testing.

The duration of clinging among those mice which clung did not reveal such a distinct difference, although *bairdii* tended to cling longer than *gracilis*. The mean duration of clinging for *bairdii* over the 18

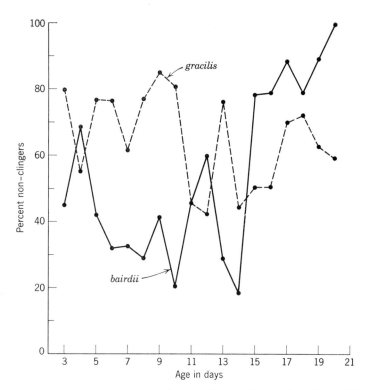

FIG. 7. *Percentage of young mice failing to cling to the nipples when held aloft for 30 seconds.*

test days was 20.5 seconds, with most individuals clinging the full 30 seconds. The mean for *gracilis* was 13.3 seconds with most individuals releasing their grasp before the 30-second test was completed. With increasing age, *bairdii* tended to decrease in clinging time, primarily after 15 days of age when their eyes are open.

Differences in the nipple-clinging tendencies of both subspecies may be related to the native habits of the two subspecies. The semi-arboreal *gracilis* often nest in trees and young clinging to the mother's nipples may be dropped to the ground when she hurriedly leaves the nest. Furthermore, the chances of young *gracilis* being destroyed by a predator in the nest are probably less than young *bairdii* encounter on the ground. When young *bairdii* cling to the nipples, they are dragged along the ground and can be easily retrieved. Our observations on this trait in foster mothers, particularly among mixed litters, reveal

Maternal Behavior in Peromyscus 77

that *bairdii* young will cling to a *gracilis* mother, whereas the young *gracilis* release their hold. Apparently, the difference is in the young and not in the behavior of the mother.[1]

VOCALIZATIONS

Young *Peromyscus* utter a high-pitched squeak when exposed to painful or noxious stimuli. A slight squeeze on the tail or rough manipulation by the mother will elicit the squeak. It is rarely heard during normal care. If the young are removed from the nest and placed where there is no external source of heat, they squeak frequently until decreased body heat and metabolism reduce squeaking frequency. Observation of the mother's reaction to the squeaking indicates that she will search for the young and retrieve them. Although the maternal response has not been examined, the squeaking frequency was measured with the assistance of J. C. Deshaies; and F. M. Hart obtained sonograms of the pitch, intensity, and duration of the squeaks.

The frequency of squeaking was counted in young removed from their mothers and placed alone upon the sawdust of a standard living cage for a period of 5 minutes in a red neon-lit room. The number of squeaks was counted with a hand counter. Each squeak, defined as a discrete expiration, was recorded, the squeaks tending to come in bursts. Since errors were introduced in counting, in temperature changes of the neonates, and by differences in the antecedent conditions, only significant differences can be considered.

The mean number of squeaks for *gracilis* was 43 and for *bairdii*, 11 during the 5-minute period throughout the ages tested; *gracilis* squeaked significantly more frequently than *bairdii* on most days. Both subspecies tended to reduce their squeaking with increasing age, but *bairdii* started the decline at 11 days of age, *gracilis*, at 15 days. The later decline of *gracilis* corresponds to their generally slower development, but the overall magnitude of the difference, even at the early ages when the subspecies are at similar stages in development, suggests a genetic difference.

A sonographic analysis of squeaks in a small sample of both *bairdii* and *gracilis* showed qualitative and quantitative differences (Fig. 8).

---

[1] Recent observations and writings of McCabe and Blanchard (1950) indicate that nipple clinging of *P. californicus* and *P. eremicus* in the subgenus *Haplomylomys* is of an entirely different order from that of *P. maniculatus*. The young *Haplomylomys* cling continuously and can be dislodged only with great difficulty. Durations for nipple clinging in these mice would run into hours rather than seconds as recorded for *maniculatus*.

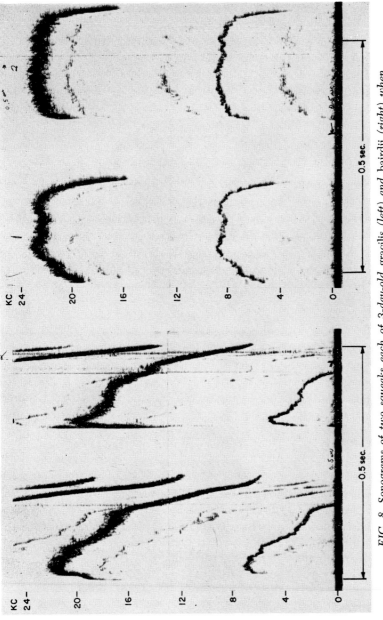

FIG. 8. Sonograms of two squeaks each of 3-day-old gracilis (left) and bairdii (right) when exposed alone to room temperature.

Young *bairdii* at three days tended to have a more sustained squeak at the same pitch, whereas the squeak of *gracilis* started high, then dropped in pitch and terminated with another high note. These differences persisted through 10 days of age, and became more extreme before they were incorporated into a more complex squeak at later ages. When *P. floridanus*, which belongs to an entirely different subgenus, was compared with both subspecies of *maniculatus*, similarities between *bairdii* and *gracilis* were revealed that were not apparent in *floridanus*. The squeak of 3-day old *floridanus* was shorter in duration and accompanied by complex overtones (Fig. 9). Differences in the squeaks of different species and subspecies of mice may provide a clue for maternal recognition of the young.

Defense of young

In the course of daily checking for litters among the breeding stock, it was noticed that pregnant females could easily be chased from their nests with 10-inch forceps. After the birth of their litters, however, the mothers often savagely attacked the forceps and retained their position over the young. This response was quantified with a rating scale from zero (no attack) to three (a savage attack). Mothers receiving a rating of three often clung so firmly with their teeth to the rubber tips on the forceps that they could be lifted from the nest. Eight mothers of *P. m. bairdii* and eight of *P. m. gracilis* were tested from parturition until the young were 30 days old. The attacks were recorded as the young were being removed from the nest with the forceps (King, 1958).

The results illustrated in Fig. 10 demonstrate that *bairdii* mothers attacked the forceps significantly more intensely than did the *gracilis* mothers. The *gracilis* mothers showed little fear; they frequently nosed the forceps, or they slowly left the nest, returned, and stuck their heads back in, as if watching the removal. Occasionally *gracilis* mothers grasped the young and pulled them from the forceps. This attentive and solicitous behavior was in sharp contrast to the severity of the attacks made by *bairdii* mothers.

Another form of defense shown by mother *Peromyscus* is related to territoriality. Dice (1929) noted that mothers frequently kept their mates from the nest during the early stages of lactation, although this is not always true (Horner, 1947). The same females in the study to be described and in the previous study were maintained in cages with only their litters, without mates or other adult mice. After the young were returned to the cage, a strange adult male was introduced and

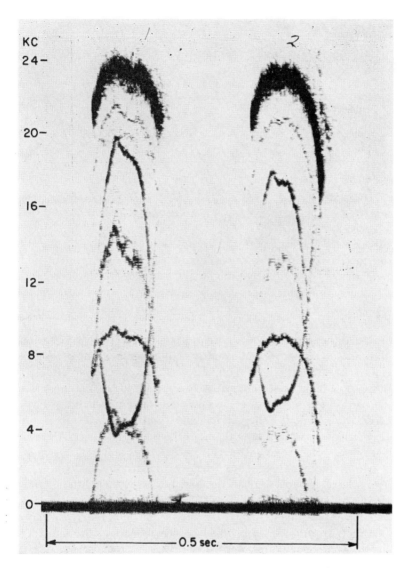

FIG. 9. Sonogram of two squeaks of a 3-day-old P. floridanus exposed alone to room temperature.

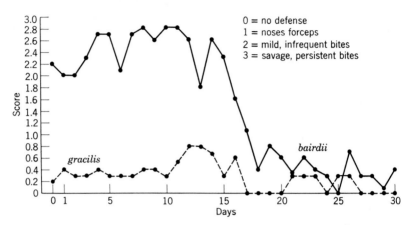

FIG. 10. Mean rating score of bairdii and gracilis mothers during attacks on forceps used to remove young from nest box. (From King, 1958, p. 180)

left there for a 5-minute period. This procedure tends to provoke attack under most circumstances, regardless of whether the resident animal is male, female, or a mother. Individual variability among nonreproducing females, however, is great and some will accept a strange male. Among lactating females, in contrast, only differences in the amount or intensity of the attack were observed.

Several different males were used as test animals. They were strangers to the mothers at the first encounter, but same males were reintroduced on alternate days. Number of attacks, latency to attack, and duration of attacks were measured. In contrast to the mildness which *gracilis* exhibited toward the forceps, they were unrelenting tigresses toward a strange male. They attacked at shorter latencies, more often, and for longer periods of time than did the *bairdii* mothers. An overlap in the scores of the two subspecies occurred in only one test period. The *bairdii* mothers were not friendly toward the male, but after several attacks usually went in the nest box with their litters. *Gracilis* mothers continued their attacks, even after the males showed complete submission. Those males which frequently encountered the attacking female soon abandoned the ineffective submissive posture and leaped wildly about the cage or attempted to dodge the female. Males rarely fought back.

When the young were old enough to come out of the nest box by themselves or to resist the retrieving attempts of the mother, they became exposed to the attacks of the mother as she chased the male. If the mother accidentally attacked a young, she released it, and then continued her attacks upon the male. Sometimes she tried to carry the young back to the nest or to localize it in a corner of the cage. A gradual diminution of the attacks upon the male occurred in both subspecies as the age of the young increased, perhaps as a result of the confusion they caused the mother.

Subspecies differences in the defense of the young in these two tests suggest that maternal defense provides a selective advantage for both subspecies, but in different circumstances. Reaction to the forceps may be an example of interspecific aggression, such as *bairdii* mothers show toward other genera of small mammals or vertebrates which may invade the terrestrial nest site. The intraspecific attacks toward the male by *gracilis* mothers may indicate that their less exposed arboreal nests are most vulnerable to the invasion of other mice.

Weaning

Under natural conditions, weaning is about the last maternal relationship *Peromyscus* mothers have with their offspring. As we have seen, some litters born in the autumn may remain with their parents, but under such circumstances maternal behavior is not apparent. The young usually depart from their natal home after they have been weaned. It has been postulated (Burt, 1940) that weaning the young may contribute to their forced departure. Actually we have little more than occasional observations on maternal behavior at weaning. Birth of another litter at weaning age can affect the relationship, but without systematic studies it is unknown how. Some mothers will nurse both litters simultaneously, whereas others seem to exclude the older litters. In the absence of a new litter, mothers can be expected to nurse longer. These variables are yet to be explored.

Most of the information about weaning concerns the age when it occurs. Svihla (1932) recorded the earliest age that young were weaned and also the oldest age that they were observed still nursing. For *P. maniculatus* and *P. leucopus*, he established 22 days as the youngest and 37 days as the oldest. The slower development of *P. truei* indicates a later weaning age, at least over a month, and one litter was not weaned until 40 days of age. *P. californicus* and *P. eremicus* are still slower in this respect, with the last suckling observed 44 days after birth. Within this genus we see one species which can be weaned at one-half the age of another species. Evaluation of these observations requires a more accurate estimate of weaning age.

The measure of weaning age that J. C. Deshaies, R. L. Webster, and the author employed was the earliest age at which the young could be kept from their mothers for 24 hours without a weight loss. Food (Purina Mouse Breeder Chow) and water were readily available at all times during the 24 hours of isolation. Unfortunately temperature varied as much as 10°F, from about 68° to 78°F. The separation and isolation of the young mice probably affected their propensity as well as their capacity to eat. In many respects this is an artificial measure of natural weaning, but it does establish accurately the age at which a mouse can maintain its own body weight apart from the mother. Young mice are usually adding body weight at this age, not merely maintaining it.

The two subspecies of *maniculatus, bairdii* and *gracilis* were used. All litters were reduced to 4 mice shortly after birth to keep nutritional variables as constant as possible. Only one mouse from each litter was tested at any given age and it was returned to the mother after the 24 hours to keep litter size constant for testing the siblings at other ages. Food consumption was measured, but only body weights are reported here. At least ten mice were tested at most ages in both subspecies, a total of 137 *gracilis* and 122 *bairdii,* from more than 65 litters.

At least half the *bairdii* were able to maintain or increase their weight by 17 days of age (Fig. 11). The number of mice gaining weight in-

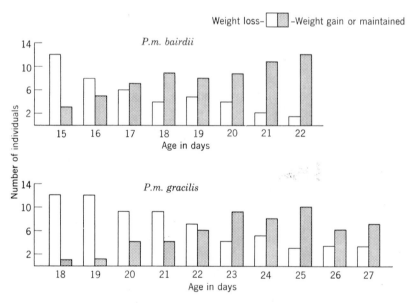

FIG. 11. Number of individual bairdii and gracilis losing or gaining body weight when separated from mother for 24 hours at age specified.

creased with age until only an exceptional individual or two failed to gain after 21 days of age. A similar shift from weight loss to weight gain occurred in at least 50% of the gracilis at 23 days of age. Furthermore, a substantial percentage of the young gracilis were still losing weight at 27 days, the oldest age examined. Although the usual age of weaning is probably later than 17 days in bairdii and 23 days in gracilis, these data reveal a significant difference in maturation rates. If similar measures were made on other species, such as the slowly developing P. truei or even slower P. californicus, the differences might be greater. Maternal influences on the young may thus be extended or abbreviated among different species and subspecies of Peromyscus.

Abnormal maternal responses

Any behavior which results in the death or injury of the young may be considered abnormal. There is almost no evidence that abnormal maternal behavior occurs under natural conditions, although it is likely that litters are occasionally deserted or eaten. Such treatment of the young may result from unusual disturbances to the nest or the mother at the time of parturition or lactation. The day-to-day disturbances of cleaning cages, feeding, inspecting for litters, as well as experimental procedures, can disrupt the normal pattern of maternal care in undomesticated mice. I am often amazed by the care mothers will give their offspring when they are transferred to a clean cage or when their young are removed each day for examination.

Captivity frequently provokes abnormal behavior. The extent of disturbance brought about by captivity is indicated by the reduction of fertility in many forms of mice brought into the laboratory. Some species adapt readily and breed soon after capture; P. m. bairdii are particularly adaptable, whereas P. m. gracilis are slower to breed. One subspecies, P. m. abietorum, has never bred for us in the laboratory without hormonal stimulation. Dice (1933) believes that the relatively warm, arid conditions of the laboratory are more suitable for breeding southern and desert form of Peromyscus than for boreal and forest forms.

Cannibalism is the most frequent type of abnormal behavior encountered in the laboratory. Of a total of 75 breeding females of P. maniculatus, 46 (61%) ate at least one of their litters. Ninety-three of 278 litters were eaten or about 34% of those recorded. To some extent these high percentages may reflect our husbandry practices. Most litters tend to be eaten at birth or shortly after, at least within the first week. A few litters are destroyed much later, even up to weaning. Usually if one individual of the litter is eaten, the others will be similarly treated later. Young mice that die are often consumed.

Some females eat every litter they produce, whereas others may destroy an occasional litter. Some females will raise several litters successfully, then start to eat them, and finally return to care for subsequent litters. The causes of cannibalism have not been explored. Although nutritional deficiencies are usually suspected, attempts to prevent cannibalism with supplemental diets have been unsuccessful. The absence of a suitable nest box in our breeding cages seems to be an important contributing factor.

Desertion, which leaves the young to die or too weak to nurse, is often preliminary to cannibalism. Extreme activity and restlessness on the part of the mother seem to be responsible for some desertions. One female that became restless after her litter was half grown was temporarily put under sedation. This single treatment was sufficient to return her to nursing the young until they were weaned, suggesting that tranquilizers might be profitably applied to restless mothers. The discomforts of mammary distension may cause the restlessness, thus depriving the mothers of the only relief possible—nursing the young (Lehrman, 1961). Other restless mothers may not produce enough milk to feed the young. Certainly there is room for some interesting hormonal and behavioral studies among mice which show such frequent deviations from normal maternal care.

Young mice frequently display on their underparts sores or scabs, usually caused by the teeth of the mother holding the young in her mouth and leaping about the cage with them. This behavior, which often develops when the young are removed frequently from the mother, tempts one to believe that it results from a displaced drive to relocate her litter. Aside from the minor chest injuries and the disturbing effect of being bumped and twirled about, the young do not appear to suffer.

Our systematic studies have not included abnormal maternal behavior, so we cannot demonstrate racial differences. However, the writer's general impression is that *gracilis* mothers are most prone toward cannibalism, whereas *bairdii* mothers more frequently exhibit excessive transport of the young. A quantitative study of these abnormalities among several species and subspecies of this genus should prove valuable.

Tuition of young

Foster (1959) concluded from her genetic study of *P. m. bairdii* and *P. m. gracilis* that parental influences were negligible, although the young hybrids raised by *gracilis* mothers and those raised by *bairdii* mothers did differ significantly in some measures. It does seem unlikely that mothers would teach their young such responses as the number of times to cross a barrier or the number of fecal boluses eliminated, as Foster suggested. On the other hand, her reciprocal crosses and back crosses provided enough differences in the behavior of genetically similar young raised by either subspecies to indicate that maternal factors were at work. Certainly this does not mean that the young are taught specific patterns of behavior by the mother, but only that each subspecies provided a distinct maternal environment to which the young respond. The subspecies differences we observed in maternal behavior have not been tested for their effects upon the young. However, the differences in care and the results Foster (1959) obtained with some reciprocal F_1 hybrids suggest that maternal effects are responsible (Ressler, 1962).

Additional evidence for the plasticity of young *Peromyscus* is provided by an experiment on the effects of early manipulation of *bairdii* and *gracilis* (King and Eleftheriou, 1959). In this experiment young mice of both subspecies were placed in a motor-driven "handling machine," which gently compressed the mice between two pads of foam rubber for 10 minutes a day from 3 to 25 days of age. When the mice were 70 days old, their performance in a shock-avoidance situation was examined. The same type of early experience had the opposite effect on the adult performance in the two subspecies. Whereas the treatment enhanced the avoidance of the *gracilis* over their controls, it interfered with the avoidance performance of *bairdii*. If the adult behavior of the two subspecies can be differentially affected by the same early experiences, it is reasonable to expect that different early experiences such as those provided by the maternal environment could also affect their behavior.

The fostering experiments with the two subspecies do not yet permit any definite conclusions. In one experiment employing an activity wheel, the fostered young behaved according to their subspecies and not according to that of their foster mother. Only one measure of five indicated a possible exception: young *gracilis* fostered on *bairdii* mothers tended to escape shock in a manner more characteristic of *bairdii* (King, 1961b). Further fostering experiments must be done, particularly after obtaining measures of behavior which may be amenable to maternal influences.

Within a particular subspecies, the behavior of the mother suggests that some training occurs, although it may be of short duration. When the mother continues to retrieve her half-grown young into the nest box, she is ultimately successful in keeping them there. Every time a young mouse leaves the box and the mother bodily returns it, the young have ample opportunity to learn to stay put. On those occasions when a strange male was introduced into the cage, the mother often pounced upon a young mouse and went through some spanking-like motions with her forefeet. This behavior kept the young still, at least for a few seconds. If the young were roughly treated by the mother upon such occasions, they soon adopted a defensive posture by rolling on their backs and kicking their feet. These observations suggest that the young can learn and often the mother is the instrument involved in the acquisition of a habit.

Discussion

Maternal behavior is only one of many adaptive responses mice make to their environment. Within a single genus, *Peromyscus*, we find the mice adapted to very different habitats, which determine the type of food eaten, the selection of nest sites, the number and developmental rates of their young, body form, as well as maternal and other social behavior. Some of these adaptations stem from the ancestral past when each species became isolated and diverged from the common ancestor. They are the basic phylogenetic characteristics observed primarily by systematists in the morphology and physiology of the mice. The current knowledge of maternal behavior throughout the genus is not adequate to discover those fundamental patterns which would occur in each species of a single subgenus, or in each subspecies of a single species. Until adequate quantitative measures are made in more species, one cannot speak about the common heritage or homologues of maternal behavior. This applies not only to the genus *Peromyscus*, but also to any group: species, genus, family, or order among the mammals, and indeed, to the class Mammalia itself.

Other adaptations to the environment are relatively recent in comparison to the phyletic adaptations. When a species increased its range and spread into new habitats, the environment imposed different selection pressures upon its patterns of maternal behavior. Whatever the selective forces were that enhanced the survival value of the different types of maternal behavior occurring between species, these forms are probably still active. Insofar as a particular pattern of maternal behavior characterizes and distinguishes one species from another, it may be regarded as influenced by the genotypes of the species, genotypes held constant by the pressure of the environment, yet with so much residual variability that they are capable of being modified to exploit new or changing environments. Those types of maternal care which distinguish geographic races of mice would be expected to form a continuous distribution between the extremes in a freely interbreeding population.

One further type of adaptation is characteristic of each individual mother whose combined experiences and the immediate situation of caring for her young, as well as her inherent capacities, form the basis of her maternal care. Each mouse becomes a mother with a unique set of experiences which will determine to some extent the type of care she gives her young. Has she just passed through a winter in cohabitation with other mice? Does she now give birth to her first litter, or is she still nursing her previous litter? Studies have not attempted to answer these and similar questions, although it is known that some of them may be significant in other species (Lehrman and Wortis, 1960; Riess, 1950; Ross et al., 1956; Seitz, 1958). Similarly, the immediate situation structures the patterns of maternal care. Is her present nest site the only one available? Must she nurse three offspring or eight? What type of predator threatens her young now? In the experiments reported here one animal varied from another, and the same animal varied from time to time and from one situation to another. Such variability in behavior enables each mother to make the most or the least of her experiences and her current situation (Scott, 1958).

A pattern or several patterns, complex, interwoven, and superimposed, prevail throughout the phyletic, specific, and individual adaptations female *Peromyscus* exhibit in their maternal care. Only the vaguest outline of a phyletic pattern is discernible now, a type of maternal care closely related to fundamental reproductive processes. Patterns are apparent in those species which have been studied, but they are not clear enough yet to relate them to the causal elements of the environment. The conclusion can be only that some aspects of maternal care are species-specific and genetically influenced, and amenable to change under shifting selection pressures. Patterns that enable one to predict maternal behavior at the individual level have not been discovered. It might be fruitfully asked if these still unknown individual patterns can eliminate or enhance those at the species level. With suitable training and in proper test situations will *gracilis* mothers exhibit the type of maternal care we now associate with *bairdii* mothers? The answers to the questions they enable us to formulate can be provided only by further research extended over many species and intensified in those species known quite well.

Summary

This chapter sought to compare the maternal behavior of two sub-species of deermice and other species within the genus *Peromyscus* in an effort to evaluate phylogenetic trends. Material for the comparisons was obtained from field and laboratory investigations.

Natal nests of deermice are located in subterranean burrows, under logs, rocks, and other materials on the surface of the ground, and in arboreal cavities. Nest material usually consists of soft fibers. Experiments on the quantity of material used in nests revealed that, regardless of their phyletic affinity, northern forms made larger nests than southern forms.

Parturition takes about an hour for the entire litter and most births occur during daylight hours before noon. Mothers spend over 20 hours each day with their young and subspecific differences occur in the duration and frequency of periods in the nest. Young mice are occasionally transported from one nest to another in the field, and mothers exhibit the retrieving response in the laboratory. The young are also transported by clinging to the nipples of the mother. Subspecies differ in the nipple-clinging response. When separated from their mother, young *P. m. gracilis* squeak more frequently than young *P. m. bairdii* and the tonal qualities of their squeaks differ.

Mother *Peromyscus* defend their young against invaders of different and the same species, with each subspecies exhibiting different responses. The age of weaning differs in the two subspecies studied, depending upon their relative stage of development. Evidence for tuition of the young is scarce. The different maternal environment provided by each subspecies in reciprocal F_1 hybrids may account for some divergence in later behavior.

Abnormal maternal behavior most often takes the form of cannibalism or desertion of the young. Comparative studies of the frequency and nature of such aberrations in maternal care are lacking.

The species level of comparison exemplified here reveals only a few homologous patterns which originate in the phylogenetic history of the species. More recent adaptations of maternal behavior to the environment currently occupied by the species appear to account for many species-specific patterns. Finally, each individual mother has her own unique genetic and experiential background superimposed upon the patterns of maternal care derived from her ancestors.

References

Adolph, E. F. (1948), Tolerance to cold and anoxia in infant rats. *Amer. J. Physiol.*, **155**, 366–377.

Barbour, R. W. (1942), Nests and habitat of the Golden Mouse in Eastern Kentucky. *J. Mammal.*, **23**, 90–91.

Barbour, R. W. (1951), The mammals of Big Black Mountain, Harlan County, Kentucky. *J. Mammal.*, **32**, 100–110.

Barbour, R. W., and W. T. Gault (1953), *Peromyscus maniculatus bairdii* in Kentucky. *J. Mammal.*, **34**, 130.

Blair, W. F. (1940), A study of the prairie deer-mouse populations in Southern Michigan. *Amer. Midl. Nat.*, **24**, 273–305.

Blair, W. F. (1951), Population structure, social behavior, and environmental relations in a natural population of the beach mouse (*Peromyscus polionotus leucocephalus*). *Contr. Lab. Vertebr. Biol. Univ. Mich.*, **48**, 1–47.

Blair, W. F. (1958), Effects of x-irradiation on a natural population of the deer-mouse (*Peromyscus maniculatus*). *Ecology*, **39**, 113–118.

Blair, W. F., and T. E. Kennerly, Jr. (1959), Effects of x-irradiation on a natural population of the wood-mouse (*Peromyscus leucopus*). *Tex. J. Sci.*, **11**, 137–149.

Blair, W. F., and J. D. Kilby (1936), The gopher mouse—*Peromyscus floridanus*. *J. Mammal.*, **17**, 421–422.

Burt, W. H. (1940), Territorial behavior and populations of some small mammals in Southern Michigan. *Misc. Publ. Mus. Zool. Univ. Mich.*, No. 45, 1–58.

Clark, F. H. (1937), Parturition in the deer-mouse. *J. Mammal.*, **18**, 85–87.

Denenberg, V. H., D. R. Ottinger, and M. W. Stephens (1962), Effects of maternal factors upon growth and behavior of the rat. *Child Develpm.*, **33**, 65–71.

Dice, L. R. (1925), The mammals of Marion Island, Grand Traverse County, Michigan. *Occ. Pap. Mus. Zool. Univ. Mich.*, **160**, 1–8.

Dice, L. R. (1929), A new laboratory cage for small mammals, with notes on methods of rearing *Peromyscus*. *J. Mammal.*, **10**, 116–124.

Dice, L. R. (1932), The prairie deer-mouse. *Cranbrook Instit. Sci. Bull.*, No. 2, 1–8.

Dice, L. R. (1933), Fertility relationships between some of the species and subspecies of mice in the genus *Peromyscus*. *J. Mammal.*, **14**, 298–305.

Drake, J. D. (1958), The brush mouse, *Peromyscus boylii*, in southern Durango. *Publ. Mus., Mich. State Univ. Biol. Ser.*, **1** (3), 97–132.

Edwards, R. L., and W. H. Pitts (1952), Dog locates winter nests of mammals. *J. Mammal.*, **33**, 243-244.

Evans, F. C. (1957), Utilization of resources by experimental populations of *Peromyscus*. *Bull. ecol. Soc. Amer.*, **38**, 66. (Abstract)

Fitch, H. S. (1958), Home ranges, territories, and seasonal movements of vertebrates of the Natural History Reservation. *Publ., Mus. nat. Hist. Univ. Kans.*, 11, 63–326.

Foster, Dorothy D. (1959), Difference in behavior and temperament between two races of deer mouse. *J. Mammal.*, **40**, 496–513.

Goodpaster, W. W., and D. F. Hoffmeister (1954), Life history of the golden mouse, *Peromyscus nuttalli*, in Kentucky. *J. Mammal.*, **35**, 16–27.

Hall, E. R. (1928), Note on the life history of the woodland deer mouse. *J. Mammal.*, **9**, 255–256.

Hall, E. R., and K. R. Kelson (1959), *The Mammals of North America*. New York: Ronald. Two vols.

Hansen, R. M. (1957), Communal litters of *Peromyscus maniculatus*. *J. Mammal.*, **38**, 523.

Hayne, D. W. (1936), Burrowing habits of *Peromyscus polionotus*. *J. Mammal.*, **17**, 420–421.

Hoffmeister, D. F. (1951), A taxonomic and evolutionary study of the piñon mouse, *Peromyscus truei*. Urbana: University Illinois Press. *Illinois biol. Monogr.*, **21** (4), 1–104.

Hooper, E. T. (1958), The male phallus in mice of the genus *Peromyscus*. *Misc. Publ. Mus. Zool. Univ. Mich.*, No. 105, 1–24.

Horner, B. Elizabeth (1947), Paternal care of young mice of the genus *Peromyscus*. *J. Mammal.*, **28**, 31–36.

Howard, W. E. (1949), Dispersal, amount of inbreeding, and longevity in a local population of prairie deermice on the George Reserve, Southern Michigan. *Contr. Lab. Vertebr. Biol. Univ. Mich.*, **43**, 1–52.

Huestis, R. R. (1933), Maternal behavior in the deer mouse. *J. Mammal.*, **14**, 47–49.

Ivy, R. D. (1949), Life history notes on three mice from the Florida east coast. *J. Mammal.*, **30**, 157–162.

Jackson, W. B. (1953), Use of nest boxes in wood mouse population studies. *J. Mammal.*, **34**, 505–507.

King, J. A. (1958), Maternal behavior and behavioral development in two subspecies of *Peromyscus maniculatus*. *J. Mammal.*, **39**, 177–190.

King, J. A. (1961a), Development and behavioral evolution in *Peromyscus*. In W. F. Blair (Ed.), *Vertebrate Speciation*, Austin: University Texas Press. Pp. 122–147.

King, J. A. (1961b), Swimming and reaction to electric shock in two subspecies of deermice (*Peromyscus maniculatus*) during development. *Anim. Behav.*, **9**, 142–150.

King, J. A., and Helen Connon (1955), Effects of social relationships upon mortality in C57BL/10 mice. *Physiol. Zoöl.*, **28**, 233–239.

King, J. A., and B. E. Eleftheriou (1959), Effects of early handling upon adult behavior in two subspecies of deermice, *Peromyscus maniculatus. J. comp. physiol. Psychol.*, **52**, 82–88.

King, J. A., and J. W. Nichols (1960), Problems of classification. In R. H. Waters, D. A. Rethlingshafer, and W. E. Caldwell (Eds.), *Principles of Comparative Psychology*, New York: McGraw-Hill. Pp. 18–42.

Lehrman, D. S. (1961), Hormonal regulation of parental behavior in birds and infrahuman mammals. In W. C. Young (Ed.), *Sex and Internal Secretions*, 3rd ed., Baltimore: Williams and Wilkins. Pp. 1268–1382.

Lehrman, D. S., and R. P. Wortis (1960), Previous breeding experience and hormone-induced incubation behavior in the ring dove. *Science*, **132**, 1667–1668.

Levine, S. (1962a), Psychophysiological effects of infantile stimulation. In E. L. Bliss (Ed.), *Roots of Behavior*, New York: Hoeber. Pp. 246–253.

Levine, S. (1962b), The effects of infantile experience on adult behavior. In A. Bachrach (Ed.), *Experimental Foundations of Clinical Psychology*, New York: Basic Books, Pp. 139–169.

Long, C. A. (1961), Natural history of the brush mouse (*Peromyscus boylii*) in Kansas with description of a new subspecies. *Publ. Mus. nat. Hist. Univ. Kans.*, **14**, 99–110.

McCabe, T. T., and Barbara D. Blanchard (1950), *Three species of Peromyscus*, Santa Barbara, California: Rood Associates.

Manville, R. H. (1949), A study of small mammal populations in northern Michigan. *Misc. Publ. Mus. Zool. Univ. Mich.*, **73**, 1–83.

Metzger, B. (1955), Notes on the mammals of Perry County, Ohio. *J. Mammal.*, **36**, 101–105.

Morrison, P., and F. A. Ryser (1959), Body temperature in the white-footed mouse, *Peromyscus leucopus noveboracensis*. *Physiol. Zoöl.*, **32**, 90–103.

Nicholson, A. J. (1941), The homes and social habits of the wood-mouse (*Peromyscus leucopus noveboracensis*) in southern Michigan. *Amer. Midl. Nat.*, **25**, 196–223.

Pournelle, G. H. (1952), Reproduction and early postnatal development of the cotton mouse, *Peromyscus gossypinus gossypinus*. *J. Mammal.*, **33**, 1–20.

Quast, J. C. (1954), Rodent habitat preferences on foothill pastures in California. *J. Mammal.*, **35**, 515–521.

Rainey, D. G. (1955), Observations on the white-footed mouse in Eastern Kansas. *Trans. Kan. Acad. Sci.*, **58**, 225–228.

Rawson, K. S. (1959), Experimental modification of mammalian endogenous activity rhythms. In R. B. Withrow (Ed.), *Photoperiodism and Related Phenomena in Plants and Animals*, Washington: Amer. Ass. Advancement Sci., Publ. No. 55. Pp. 791–800.

Ressler, R. H. (1962), Parental handling in two strains of mice reared by foster parents. *Science*, **137**, 129–130.

Riess, B. F. (1950), The isolation of factors of learning and native behavior in field and laboratory studies. *Ann. N. Y. Acad. Sci.*, **51**, 1093–1102.

Ross, S., V. H. Denenberg, P. B. Sawin, and P. Meyer (1956), Changes in nest building behaviour in multiparous rabbits. *Brit. J. anim. Behav.*, **4**, 69–74.

Schorger, A. W. (1956), Abundance of deer mice in Tuscola County, Michigan in 1854. *J. Mammal.*, **37**, 121–122.

Scott, J. P. (1958), *Animal Behavior*, Chicago: Univ. Chicago Press.

Seitz, P. F. D. (1958), The maternal instinct in animal subjects: I. *J. Psychosom. Med.*, **20**, 215–226

Smith, W. P. (1939), The transfer of a *Peromyscus* family. *J. Mammal.*, **20**, 108.

Sumner, F. B., and J. J. Karol (1929), Notes on the burrowing habits of *Peromyscus polionotus*. *J. Mammal.*, **10**, 213–215.

Svihla, A. (1932), A comparative life history study of the mice of genus *Peromyscus*. *Misc. Publ. Mus. Zool. Univ. Mich.*, No. 24, 1–39.

Thorne, O. (1958), Shredding behavior of the white-footed mouse, *Peromyscus maniculatus osgoodi*, with special reference to nest building, temperature, and light. Boulder, Colorado: *Thorne Ecol. Res. Station Bull.*, No. 6, 1–75.

Maternal Behavior in Peromyscus   93

3

maternal behavior in the
RABBIT

Sherman Ross, P. B. Sawin, M. X. Zarrow, and V. H. Denenberg

The rabbit, *Oryctolagus cunniculus,* Linnaeus, 1758, has been the animal of choice in a wide variety of biological experiments and is a commonplace bio-assay preparation. It is a well-known mammal both in its wild and domestic forms; yet many aspects of its biology and behavior have been given no sound experimental investigation. This chapter seeks to (1) describe rabbit behavior which relates to maternal care, (2) summarize experimental attempts to quantify overt events associated with such care, and (3) discuss the behavior with reference to its possible underlying genetic or endocrinological etiology and its susceptibility to varied environmental influences. The chapter is organized around several major considerations: (1) species characteristics of the rabbit which, compared with those of other animals, enhance its value in the study of maternal behavior, (2) individual treatment of genetic, endocrinologic, and behavioral approaches and findings, and (3) some promising areas of investigation.

Supported in part by PHS research grants MY-1604 from the National Institute of Mental Health to the University of Maryland, and by RG-5228 and RG-6263 from the Division of General Medical Sciences to Roscoe B. Jackson Memorial Laboratory and Purdue University respectively.

General considerations

Maternal care may be considered a limited but major portion of a larger sequence of biological events running from infancy through puberty, sexual development, mating, birth, and the recycling of these events in the next generation. Although maternal care is particularly concerned with relations between mother and newborn young, it is also a part of physiological reproduction. Success in all these events accounts for survival of the species, and in the wild the rabbit can be considered highly successful. The extensive restrictions placed upon the rabbit under domestication and experimental laboratory procedures demonstrate its wide adaptability. These manipulations may also help in evaluating the important biological and behavioral processes involved. Hence, critical effects of nutrition, environmental stresses (including protection from elements and predators), and antecedent irregularities in reproduction are important considerations in addition to readily observable genetic differences.

ADVANTAGES OF THE RABBIT

The rabbit as a biological preparation has unique advantages in its size. The range in size and genetic characteristics of the rabbits available at the Roscoe B. Jackson Memorial Laboratory is shown in Table 1. Others, including both larger (Flemish Giant) and smaller (Polish) breeds, are available from fanciers. The rabbit is large and durable enough for repetitive surgery and electrophysiological experiments; it also provides urine, blood, and various tissue samples for biochemical analysis and therapeutic assays. Substantial numbers can be obtained with reasonable economy. As a final point, the rabbit is easy to maintain and handle in laboratory and field situations, and its method of rearing young is, by comparison with other species, relatively simple, as will be subsequently described.

Ovulation, which initiates the reproductive process in the rabbit, is normally dependent upon the coital stimulus. Thus a time referent is available for later events and makes possible many experiments on the reproductive process which would be more difficult in spontaneously ovulating species. The available knowledge of the physiology of reproduction in the rabbit provides a background for the study of relationships between behavioral and endocrine aspects, whereas the genetic approach reveals the degree to which they are under the same inherent physiological control.

TABLE 1
Rabbit Races Available at the Roscoe B. Jackson Memorial Laboratory

Race (Name and/or Symbol)	Color	Genotype	Origin	Inbreeding*	Approx. Mature ♀Weight	Genes Occasionally Segregating
III	Albino	ccAAE^{d}E^d	New Zealand White Castle, 1932	.70	3800	*l,bu,ep,*scoliosis†
IIIc	Albino	ccAAE^{d}E^d	Subline of III	.53	4000	*bu,* scoliosis†
X‡	Sooty yellow	aaeebbC(Ch²)	Castle's small race	.53	2200	*r², dk, Dw*‖ scoliosis†, *As*
AC§	Black, recessive white marking	aa or AE^{d}E^d du	Dutch	.36	2200	*y, ac*
ACEP§	Black, recessive white marking	aa or AE^{d}E^d du, epep	Dutch	.70	2400	*v,* agonadia
DA	Albino	cc, A, E^d	New Zealand White California, 1949	.53	4200	
Os	Black, minimal recessive white marking	aa or E^{d}E^d Osos	Rockefeller Institute, 1948	.53	3200	*hydrocephaly*†
AX	Chinchilla	Ach^{d}ww, Axax forced heterozygosis	Outcross of Chinchilla race V to races III and X	.36	3500	*du, ep, bu, ch^m, c*

Genes of importance to studies of constitutional disease being maintained in the colony are

achondroplasia (ac)	angora (l)	ataxia (ax)
dachs (Da)	furless (f)	buphthalmia (bu)
diminutive dwarf (di)	rex² (r²)	epileptic (audiogenic) seizures (ep)
dwarf (Dw)[5]	satin (sa)	lethal muscle contracture (mc)
	wirehair (Wh)	osteopetrosis (os)

For other gene symbols, see *Bibliographica Genetica*, **17:** 229-558 (1958)

---

* Breeding is by sib mating or as close to sib mating as possible consonant with maintenance of the specific lethal or semi-lethal genes (indicated by underlining) and an optimal reproductive capacity and viability.

† Transmitted under conditions of suboptimal mutation or health.

‡ Reached F_9 in 1958, declined, and is now reestablished by five generations of successive backcrosses to F_9 males.

§ Sublines of the same Dutch stock obtained from Rockefeller Institute in 1948.

¶ Formerly *dw*, now recognized in the heterozygote.

Basic to understanding the more technical aspects of maternal behavior in the rabbit, particularly as observed under laboratory conditions, is knowledge of its morphology, habits, and habitat in the field. Formerly classified among the rodents, the rabbit more recently has been placed in the order *Lagomorpha*, principally on the basis of two pairs of incisors instead of one as in the rodents. This difference has probably little to do with its habits as compared with those of the rodents. An excellent description of rabbit behavior may be found in the chapter by Worden and Leahy (1962).

The rabbit is a herbivorous animal living, in the wild, upon vegetation, such as bark, twigs, and limbs. Much of this can be utilized at certain seasons by use of the long chisel-like incisor teeth. It is built for ease of locomotion, not only in feeding but also in protecting itself. The rabbit's survival as a species depends greatly upon its speed in escaping from enemies as well as its range of vision and hearing. Other survival elements include its ability to excavate, and thus protect its young underground, and its extraordinary reproductive capacity.

Supplementing the above are several unique specializations of activities such as the speed and short duration of suckling (a few minutes per day), and the addition to the nest of hair plucked from the mother's own body. The latter feature offers further indications of the basic physiological mechanisms involved since prior to nest building the normally fast hair becomes loose for a short time.

Maternal behavior patterns

The activities involved in maternal care are relatively simple. Although similar to those of the rat, they are different in ways which are experimentally useful. The most striking characteristics as compared with other species are the provisions for the young at or just prior to birth. These are digging or excavating of a burrow, gathering of hay, straw, or comparable materials, loosening of the normally fast hair and plucking, and nest construction. Collectively, these activities are commonly referred to as nest building, although each component may be distinguished and treated experimentally (Zarrow, Sawin, Ross, Denenberg, Crary, Wilson, and Farooq, 1961).

As in many other animals, consumption of the fetal membranes by the mother during or directly following parturition is a normal occurrence. Eating and scattering the young occur in a small proportion of cases and are recognized as abnormal behaviors. They do not involve stillbirths exclusively as is sometimes believed.

Retrieving the young, one of the most interesting patterns of maternal care in some species, has not been reliably observed in the rabbit either in the wild or in the laboratory (Ross, Denenberg, Frommer, and Sawin, 1959). A special temporal mechanism, probably oxytocin as in cattle, goats, etc., exists for the release of milk, and suckling time appears to be in the order of a few minutes per day.

Attention to molestation by humans and aggressive protection are present in many rabbits and tend to be strongest after the young leave the nest. A description of other behavior variables may be found in Worden and Thompson (1962).

GENETICS

Before the initial studies of Sawin and Curran (1952) and Sawin and Crary (1953), no attempt had been made to analyze maternal behavior in the rabbit, much less its genetic or endocrine background or its association with other facets of reproduction. These studies have focused on the species pecularities in the maternal-young relationship during the period of 15 days before and after parturition, and have revealed racial differences which are useful both in differentiating the fundamental processes and the nature of the genetic backgrounds.

The pattern of maternal behavior in four races of rabbits with respect to twelve characteristics of reproduction is shown in Table 2. Each race had certain differentiating characteristics. It can be assumed that perpetuation of the race depends upon the achievement of at least a certain minimal threshold for each of these characteristics.

Race III had medium fertility and high fecundity, tended to construct a good nest, but ceased lactation early and was not overly protective of its young. In contrast, race X, in spite of lower fertility, was more precocious and consistent in its nest building. It was in general more aggressive to humans but less aggressive in the protection of its young. Each race through inbreeding or genetic drift appears to have developed its own specific pattern.

The nine types of maternal behavior in Table 2 have been studied further, both individually and in relation to each other, as described below.

Time of nest construction. Sawin and Crary (1953) studied components of nest building and lining in races III, IIIc and X. They found a close correlation between time of nest building and time of lining with hair. This observation has been confirmed in a later study of some other variables (Denenberg, Sawin, Frommer, and Ross, 1958; Ross, Denenberg, Sawin, and Meyer, 1956; Ross, Zarrow, Sawin, Denenberg,

TABLE 2
Reproductive Pattern in Four Inbred Races

Character	Races			
	III	IIIc	V	X
Fertility	Medium 69%	Medium 75%	Medium 62%	Medium 66%
Fecundity	High 9.5	High 9.2	Good 6.5	Good 5.1
Milk production	Deficient toward weaning	Very deficient toward weaning	Two days delayed onset	Normal and steady
Maternal behavior				
(1) Cannibalism	Low 5%	High 16%	Medium	Medium
(2) Scattering	Low 9%	High 23%	Medium	Medium
(3) Nesting time	32% prepartum	21% prepartum	29% prepartum	58% prepartum
(4) Nest location	11% displacement	26% displacement	10% displacement	6% displacement
(5) Nature of nest	Better than average 89%	Below average 77%	Average 86%	Average 84%
(6) Time of lining nest	28% prepartum	31% prepartum	28% prepartum	57% prepartum
(7) Lining of nest	Average 91%	Average 87%	Average 94%	Average 61%
(8) Aggression	19% aggressive	30% aggressive	7% nonaggressive	61% very aggressive
(9) Interest in young	Better than average 65%	Average 54%	Below average 50%	Average 53%

From P. B. Sawin and R. H. Curran, *J. Exp. Zool.*, 1952, **120**, 165-201.

and Blumenfield, in press). Data on both building and lining were based on a scale of 0 to 7, 0 being no nest, 1 a partum nest, and 2 to 7 representing the range of 6 days prepartum.

Nest quality. This variable was originally found to differ in three ways: (1) location, whether within or outside the nest box, (2) the nature or quality of construction, and (3) quantity of nest lining, based on a scale of 0 to 6+. At the Jackson Laboratory the doe is provided with a nest box several days before parturition (Ross et al., 1956). The box contains a 6 inch high partition, which divides it into two compartments. A removable lid covers two-thirds of the box. The floor of the rear compartment is covered with a ½ inch thick layer of shredded sugar cane to absorb excess moisture in the box. The other compartment is approximately three-quarters filled with loose excelsior. Figure 1 illustrates graded classes of nests as categorized by Sawin and Crary (1953). Number 0 illustrates the case in which no apparent effort was made to build a nest. Number 6 illustrates a well-hollowed packed

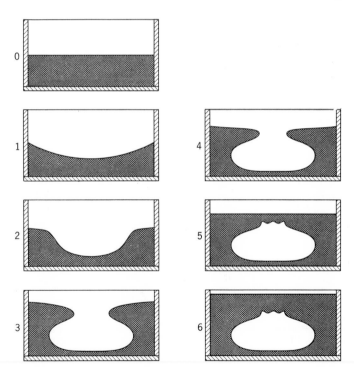

FIG. 1. *Graded classes of nests. (From P. B. Sawin and D. D. Crary,* Behaviour, *1953,* **6,** *128–146.)*

Maternal Behavior in the Rabbit 101

nest. In constructing the nest the doe interweaves with the nesting material hair plucked from her body.

All three measures varied significantly between races, but the associations were not as close as those for time of nest building (Sawin and Crary, 1953). Some evidence was found by Denenberg et al. (1958) of a weak positive correlation between nest quality and time of nest building. Correlations for first litters were highest in races III and IIIc, and low for the fourth litter in race ACEP, as shown in Table 3. Nest quality was also found to be correlated with the percentage of young suckled the first day of birth.

TABLE 3
Correlation of Nest-Building Time and Nest Quality

Race	Litter Number							
	1		2		3		4	
	r	N	r	N	r	N	r	N
IIIc	.58*	27	.53*	26	.55*	27	.33	27
X	.06	27	.17	27	.24	27	.53*	27
ACEP	.30	26	−.02	26	.23	26	−.06	26
III	.38	21	.59*	22	.25	22	.16	21

*Significant at .01 level.

From Denenberg et al., Genetic, physiological and behavorial background of reproduction in the rabbit: IV. An analysis of maternal behavior at successive parturitions. *Behaviour*, 1958, **13**, 136. (E. J. Brill, Pub., Leiden, Holland).

If we consider the percentage of young suckled as a measure of the mother's ability to feed her young, quality of nest and lactation appeared to be strongly correlated throughout the four litters of race IIIc females. Similar correlations were found for the first two litters of race III mothers and the first litter of those of race ACEP. Race X, however, appeared more erratic although correlations of litters two and four were highly significant. In this study as a whole there tended to be improvement in quality of nest in successive litters. When, however, nest quality is considered in relation to lactation, the racial differences in the association of the two characters are suggestive of some degree of genetic interaction which differs among races.

Aggression. Protection of the young in nature is essential for preservation in most mammalian species. Preparturient and postparturient aggression toward the laboratory attendant was rated on a scale of 1 to 4, (1) timid, (2) nonaggressive, (3) aggressive, including laying back of the ears, foot stamping, vocalization, and attack, and (4) very aggressive or vicious attack, including biting and kicking. Females in most races are relatively docile, except during pregnancy or lactation, and may be confined together without serious trouble. Sawin and Crary (1953) reported that one small-sized race never showed aggressive tendencies. Among the races studied here, X has consistently, at an early age in both sexes, manifested aggressiveness both between individuals and in relation to attendants. Thus aggression, per se, is not necessarily a maternal characteristic in the rabbit.

Table 2 shows distinct racial differences in aggression. In race X, 61% of the mothers were aggressive. They also tended to show high interest in their young. Race IIIc and V mothers showed high interest without being protective to the point of aggression. A further study of these two characteristics (Denenberg et al., 1958), based on new data and examined over four successive litters, again showed a significant racial difference in postparturient aggression, with race X being the least aggressive and race ACEP the most aggressive. In the seriation analysis of successive litters, race III was particularly interesting since mothers of litters one and two were not aggressive, but showed a significant increase in aggression with later litters. The apparent decline in aggressiveness in race X in the second of the two studies may reflect laboratory efforts to select against the preparturient aggressive type for convenience in handling. It is possible, however, that there are actually two kinds of aggressive behavior of genetic origin. One of these, characteristically found in race X, tended to be manifest throughout the life of the animal. The other appeared in several races only during lactation. In race III it tended to become more apparent in later litters and in many cases was more pronounced as lactation progressed.

Cannibalism and scattering. In a normal rabbit parturition, the mother consumes the fetal placenta and membranes and severs the umbilical cord. As a rule there is no appreciable loss of blood and the fetus is uninjured. The mother discriminates between membranes and placentae on one hand and the infant on the other. On occasion the young may be partly or completely consumed, even while still alive. No consistent pattern of eating the young has been noted. In some cases the procedure is initiated with the placentae but as often ears, limbs, or skin are first stripped from the body. The phenomenon rarely occurs after one or more days of parental solicitude, but maternal behavior can vary in this respect from one delivery to the next.

Often associated with eating the young is a tendency to scatter them on the floor of the cage or elsewhere, rather than to group them in the nest or nest box. Sometimes a nest is built on the cage floor rather than in the box. In our data, cannibalism and scattering have been recorded as either present or absent. Race differences in these two characteristics were first described by Sawin and Curran (1952) and confirmed in a later study (Denenberg, Petropolus, Sawin, and Ross, 1959). As shown in Table 4, significant amounts of both cannibalism and scattering occurred in race IIIc, whereas in the earlier study the amount of cannibalism was much less. Results from 31 race IIIc mothers, each having four successive litters, showed no significant seriation effects for either scattering or cannibalism. The numerical values of the intraclass correlations of .55 for scattering, and .72 for cannibalism, indicate a fair amount of individual variability. A correlation of .40 between total scores for cannibalism and those for scattering indicates that the two characters are related only to a moderate degree. Correlations of scattering and cannibalism with nest quality and time of nest building were significant (Table 5). Scattering and cannibalism appear to be under genetic control and are related to ability to suckle the young. Mothers who built good quality nests showed significant tendencies not to scatter or cannibalize the young. Significant correlations found for scattering and cannibalism in relation to suckling and interest in young are considered a result of the mortality attending them and therefore probably artifactual.

TABLE 4

Racial Differences in Cannibalism and Scattering over Four Litters

Race	N	Scattering Mean	Cannibalism Mean
ACEP	27	1.25	0.75
X	11	0.50	0.25
III	20	3.00	1.25
IIIc	31	9.75	9.00

From Denenberg et al., Genetic, physiological, and behavorial background of reproduction in the rabbit: VI. Maternal behavior with reference to scattered and cannibalized newborn and mortality. *Behaviour*, 1959, **15**, 71-76. (E. J. Brill, Pub., Leiden, Holland.)

Infant mortality. Mean behavioral scores of does with high and low mortality among the young were also compared for races III, IIIc, X, and ACEP by Denenberg et al. (1959), using the same five measures of maternal behavior. As a group, the low mortality does of race ACEP showed significantly more interest in their young and were significantly better nursing mothers (% nursed) than the high mortality does.

TABLE 5

Correlation of Scattering and Cannibalism with Nest Quality and Nest-Building Time

Scattering	Litter Number			
versus	1	2	3	4
Nest quality	.775‡	.309°	.516‡	.395†
Nest time	.582‡	.160	.196	.288
% nursed	.373†	.395†	.474‡	.435†
Interest	.350°	.382†	.341°	.307°
Aggression	.155	.260	.090	.260
Cannibalism versus				
Nest quality	.406†	.081	.637‡	.418†
Nest time	.228	−.137	.419†	.331°
% nursed	.351°	.201	.460‡	.217
Interest	.284	.240	.374†	.216
Aggression	.159	.003	.080	.193
Cannibalism versus				
Scattering	.532‡	.075	.671‡	.595‡

° Significant at .10 level.
† Significant at .05 level
‡ Significant at .01 level.

From Denenberg et al., Genetic, physiological, and behavorial background of reproduction in the rabbit: VI. Maternal behavior with reference to scattered and cannibalized newborn and mortality. *Behaviour*, 1959, **15**, 71-76. (E. J. Brill, Pub., Leiden, Holland.)

Nest-building season. Although all races tended to have their greatest proportion of prepartum nests during the first three calendar months of the year, race X had a higher proportion than the others throughout the year (Table 6). Races III and IIIc, which tended to be partum nest builders, had a larger proportion of partum nests in the fall. It is also interesting to note that race IIIc not only had the greatest number of mothers building no nests, but that there was also a distinct seasonal maximum during spring and summer when reproduction is normally highest. In race III nests were most frequent in fall and winter, which may be an indication that reason for failure is not the same in the two races.

TABLE 6
Per Cent of Nests Built in Four Races of Rabbits
as a Function of Season*

	Race IIIc				Race III			
	J-M	A-J	J-S	O-D	J-M	A-J	J-S	O-D
No nest	6.9	18.6	13.3	8.3	4.7	0.9	0.44	5.2
Partum nest	55.1	57.3	60.5	66.4	60.3	66.0	69.1	73.0
Prepartum nest	37.9	24.0	26.6	24.9	34.9	33.0	26.4	21.1

	Race ACEP				Race X			
No nest	1.1	0.9	3.1	—	.21	.12	2.9	—
Partum nest	58.1	69.8	68.7	67.8	32.6	45.1	41.1	43.4
Prepartum nest	40.7	29.2	28.1	32.1	65.2	53.6	55.8	56.5

* Seasons arbitrarily classified as January-March, April-June, July-September, and October-December.

From Ross et al., Maternal behavior in the rabbit: yearly and seasonal variation in nest building. *Behavior*, 1961, **18**, 157. (E. J. Brill, Pub., Leiden, Holland.)

ENDOCRINOLOGY

Only a few aspects of the maternal behavior complex were considered appropriate for studies on endocrine control of maternal behavior in the rabbit (Zarrow, Sawin, Ross, and Denenberg, 1962). These were lactation, hair loosening, and maternal nest building. Each of these response complexes possesses a specific endpoint which can be utilized in an experimental attack on the problem.

The hormonal requirements for lactation have been fairly well-known for the rabbit as well as for other mammals for some time. In the rabbit, where suckling occurs almost at once after birth, milk can be recognized through the skin of the young within a few minutes after birth or upon postmortem examination. Milk, which can often be expressed from the mother's nipples before parturition, can be measured quantitatively and related to growth of the young.

Our observations reveal nest building to consist of two specific activities, sometimes carried out independently, but usually in sequence or almost simultaneously in the pregnant female. The first consists of scratching and digging, which in a natural or seminatural environment results in the so-called burrow. In the limited laboratory environment it is usually only apparent when a box containing straw or similar material is available. This phenomenon has been observed in both sexes and under diverse conditions.

The second activity consists of the gathering, transportation, and manipulation with the mouth of straw, dried grass, excelsior, or similar available material. In the wild, the rabbit, using nose and forepaws, deposits and fashions this material into a hollow nest. In addition, the animal plucks hair from its dewlap, body, hind quarters, or other accessible parts, and deposits it in the nest as lining and covering. Often hair plucking precedes straw gathering by hours or even several days, the hair being deposited on the floor of the cage. Sometimes before parturition, but usually after it is complete, the hair is picked up and deposited in the nest.

The final result is referred to as the maternal nest and should be contrasted with the straw nest. Maternal nests are also frequently seen around the 17th day after copulation in animals which are pseudopregnant. This varies from the 15th to the 21st day, and is in contrast to the burrowing and hollowing activity, which are not exclusively maternal. Failure of the mother to build a maternal nest at parturition usually results in reproductive failure even in the most favorable season, presumably due to exposure, although sometimes other evidence of carelessness with the young is manifest. Preliminary experimental evidence for this relationship, whose entire pattern seems important, has been obtained recently. There may also be a factor in the doe which relates failure to nurse and failure to build a maternal nest.

Since the hair of this species is normally fast, except at the time of seasonal molt, it is apparent that hair loosening at the time of parturition is an integral part of maternal nest building. In designing our experiments we have assumed that it is a separate event or the result of an independent process, an assumption which later work seems to confirm. It will therefore be considered under a separate heading.

Lactation. Isolation of the female sex steroids (estradiol and progesterone) and prolactin led to the current understanding of the role these hormones play in lactation. As a consequence it has been possible to obtain lactation in both the castrated female and the male with the injection of the above three hormones. In 1954, Meites and Sgouris showed that their injection led to lactation in the castrated female rabbit. In a series of experiments in our laboratory 13 female and 4 male castrated rabbits were injected with an estrogen (10 mg stilbestrol) and 1 to 2 mg progesterone daily for 14 days. This was followed with 200 IU of prolactin daily for 5 to 7 days. Complete growth of the mammary gland was obtained in all 17 animals and milk could be expressed manually from the mammary gland. Eleven of the 17 rabbits built straw nests in the course of the treatment with the hormones and

4 of the 17 or 22% built maternal nests, that is, incorporated hair into the straw nests. None of the 4 males built maternal nests.

To precipitate early lactation and nest building in 5 pregnant rabbits, 200 IU of prolactin were injected twice daily for 8 days starting on the 20th day of gestation. Although early lactation was stimulated, the treatment failed to induce maternal nest building. It is apparent from these results that although there is a significant correlation between good lactation and maternal nest building, the two phenomena are not under the same controlling mechanism. It is possible and indeed a simple matter to induce lactation, but such treatment may not necessarily result in nest building. One may therefore conclude that lactation and maternal nest building are correlated because both are necessary in the maternal behavior complex. Furthermore, the hormones involved in both instances are different, or are the same with differences in the dose and time requirements. Since both phenomena require estradiol and progesterone, and prolactin is necessary for lactation, it would appear that at least some of the requirements are identical for the two phenomena.

Hair loosening and maternal nest building. The early work of Tietz (1933) and general observations by naturalists (Cahalane, 1947) indicate that hair loosening occurs in the rabbit toward the end of pregnancy and pseudopregnancy. Recently, the degree of hair loosening has been measured by obtaining the weight of the hair combed from a specific area on the body and following a specific number of passes with the comb. The degree of hair loosening is then expressed as the percentage increase in the weight of the hair obtained before and after a treatment period (Sawin, Denenberg, Ross, Hafter, and Zarrow, 1960). This technique has been shown to be reproducible and valid for determining the degree of hair loosening observed either in the laboratory or under seminatural conditions and following various treatments.

The data obtained with the above technique indicate that significant increases in hair loosening occur during both pregnancy and pseudopregnancy. In general, the hair loosening takes place as a peak response and falls immediately. The peak response in one animal may occur on the day of parturition (Fig. 2) or in another several days before delivery (Fig. 3). The time of the peak response appears to correlate with the time of maternal nest building, that is, partum or prepartum. The degree of hair loosening obtained in a Dutch-belted strain showed a 153% increase for the peak loosening of the hair in a group of rabbits all of which built maternal nests (Table 7). In a group of 10 rabbits made pseudopregnant with human chorionic gonadotropin, 9 built maternal

TABLE 7

Hair Loosening in the Rabbit

Treatment	No. of Rabbits	Maternal Nest		Hair Loosening		
		Number Built	Number Failed	Control wt. mg.	Maximum wt. mg.	Per Cent Increase
Pregnancy	10	10		16.5	42.2	153.3
Pseudopregnancy	10	9		18.1	38.5	112.5
			1	33.3	33.1	0.0
E*, P† and Pr‡ for 8 weeks	3	3		20.0	45.4	127.3
E* and P§ for 32 days	2	2		70.1	76.4	9.1
Pregnant¶ 2 mg P	4	4		55.7	75.8	36.1
Pregnant¶ 4 mg P	8	8		57.8	83.7	46.5

* Estradiol, 5μgrams daily through the period.
† Progesterone, 1 mg daily on weeks 2 and 3 followed by 2 mg daily on weeks 4 through 8.
‡ Prolactin, 20 IU daily on weeks 7 and 8.
§ Progesterone, 2 mg daily on days 10 to 20 and 4 mg on days 20 to 30.
¶ Progesterone, daily from day 28 to 35 after coitus.
From A. Farooq, Ph.D. thesis, Purdue University, 1961.

nests and showed a hair loosening of 112.5%. The one pseudopregnant rabbit which failed to build a nest also failed to show any hair loosening. Treatment of three ovariectomized rabbits for 8 weeks with estradiol (5 mg daily), progesterone (1 mg on weeks 2 and 3, followed by 4 mg on weeks 4 through 8), and prolactin (20 IU on weeks 7 and 8) induced a 127% increase in hair loosening and maternal nest building in all three animals. Figure 5 is an example of the data obtained in this experiment. It may be noted that the animal built several straw nests before hair loosening occurred and that both the hair loosening and maternal nest building occurred after treatment was stopped. It may also be noted that hair loosening lasted for only 2 days. However, a reduction in the length of treatment to 4½ weeks and elimination of the prolactin treatment failed to cause any increase in hair looseness, although nest building occurred.

Further evidence for the separation of hair loosening and nest building is seen in an experiment in which pregnant rabbits were treated with progesterone from the 28th day of gestation until the 35th day.

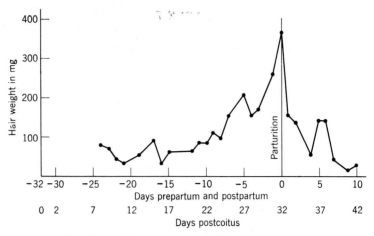

FIG. 2. *Partum hair loosening in a pregnant rabbit. (From Sawin et al.,* Amer. J. Physiol., *1960,* **198,** *1099-1102.)*

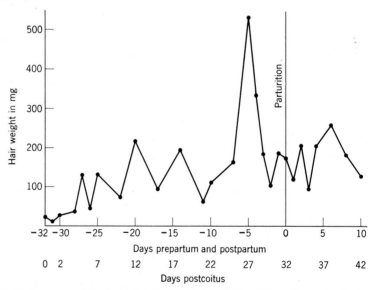

FIG. 3. *Prepartum hair loosening in a pregnant rabbit. (From Sawin et al.,* Amer. J. Physiol., *1960,* **198,** *1099-1102.)*

Treatment with either the 2 or 5 mg dose delayed parturition in all instances, so that delivery of the dead fetuses did not occur until day 37 to 39. However, maternal nest building was inhibited only by the 4 mg dose. Rabbits treated with 2 mg of progesterone built maternal nests on days 32 or 33, indicating possibly a slight delay. A slight degree of hair loosening was noted with both treatments, but the degree was less than half of that seen during pregnancy and pseudopregnancy. It is obvious thus that hair loosening occurs during pregnancy and after prolonged treatment with estradiol, progesterone, and prolactin. It is interesting that the rabbits treated with 4 mg of progesterone eventually delivered the dead fetuses on approximately day 38, but nest building failed to occur. The treatment with 2 mg of progesterone failed to inhibit maternal nest building, although parturition was delayed.

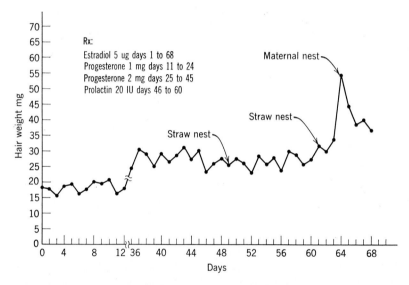

FIG. 4. *Maternal nest building and hair loosening in a castrated female rabbit treated with estradiol, progesterone, and prolactin for 8 weeks. (From A. Farooq, Ph.D. Thesis, Purdue University, 1961.)*

Maternal nest building. Analysis of nest-building data collected on a heterogeneous group of rabbits of various races at the Jackson Laboratory and a single strain at the Purdue Laboratory indicates a remarkably comparable picture (Table 8). In a total of 941 normal pregnancies at the Jackson Laboratory and 54 at Purdue, 96% nest building was obtained with the former and 98% with the latter. Similarly, an incidence of 84% and 85% nest building was obtained for maternal nest building in pseudopregnancy induced by injection of chorionic gonadotropin or mating with a vasectomized buck.

TABLE 8

Maternal Nest Building in the Rabbit Following Endocrine Manipulation

Treatment	Number Rabbits	Maternal Nest Total Number	Per Cent
Compilation of all available races at Jackson Laboratory			
Controls	941	901	96
Caesarian*	250	209	84
Castration during pregnancy†	16	12	75
Pseudopregnancy	11	5	45
Stilbestrol, progesterone, prolactin	17	4	22
Dutch-belted race at Purdue University			
Controls	54	53	98
Pseudopregnancy	20	17	85
Caesarian*	5	4	80
Castration during pregnancy†	5	5	100

* Total conceptus mass removed on days 20 to 27 of gestation.
† Ovaries removed on days 21 to 24 of gestation.
From Zarrow et al., *J. Reprod. Fertil.*, 1961, **2**, 152–162.

Castration and Caesarian section. Castration during the 21st to the 24th day of gestation invariably led to abortion and a 75% incidence of nest building in the Jackson colony and 100% nest building in the Dutch-belted strain (Table 8). This incidence was approximately the same after Caesarian section. Attempts to rule out uterine distention as a factor in the onset of nest building were made by inserting paraffin rods following Caesarian section. Under these conditions six of eight rabbits built nests. These data indicate that nest building is triggered by a change in hormone balance.

Hormone treatment. The original studies on the induction of maternal nest building in the rabbit utilized the animals previously described under lactation (page 107). As indicated in that section, lactation was obtained in all 17 rabbits, but only 11 of the 17 built straw nests and 4 of the 17 or 22% incorporated hair into the nests, that is, built maternal nests.

In a second experiment, an attempt was made to precipitate maternal nest building in five pregnant rabbits prior to the predicted time for such behavior by treatment with 200 IU of prolactin twice daily for 8 days starting on the 20th day of gestation. Premature nest building failed to occur in any of the treated animals.

Additional experiments involving the induction of maternal nest building in the castrated female rabbit have indicated that nest building can be induced in 100% of the animals with a prolonged hormone treatment of estradiol, progesterone, and prolactin. Originally, such a treatment lasted for approximately 60 days. It has now been possible to reduce the length of treatment to 3 weeks and eliminate prolactin. Maternal nest building can be obtained consistently in the castrated female rabbit treated with estrogen and progestogen, but thus far it has not been possible to obtain maternal nest building in the normal or castrated male.

Maternal nest: a critical period. Preliminary observation on interruption of pregnancy by castration or Caesarian section has indicated that a critical period exists for exposure of the animal to pregnancy before the experimental termination of gestation can lead to maternal nest building. This period occurs between days 12 and 17 of gestation, but may differ for the different strains of rabbits.

Evidence for endocrine control. The evidence for an endocrine control of maternal nest building in the rabbit is not complete but is strongly suggested by the available data. The hormonal substrate appears to include estradiol and progesterone, the two major hormones of pregnancy. This is apparent from the occurrence of maternal nest building during pregnancy and pseudopregnancy and after treatment with the two hormones. As yet the question of the role of prolactin in maternal nest building is still unsettled. Since our experiments were not conducted on hypophysectomized animals, and in addition since Robson (1937) failed to get nest building in rabbits hypophysectomized during the latter part of pregnancy, we cannot rule out prolactin at this time.

What triggers the onset of maternal nest building is a second phase of the problem. A likely explanation of the onset following induced abortion or Caesarian section is the change in hormone balance with the termination of gestation. However, since the nest is built just prior to parturition in a normal pregnancy, it is impossible to explain both instances on the basis of hormonal changes following termination of pregnancy. Nevertheless, it has been recently demonstrated that the progestogen-estrogen ratio is reversed in the rabbits several days before parturition, and that the progestogen dominance seen throughout the major portion of pregnancy is reversed to an estrogen dominance several days prior to delivery (Schofield, 1957). Hence a change in hormonal balance does occur in both instances of maternal nest building, and the same explanation can be advanced for the nest building seen with abortion, Caesarian section, pseudopregnancy, and normal pregnancy.

EFFECTS OF PREVIOUS EXPERIENCE

One of the major characteristics of mammals is the ability to profit from experience, that is, to learn. Learning may take place very quickly or it may be spread over a number of trials. The latter is more likely to be the case when the sequence of acts to be learned is relatively complex. The construction of the maternal nest by the female rabbit is a complex act, which suggests that the doe might profit from the experience of building a nest so that the subsequent nest would be better.

To determine whether the quality of nest building improved with successive parturitions, a study was made of females which had had four litters and had come from three different races, ACEP, X, and III, and two sublines of race III, IIIc, and IIIr[2] (Ross et al., 1956). The nest quality was rated according to the scale previously described (Fig. 1). Figure 5 presents the major finding of this study. The characteristic pattern for all strains and sublines was a significant improvement in nest construction from the first to the third litter and then a leveling off. Although the results are consistent with the hypothesis that the female learns to improve her nest, still another hypothesis which must be considered is that there may be systematic hormonal changes with successive litters, and it is these changes which result in the improvement of nest quality. Information on the effects of repeated litters upon endocrine activity is not yet available to test this hypothesis. Still, it

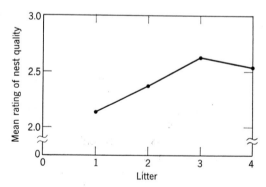

FIG. 5. Mean rating of nest quality for the first four litters of 84 females. (From Ross et al., Brit. J. Anim. Behav., 1956, 4, 69–74.)

appears unlikely that the endocrine activity is affected by successive pregnancies.

Quality of nest. To gain further understanding of the factors affecting the quality of nest construction a series of correlational analyses were carried out (Denenberg et al., 1958). The nest quality score was correlated against age of mother at parturition, time of nest building relative to parturition, number of young born (including stillbirths), and percentage of young born alive and suckled on the day of birth. In addition, the time of nest building was correlated with the percentage of liveborn suckled young. These correlations were obtained for each of four successive litters for four different groups of rabbits (X, ACEP, III, and IIIc). No significant relationships were found between nest quality and age of mother at birth or between nest quality and number of young produced. A definite relationship was found between nest quality and percentage of liveborn suckled. Those mothers which built the better nests suckled a higher percentage of their young on the day of birth. In addition, there was a tendency for nests of better quality to be built earlier in time and a weak positive relationship between the time of nest building and the percentage of young suckled on the day of birth. These findings suggested the possibility of some common factor or factors in nest building (time and quality) and suckling activities.

The question of changes in behavior with successive parturitions was extended by Denenberg et al. (1958) to include the variables of maternal interest, preparturient maternal aggression, postparturient maternal aggression, and time of nest building. Using animals from four races (X, ACEP, III, and IIIc), separate analyses were made for does which had maintained four or more litters. In the latter case only the data from the first four litters were analyzed. No significant seriation effects were found on the measures of maternal interest, preparturient aggression, or time of nest building relative to parturition. On the postparturient aggression measure, only strain III showed any seriation effect. This strain showed the same aggression score for the first and second litters and then a significantly increased score for their third and fourth litters.

The use of different genetic stocks reared in a laboratory environment raises two critical methodological issues:

Long-term stability. One is whether the behaviors which have been studied are stable over time or whether there have been marked changes due to genetic drift, selection, or environmental changes. To answer this question Ross, Sawin, Denenberg, and Zarrow (1961) analyzed the

Maternal Behavior in the Rabbit 115

records of does which had successful pregnancies. A successful pregnancy was defined as one in which viable young were brought to term with one or more live animals at the first postpartum observation. This analysis covered data from January 1953 through June 1959, and included a total of 941 successful pregnancies. Analyses were made of the percentage of animals which failed to build nests and the time of construction for those rabbits which did build nests. Neither of these measures showed any significant change over the 6½ years which were investigated. The findings both extend and confirm the work of Sawin and Crary (1953) who had obtained similar findings on nest building. The present information is inadequate for the analysis of genetic drift and selection effect.

Laboratory and field study. The second methodological point is concerned with the generality of findings obtained in a laboratory setting. To answer that question 18 pregnant does of different backgrounds were placed in a field situation and their behavior was observed as they approached parturition and during the early rearing of the young (Ross et al., in press). The females were put into foundation silo pits measuring 31 square feet and containing gravel subsoil overlaid with natural compost from silage, grass, straw, and leaves. It was relatively easy for the rabbit to dig in this soil.

Complete observations were not possible in all instances. Sometimes the nests were hidden in a burrow, or a miscarriage took place, or the young were eaten. The following statements are based upon cases where valid observations could be obtained. The gestation period of these rabbits was the same as the gestation period for animals reared in the laboratory (31.9 days and 31.8 days, respectively). All does pulled hair from their bodies and 14 of 15 does (93%) built some form of maternal nest as compared to 96% of laboratory reared animals (Ross et al., 1961). As best as could be determined without disturbing the nest or mother, the average number of young per litter was 5.9 as compared to 6.6 young born in the laboratory. In 5 out of 13 cases (38.5%) definite aggression was noted after parturition; Sawin (1954) has reported that 62.6% of strain X and 31.8% of strain IIIc rabbits exhibited postparturient aggression. The incidence of scattering and cannibalism was higher among the mothers in the seminatural setting than has been reported for laboratory animals (Sawin, 1954).

The results establish that the same qualitative and quantitative results are obtained in the field as are found in the laboratory, and that the behavior of burrowing occurred in the field. The does averaged 3.6 burrows, although no doe built more than one maternal nest. Of eight rabbits which had nest boxes placed into their fields, only two built nests in the boxes; the others burrowed nests in the ground. Figure 6 shows two entrances to an underground burrow and Fig. 7 shows a doe sitting in her burrow. Even though burrowing cannot occur in the laboratory, it should be noted that its occurrence in the field environment in no way changed the characteristics of the maternal behavior pattern observed in the laboratory.

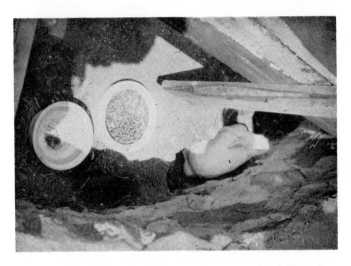

FIG. 6. Entrance to an underground burrow in the field study.

Retrieving. One characteristic of the rabbit which is different from that of other mammals is the apparent absence of retrieving behavior (Ross et al., 1959). Investigation of this behavior was done as follows. An alleyway was attached to the rabbit's nest box, the young were removed from the box and placed on the alleyway, and the mother's reactions were observed. This procedure, begun a few hours after birth, continued at intervals for a few days. No doe made any attempt to move her young. Different mothers showed varying degrees of interest in their young. Some showed no apparent interest, others nosed and sniffed the pups, whereas others licked the pups extensively. One doe stood on her young despite their loud vocalized protests. The young of another doe attempted to nurse while on the alleyway. The females' reactions to the experimenter ranged from indifference to threats of active attack.

Scattering and cannibalism. Scattering and cannibalism are forms of abnormal behavior which are influenced by genotype since strain IIIc rabbits exhibit a significantly higher incidence than other rabbit

FIG. 7. A doe sitting in her burrow in the field study.

strains (see Table 4). An analysis of scattering and cannibalism by Denenberg et al. (1959) found that these two events were significantly correlated and that those females that scattered or ate their young also built a nest of poorer quality and built their nests later in the gestation period. Neither scattering nor cannibalism correlated significantly with postparturient aggression or with maternal interest in the young. These findings, in combination with the prior work of Denenberg et al. (1958), showed positive intercorrelations for better nest quality, earlier time of nest building, greater percentage of liveborn young suckled on the first day, lack of scattering, and lack of cannibalism. This pattern suggested a maternal care complex, which appears to be different from a second group of factors involving interest in the young and aggressive protection of the young.

Summary

Any definitive genetic analysis of maternal behavior is dependent upon extensive refinement of the biological materials, the yardsticks used to define them, and a knowledge of the environmental factors which influence their expression. In the present state of our knowledge, maternal behavior in the rabbit appears to have a strong genetic background, well established in the species, but sufficiently variable between breeds and genetic races to yield to investigative procedures. It is the basis of the wide range of adaptability of the species, in the wild, under domestication, and in the laboratory. Although interpretation in terms of specific gene activity is at present impossible, the constancy of the racial pattern over the interval during which our races have been examined indicates its importance. Furthermore, the complexity of the endocrine pattern in reproduction, together with the evidence of correlation between endocrine and behavioral reactions, suggests that the underlying physiological mechanism is responsible in considerable measure for both. Our studies have emphasized the importance of carefully controlled genetic analyses of the major variations in both patterns, under as controlled environmental conditions as possible, and consideration of the possible interrelations.

Present knowledge of the endocrinology of maternal behavior demonstrates that the hormones, estradiol and progesterone, are necessary in lactation, hair loosening, and maternal nest building. Although prolactin also is necessary for lactation, the evidence suggests that it may not be a factor in hair loosening or nest building. The mechanism that triggers nest building is still unknown, although evidence points to a change in estrogen-progesterone dominance as crucial.

Studies of the behavioral aspects of maternal care in the rabbit permit a number of conclusions. The quality of nest built by the mother improves with successive litters, up through three litters. The quality of nest is not related to the age of the mother or to the number of young born. Nest quality is significantly related to the percentage of young suckled by the doe on the day of birth and to the time of nest construction. The percentage of does building prepartum or partum nests in four different strains has not changed over a period of 6½ years. A study of the behavior of rabbits in a seminatural field situation found essentially the same qualitative and quantitative results as in the laboratory. Although rabbits in the field burrowed, this in no way changed the characteristics of the maternal behavior pattern in the laboratory. No evidence of retrieving by the doe was found. Scattering and cannibalism of young are correlated and appear to have a substantial genetic basis. In addition, does which scatter or cannibalize build nests of poorer quality and later in the gestation period.

Although the genetic-endocrinological-behavioral approach has been productive in many ways, it is clear that many fundamental problems remain to be attacked. We recommend the rabbit for the further exploration of these complex interactions.

References

Cahalane, V. H. (1947), Mammals of North America, New York: Macmillan.

Denenberg, V. H., S. F. Petropolus, P. B. Sawin, and S. Ross (1959), Genetic, physiological, and behavioral background of reproduction in the rabbit: VI. Maternal behavior with reference to scattered and cannibalized newborn and mortality. Behaviour, 15, 71–76.

Denenberg, V. H., P. B. Sawin, G. P. Frommer, and S. Ross (1958), Genetic, physiological and behavioral background of reproduction in the rabbit: IV. An analysis of maternal behavior at successive parturitions. Behaviour, 13, 131–142.

Meites, J., and J. T. Sgouris (1954), Effects of altering the balance between prolactin and ovarian hormones on initiation of lactation in rabbits. Endocrinology, 55, 530-534.

Robson, J. M. (1937), Maintenance of pregnancy and of the luteal function in the hypophysectomized rabbit. J. Physiol., 90, 145–166.

Ross, S., V. H. Denenberg, G. P. Frommer, and P. B. Sawin (1959), Genetic, physiological, and behavioral background of reproduction in the rabbit. V. Nonretrieving of neonates. J. Mammal., 40, 91–96.

Ross, S., V. H. Denenberg, P. B. Sawin, and P. Meyer (1956), Changes in nest building behaviour in multiparous rabbits. Brit. J. Anim. Behav., 4, 69–74.

Ross, S., P. B. Sawin, V. H. Denenberg, and M. X. Zarrow (1961), Maternal behavior in the rabbit: yearly and seasonal variation in nest building. Behaviour, 18, 154–160.

Ross, S., M. X. Zarrow, P. B. Sawin, V. H. Denenberg, and M. Blumenfield (in press), Maternal behavior in the rabbit under semi-natural conditions. Anim. Behav. (in press).

Sawin, P. B. (1954), The influence of age of mother on pattern of reproduction. Ann. N. Y. Acad. Sci., 57, 564–574.

Sawin, P. B., and D. D. Crary (1953), Genetic and physiological background of reproduction in the rabbit. II. Some racial differences in the pattern of maternal behavior. Behaviour, 6, 128–146.

Sawin, P. B., and R. H. Curran (1952), Genetic and physiological background of reproduction in the rabbit. I. The problem and its biological significance. J. Exp. Zool., 120, 165–201.

Sawin, P. B., V. H. Denenberg, S. Ross, E. Hafter, and M. X. Zarrow (1960), Maternal behavior in the rabbit: hair loosening during gestation. Amer. J. Physiol., 198, 1099–1102.

Schofield, Brenda M. (1957), The hormonal control of myometrial function during pregnancy. J. Physiol., 138, 1–10.

Tietz, Esther G. (1933), The humoral excitation of the nesting instincts in rabbits. *Science*, **78**, 316.

Worden, A. N., and J. S. Leahy (1962), The behaviour of rabbits. In E. S. E. Hafez (Ed.), *The Behaviour of Domestic Animals*, London: Baillière, Tindall and Cox. Pp. 397–414.

Zarrow, M. X., P. B. Sawin, S. Ross, and V. H. Denenberg (1962), Maternal behavior and its endocrine basis in the rabbit. In E. L. Bliss (Ed.), *Roots of Behavior*, New York: Hoeber. Pp. 187–197.

Zarrow, M. X., P. B. Sawin, S. Ross, V. H. Denenberg, D. Crary, E. D. Wilson, and A. Farooq (1961), Maternal behavior in the rabbit: evidence for an endocrine basis of maternal-nest building in the Dutch-belted race. *J. Reprod. Fertil.*, **2**, 152–162.

4

maternal behavior in the CAT

T. C. Schneirla, Jay S. Rosenblatt, and Ethel Tobach

The apparent maternal efficiency of cats suggests to many that the animals carry out the essential series of acts in a rigid order and on a fixed native basis. The prevailing concepts are derived from observations of domestic cats; much less is known about conditions among pumas, jaguars, lions, leopards, and tigers—the wild cats. Knowledge essential for comparisons is sparse, not only about different species but also about variations within any species (Lindemann, 1955; Rosenblatt and Schneirla, 1962). Even the question of how domestic cats behave maternally when they become wild, as happens often in large cities or out-of-season in resort areas, is largely a matter of conjecture. For these reasons, this article will concern itself mainly with maternal behavior in the domestic cat, *Felis catus,* which the writers of this chapter and others studied intensively in the seven years following 1949 (Rosenblatt, Turkewitz, and Schneirla, 1961; Schneirla and Rosenblatt, 1961; Tobach, Failla, Cohn, and Schneirla, in preparation).

Supported from September 15, 1953 to September 15, 1956 by Grants B-413 and B-1299 from the National Science Foundation and by a grant from the Rockefeller Foundation for the following year of research. Dr. Alan Frank participated in the early stages of this investigation during the year 1950–1951 as a Postdoctoral Fellow of the National Institute of Mental Health.

Cats have altricial young, in which the eyes open some days after birth (about one week in the domestic cat) and action advances slowly in strength and coordination. Maternal-young relations consequently have a development quite different from that of the precocial young of other mammals such as ungulates.

Maternal behavior for the cat may be defined as characterized by exaggerated licking of self and of young, and encircling, nursing, retrieving, remaining near, and returning to the young. Maternal functions in cats have been discussed in one or another respect by Cooper (1942, 1944), Günther (1954), and Leyhausen (1956, 1960), often to limited extents by others in scientific articles, and of course still more often in popular publications.

It is well established that the conditions under which maternal behavior occurs are dependent on neurohormonal processes. Discussions of recent evidence of the neurohormonal basis of reproductive behavior have been offered by Beach (1948, 1958) and by Lehrman (1956, 1961). Physiological processes underlying the initiation and maintenance of lactation have been described in great detail (Hain, 1935; Hall, 1957; Harris, 1955; Leblond, 1937; Meites, 1959; Nicoll, Talwalker, and Meites, 1960; Riddle, 1935; Riddle, Lahr, and Bates, 1935, 1942; Rothchild, 1960a; 1960b). The bases of retrieving, nestbuilding, and other aspects of maternal behavior are not yet as clear. Although most of the research has been done with the rat, rabbit, and dog, it is likely that the primacy of a neurohormonal control of maternal behavior will be found applicable to the cat as well. Bard's (1936) findings indicate that the full pattern of sexual behavior in the female domestic cat may depend strictly upon hormones; Michael (1958) found that in the cat, in contrast to the rat and rabbit, both sexual receptivity and the associated postural responses depend upon ovarian hormones. Racadot (1957a, 1957b) found indications of modified thyroid function in female domestic cats during parturition which reach their peak soon thereafter and persist in nursing individuals to the end of lactation. As far as a relationship exists between this function and that of the neurosecretory axis (alterations in which follow it in time), he believes that the thyroid modifications may be primary.

Certain factors underlying maternal behavior are significant for what follows. First, because maternal behavior in its developed form constitutes a *pattern* (that is, an organized system of activities and processes), it is important always to specify whether all the activities and processes, or just certain ones, occur under given conditions. Second, it is essential to know not only the extent and intensity of the activities and processes, but also their degree of organization under the conditions of study. For example, the fact that pregnant rats, as well as hormone-injected virgin females and males, retrieve young although not lactating does not necessarily supply evidence of what lactation may contribute to the more complete pattern. Nor does the finding that full-term female rats after Caesarean deliveries continue to retrieve young and build nests (Labriola, 1953) contribute any evidence of the function of absent factors such as licking membranes and neonates and ingesting placenta in the normal development of the pattern (Schneirla, 1956). Third, as maternal-like behavior is always in flux, undergoing consecutive changes of some type from the time of the first effects in pregnancy to the time of weaning, the appearance and the change of both the elements and the pattern must be viewed always as matters of development. That the whole process of maternal behavior is neurohormonally controlled, rather than only hormonally controlled (Clegg, 1959), emphasizes the value of psychological and behavioral factors as well as situational factors affecting general physiology for understanding both the pattern and its elements (for example, Nicoll et al., 1960).

For the preceding reasons we regard strictly nativistic theories as outworn (Schneirla and Rosenblatt, 1961). To understand maternal behavior, we need the evidence of biochemical and neurophysiological excitation and transmission as well as the facts of experience, learning, and socialization (Schneirla, 1951, 1956). We need to know also the factors of early experience which play an elusive but important role in the development of sexual behavior in the male domestic cat (Rosenblatt and Aronson, 1958). As Lehrman (1956) has pointed out, there is evidence that the hormonal setting of maternal behavior and of its basic processes appears susceptible to exteroceptive stimulation, that anterior pituitary (as well as other) secretions may be conditioned to specific stimuli (for example, those provided by the young), that qualitatively different responses may be conditioned to the same internal excitatory condition at different intensities, that a particular activity may be based upon an organic need and appetite (as in the case of licking for salts, Barelare and Richter, 1938) and that for all these processes the peripheral conditions of the animal (for example, local cutaneous sensitivity; heat exchange) may have important and changing relationships to pertinent intraorganic conditions and the progress of behavior.

In keeping with the mating cycle of cats in northern latitudes, litters tend to occur during two seasons, from mid-March to mid-May and from mid-July to late August (Scott and Lloyd-Jacob, 1955). Many wild species may be similar (Eckstein and Zuckerman, 1956), but the lion and tiger have no fixed breeding seasons. Domestic cats in northern Europe have heat periods twice a year, in spring and early fall; in the northern United States anestrum lasts from September to January; variations in amount of illumination, however, influence these periods (Asdell, 1946). In our laboratory, with light maintained at approximately springtime conditions and certain other conditions observed, litter production tends to be fairly uniform throughout the year. In contrast to the conventional range in term for housecats of 60 to 65 days, under our conditions the range has tended to be 63 to 68 days, and similarly Scott and Lloyd-Jacob (1955) reported a range of 64 to 68 days with an average of 66 days. Records for number of young in the litter under our conditions give a range of 1 to 7 and a mode around 4. The reported range of litter size for the lion is 2 to 6,[1] that for the tiger 1 to 6, and most other Felidae tend to have fewer than six cubs in a litter (Asdell, 1946).[2]

Behavior and conditions of pregnancy

Advance of pregnancy is marked behaviorally in the domestic cat by decreasing activity and agility, with less frequent climbing or jumping. In the last third of pregnancy, when weight is accelerating, appetite increases and licking of genital and abdominal areas is likely to be augmented. Distention of the mammae with occasional signs of active secretion, together with tumescence at the vulva, rising body weight, and evident maximum size of embryos on palpation, indicate approach to term.

In the last weeks of pregnancy, the cat is described, conventionally, as seeking a dry, dark, wind-protected, and undisturbed situation with cover and preferably with a soft substrate, in which the young are delivered and reared (Cooper, 1944; Leyhausen, 1956); the lioness, similarly, as taking a sequestered place near water and a good hunting ground (Wells, 1934). The fixation of a desirable locality seems to be

---

[1] Cooper (1942) reported a total of 159 lion cubs born in 64 zoo parturitions (mean = 2.48); Steyn (1951) found that in four different zoos, over periods of ten or more years, the litters of lions contained 1 to 6 young with an average close to 3.

[2] Problems of health and maintenance are of paramount importance. A large screen-wire cage equipped with wall shelf, adequate diet supplemented for lactating females with five drops of viosterol and a pinch of edible bone meal daily, careful handling including abdominal support for pregnant animals, and prompt attention to all disorders are features to be emphasized.

usual, but the degree of seclusion essential may vary with the female and her background—wild or untamed individuals virtually going into hiding, sociable and home-adjusted housecats more often taking exposed places. Among alternatives, the one with softer substratum, if darker and thermally optimal, is likely to be adopted.

As pregnancy advances, the females of wild species are reported to become more retiring. A nesting place or den, frequented and used for sleeping, is saturated with the odors of urine, food, and body secretions. With the four corners of a large, screened cage available, our pregnant domestic cats nearly always settled on one corner at the back as the resting place in pregnancy, maintaining it as the site of parturition and of litter care. Nervous, maladjusted females tend to be more variable. Place-fixation constitutes an important although incidental contribution to the early habituation and orientative development of the young.

Increased cutaneous sensitivity of thoracic, abdominal, and pelvic areas—apparently general in cats late in pregnancy—may facilitate the characteristic place-fixation of that time as well as the later encircling of neonates. The African lioness in advanced pregnancy pulls out with the incisors hair around the nipples, as do also pseudopregnant and parturient females (Cooper, 1942). Beginning often before parturition, females of various cat species may become irritable, defensive in general, and even actually aggressive.[3] Self licking, normally a frequent item in the domestic cat's repertoire (Leyhausen, 1956), is prominent in behavior from the time of pregnancy, presumably in relation to increased endogenous excitation as well as to the increased sensitivity of ventral zones and to special secretions and fluids. Sensory and other organic conditions fundamental to such behavior changes may be reasonably attributed to the neurohormonal factors of pregnancy.

Preliminaries to parturition

The imminence of delivery is indicated by the appearance of colostrum in the mammae, vulvar distension, sometimes with a pinkish mucoid discharge, and by scratching of the substratum, alternating with a squatting posture resembling the defecatory crouch of normal females

---

[3] The possibility that events of the late stages of pregnancy may constitute a "stressor" complex inducing neural and hormonal changes leading to general irritability and facilitating later changes such as colostrum and milk letdown is indicated by the finding of Nicoll et al. (1960) that nonspecific stressors can induce lactation in rats primed with extradiol.

and kittens. "Calling," although uncommon among our laboratory females, is described by Cooper (1944) as a frequent and "distinctly recognizable vocal pattern" in his Siamese housecats at this time.

An abbreviated protocol of typical behavior just preceding parturition in the domestic cat is presented in Appendix 1.

Parturition

A few general descriptions of delivery in various feline species have appeared, notably those of Cooper (1944) and Leyhausen (1956) for the domestic cat, and of Cooper (1942) for the lion. Cooper (1942) noted these activities of a parturient lioness: a considerable amount of vocalizing, squatting and lying supine, kneading of the abdomen and hair pulling from abdomen and tail, rolling and pacing, and frequent licking of the genitalia. Cooper (1944) reported a detailed description of parturition in a multiparous pure-breed Siamese housecat. Although it showed marked behavioral disturbances unless her owners were nearby, in certain respects his findings are comparable with those we obtained for the births of 66 kittens in 17 parturitions.

Our study (Tobach et al., in preparation) used females of heterogeneous stock excluding selected strains. Each female was habituated during pregnancy to a standard 36 inch square and high mesh-wire cage and was accustomed to the presence of observers and to a routine of observations. The main course of events and the occurrence of definite activities were recorded either with routine symbols on a time-scale or for quantitative data with an Aronson keyboard controlling the chart of an Esterline-Angus recorder. The observer did not intervene during parturition except to mark neonates with tape-collars on delivery, to remove the sac when loss of the neonate seemed imminent, and to palpate the female when parturition seemed near its end. In the 17 parturitions, all the young were viable except for two stillborn kittens of one female and one of another.

An abbreviated protocol of typical behavior in the domestic cat in parturition is presented in Appendix 2.

The cat is a multiparous animal, that is, giving birth to more than one offspring in a litter. The succession of deliveries of kittens in a litter provides an opportunity for comparing not only the actions of any one female during the different kitten births of a given litter but also the parturitive behavior of different females. The results are presented in a form to facilitate both such comparisons; a kitten birth is distinguished from a parturition, the delivery of a litter.

The data support the following formulations:

1. Female behavior is the outcome of an interplay or competition between the stimulative effects of endogenous events (such as uterine contractions and the passage of the fetus) and of exogenous stimuli resulting from the by-products (that is, fluids, neonate, and placenta) of these organic processes. Although the female displays a fairly predictable repertoire of parturitive behavior, no pattern of behavioral acts is indicated in our evidence.

2. Parturitive behavior is exemplified by variable actions of licking which, in being shifted variably from the female's own body to the newborn or surroundings, indicate the path of the female's attention. Intrinsic or extrinsic stimuli may affect her behavior according to the rate, intensity, and distinctness of their appearance in the scene of parturition.

ORGANIC EVENTS MARKING KITTEN BIRTH INTERVALS

From our evidence, certain organic events in parturition are sufficiently distinct to be used as means of distinguishing successive intervals within any kitten birth. These events are (1) onset of abdominal contractions; (2) appearance of the fetus as it pauses in the vulva; (3) passage of the fetus from the vulva (fetus-delivery); and (4) passage of the placenta from the vulva (placenta-delivery). By these events we have reliably distinguished four successive intervals in a kitten birth as: (1) the contraction interval; (2) the emergence interval; (3) the delivery interval; and (4) the placental interval. In this way, characteristics of the kitten births, such as duration and activities of the intervals, may be compared from case to case.

Empirically, the termination of a kitten birth was set as the onset of contractions for the next kitten birth; termination of a parturition, however, could not be set by delivery of the placenta of the last kitten born; hence at times after placental deliveries palpation was necessary to determine whether there were any unborn fetuses.

In 38 of 51 kitten births analyzed, contractions, fetus-delivery, and placenta-delivery occurred consistently and in that order (Table 1). These occurrences were therefore considered standard and as those regularly influencing the behavior of the parturitive cat. Fetus-pausing-in-vulva occurred twenty-six times in these otherwise typical sequences; placenta-pausing, in contrast, occurred only five times.

The data did not indicate a relationship between the durations of

TABLE 1
Frequency of Common Sequences of Organic Events in Delivery

Sequences	Birth Order of Neonate in Litter						Total
	First (K-1)	Second (K-2)	Third (K-3)	Fourth (K-4)	Fifth (K-5)	Sixth (K-6)	
C,FA,FD,PA,PD*	1			2	1		4
C,FA,FD,PD	3	4	7	4	3	1	22
C,FD,PD		2	3	4	2		11
C,FD,PA,PD			1				1
Total	4	6	11	10	6	1	38

* C, onset of contractions; FA, fetus arrested in vulva during emergence; FD, delivery of fetus; PA, placenta arrested in vulva during emergence; PD, delivery of placenta.

kitten births and their order in the sequence. For example, short kitten births did not tend to be early in a parturition and longer ones late, or the reverse. There was a wide range of variation in the durations of the intervals in kitten births (for example, contraction intervals lasting from 12 seconds to 1½ hours and delivery intervals from 32 seconds to over 50 minutes). As might be expected, intervals of long duration, because they contained a greater frequency of specific female activities than those of shorter duration, complicated statistical analyses of the data.

Among 51 kitten births observed, 13 were atypical by our criteria. In 6 of the latter, a fetus and placenta were delivered simultaneously. In two cases there was an overlapping of kitten births; in one the interval began with the delivery of one fetus and ended with contractions referable to the next, in the other it began with the delivery of one placenta and ended with the delivery of that referable to a forthcoming fetus. The other cases were scattered and variable in nature. No evidence was found for significant differences in the duration of typical and atypical kitten births.

FEMALE BEHAVIOR DURING KITTEN BIRTH INTERVALS

The definition of the kitten birth intervals as bounded by endogenous events aids in relating the female's activities in each phase of a kitten birth to the changes in stimulative conditions. At any one time, endogenous stimuli (such as those arising from uterine contractions and the passage of the fetus) and exogenous stimuli (that is, from by-products such as fluids, membranes, fetus, and placenta) of the organic processes produced a changing stimulus scene to which the female responded differentially. The shifts in the female's behavior in successive intervals (Table 2) reflect the predominance of the one as opposed to the other source of stimulation.

TABLE 2

Parturitive Behavior in Kitten Birth Intervals

Items	Contraction	Emergence	Delivery	Placental
Gross body movements				
Scratching floor	3	2		
Squatting, straining, or				
crouching	10	9	4	1
Bracing body	2	1		3
Rolling or rubbing	6	1	1	
Lordosis	2	1		
Circling		2	2	1
Nosing				
Kitten: last born	2			1
born previously		1	4	1
Placenta	2			2
Surroundings	2	3	1	1
Licking				
Self: general	15	13	27	18
genital-abdominal	20	11	22	18
Kitten: last born	18	8	33	21
born previously	15	8	22	16
Fetal membranes		1	1	
Cord			9	2
Placenta	2		1	9
Surroundings	7	8	6	5
Chewing				
Cord	1		1	1
Placenta			1	1
Ingesting				
Fetal membranes			7	2
Cord			4	1
Placenta	1	1		23
Action with kitten				
Dangling kitten from: vulva	1	2	7	
mouth	1		1	1
Sitting or lying on kitten	3	3	1	5
Stepping on kitten	1			1
Pawing kitten	2			1

TABLE 2 (continued)

Items	Contraction	Emergence	Delivery	Placental
Curling or rolling up		1		2
Carrying, mouthing, or				
retrieving	3	2	1	6
Nursing	4	2	3	4
Number of intervals observed	37	29	38	29

Note: The table may be read as follows: for example, in 3 out of 37 contraction intervals, a parturient female scratched the floor. The frequencies in each column are not additive; a female may have been observed doing any number of the listed activities during an interval.

The following descriptions of parturitive behavioral items will aid in tracing the flow of events from interval to interval.

A reliable sign of the actual onset of parturition is the first clear indication of contractions of abdominal musculature, considered the accompaniment of uterine contractions. We have distinguished reliably between displacements of the abdominal wall due to uterine contractions and those from fetal movements alone; the first but not the second is accompanied by leg movements (flexing, also raising) of slight or greater amplitude.

During the contraction and emergence intervals one type of activity, gross body movements, is more in evidence than in the delivery and placental intervals (Table 2). These postural changes were attributed predominantly to excitation from endogenous sources because no specific extrinsic changes were found regularly coincident with them. Thus squatting, straining, and crouching, brought together because they could not be reliably differentiated, often resembled the normal female postures of defecation and micturition and commonly occurred at times when the progress of a fetus in the birth canal might have been acute. Scratching, which appeared in the contraction and emergence intervals but not later, markedly resembled the normal feline action of covering urine or feces. Rolling (Fig. 1), rubbing, and lordosis, other gross bodily actions observed during kitten births, occur in female mating behavior. Circling, as we observed it (Fig. 2), had all the earmarks of a perceptual adjustment to a disturbance localized in the posterior body; hence Cooper's (1944) term, "nesting," is misleading for this activity as it suggests a purely extrinsic orientation.

During the first two intervals (contraction and emergence), as well as in subsequent intervals of the kitten birth, actions of nosing and licking the kittens, as well as self and surroundings, were observed.

FIG. 1. Sudsie rolling during an apparent episode of uterine contractions preceding the delivery of the fourth kitten.

FIG. 2. Persian carrying out a rapid circling movement, dragging a partially delivered fetus still attached by its cord.

FIG. 3. *Mabel, early in parturition, responding to birth fluids by licking damp spot on floor.*

FIG. 4. *Mabel in posture characteristic of anogenital licking.*

Maternal Behavior in the Cat   133

FIG. 5. *Rita licking neonate which is still attached; the placenta remains undelivered.*

Licking (Figs. 3, 4, 5), by far the most frequent response in parturition, was recorded whenever the female passed her tongue over a surface such as her body, a neonate, or the floor.

Our females in all phases of parturition often actively touched the nose to a fetus, placenta, or to fluids on the floor. This action, termed nosing to include the item sniffing, often difficult to distinguish, may not infrequently have been based on very slight olfactory cues; for example, when a female touched her nose to a place where she or a neonate had been lying.

The parturitive female's actions with her kittens varied from direct responses to a neonate as pawing (Fig. 6) or licking to clearly incidental responses as dragging it about the cage while still attached by the cord. An incidental action was sitting or stepping on kittens during responses to herself or to the fetus in delivery. The female's enclosing response was a response to neonates which differed sharply from rolling or rubbing. Clearly directed at the kittens, it involved the female's approaching and standing close to one or more of them, then lying on her side as she drew the front legs ventrocaudally and the rear legs ventroanteriorly, thus enclosing the kittens near her abdomen. This occurred most frequently near the kittens, whereas no identifiable extrinsic situation accompanied rolling or rubbing.

FIG. 6. Sudsie makes a quick postural thrust of left rear leg, thereby "pawing" against body of neonate just delivered.

Under our conditions, retrieving was infrequent in the parturitive situation. In different occurrences, it varied from lifting and transporting a neonate to grasping its body briefly in the jaws and releasing it promptly with or without lifting. These responses did not differ reliably in frequency in the intervals of parturition.

Although enclosing occurred, nursing was infrequent in the parturitions observed, being recorded in only 4 of 14 kitten births in 3 females. Whether or not nursing occurred did not appear to affect other activities in the respective intervals.

BEHAVIORAL SHIFTS IN RELATION TO STIMULATIVE EVENTS

Licking. To examine the hypothesis that the different organic events of parturition and their by-products set off different female activities, each of 14 kitten births, recorded in its complete form, was analyzed for the frequency of the various groups of behavioral items which occurred in each interval. The items of each of the principal activity groups: (1) scratching floor, (2) squatting and bracing, (3) rolling, rubbing, and lordosis, and (4) licking and ingestion (Table 2) were found to be aroused in a different birth interval with frequencies approaching significance ($p = .10-.05$, Friedman two-way analysis of

Maternal Behavior in the Cat　135

variance). Each birth interval may therefore be viewed as characteristically different from any of the others with respect to the relative potencies as well as the specific nature of endogenous and exogenous stimuli acting on the parturient female.

Further evidence of significant changes in the female's activities from interval to interval in a kitten birth appears in two types of analysis of the data. First, although no one type of activity initiated any one interval more often than did any other type of activity, it was found that most of the intervals began with a new overt response by the female, sharply breaking her foregoing actions. Genito-abdominal licking and licking the last kitten born are responses exemplifying this conclusion. The contraction interval was initiated more frequently by genito-abdominal licking than was the placental interval, whereas licking the latest born kitten was seen more frequently as the first response during the delivery interval than during the placental or emergence periods. These data show that, although no particular activity consistently followed any given organic event, that event influenced the probability of the occurrence of one of at least two actions in the female's repertoire immediately after the event. Thus the initiation of a contraction period by a series of intrusive endogenous stimuli had a greater likelihood of causing the female to orient to her genito-abdominal region, and thus lick herself specifically, than did stimuli associated with placental delivery. To the latter stimuli, as will be shown, the female was likely to react by promptly ingesting the placenta after its delivery. Similarly, licking the neonate followed the complete passage of the fetus from the female's body more frequently than it followed either the arrest of the fetus or the delivery of the placenta. During the emergence interval, gross body movements dominated to the exclusion of licking the neonate; also, after the delivery of the placenta, when the placenta itself offered a stimulus which for the time being was more potent than others, the newly emerged fetus was licked to a lesser extent than after its own delivery.

Second, a comparison of the frequency and duration of the various behavioral items shown by the female during the different kitten birth intervals indicated that changes in stimulus conditions strongly tended to be responsible for changes in the female's behavior. As mentioned, by-products of the organic processes (such as fluids, neonate, and placenta), variably present during the different intervals, served as potent organizers of behavior, witness the prominence of licking and ingestion. It is important to note, however, that the presence of these by-products was subject to individual differences in the sequence of the organic events themselves and in reactivity among the females (Table 1), being highly variable among the different females.

Not only were the activities of different females in any one interval of a kitten birth highly varied, but the same female might, in any given interval of different kitten births, display one, a few, or all of these actions in almost any combination. With licking the item emphasized, some 25 sequences of activities were found for each of the four intervals in kitten births, without any of the combinations proving to be characteristic of any one interval. With the focus on activities other than licking, appropriate analyses showed the same result. Cooper's (1944) conclusion that variability prevails in the cat's parturitive activities may be clarified by the statement that our data offer no evidence for patterning except for conjunctions of events arising through interactions between the parturitive female, her organic processes, and the external environment.

Because of this lack of patterning in the parturitive process, dealing with the individual behavioral items became more feasible. As can be seen in Table 2, the frequency of the intervals in which licking occurred was greater than the frequency with which any other behavioral item occurred in all intervals. Between 27 and 53% (median 30%) of the parturient female's time was spent in one or another form of licking. No other activity approached licking in the amount of time devoted to it.[4] The predominance of licking made it desirable to differentiate the stimuli to which the licking response was made. The following areas were distinguished: (1) female's body, that is, genito-abdominal area versus general self licking; (2) kitten, that is, the latest born; (3) fetal membranes; (4) cord; (5) placenta; and (6) surroundings (Table 2). Signs of the interplay or competition of endogenous and exogenous stimuli are most clearly indicated in the changes that occur in licking in the different intervals.

Self licking, common in all phases of kitten birth, was more frequent than neonate licking in the emergence interval and not reliably less frequent at other times. During the contraction intervals, self licking, usually genito-abdominal in locus, was predominant and more frequent than licking of latest kitten. The general level of licking activity was heightened in the fetus delivery and the placenta delivery intervals;

---

[4] A very considerable quantity of fluid, attractive to the female, appears from the vulva in connection with neonate delivery. Wislocki (1935) reported that the quantity of amniotic fluid attached to the hair of the embryo at term amounts to as much as 10 to 20 grams, and may exceed by two to four times the volume of the free fluid within the cavity.

these were the times when both the newborn and the earlier born kittens were licked most frequently.

On the whole, the orientation of licking in the cat's parturition does not seem to be a devious question. Self licking and neonate licking often occurred in close sequence, practically as parts of the same act, suggesting that licking occurred rather indiscriminately when fluids were present. In 31 of 39 cases of fetus-arrested-in-vulva, for example, when the fetus emerged, the female directed her licking equally at herself genito-abdominally, at the floor and at the fetus; 8 females did not lick anything. This fact, together with the equivalent latencies of fetus licking and self licking, as discussed below, indicates that licking activities tended to occur as responses to fluids rather than to the neonate or to other objects.

Consistent with this point, genito-abdominal self licking occupies significantly more time within delivery intervals when the focus of stimulation centers more specifically on the vulva than within contraction intervals when stimulation is predominantly intraorganic and diffuse. The excitatory effect is then intense and dominates attention just as in contraction intervals general self licking was more frequent than either genito-abdominal self licking or licking of the latest born kitten. But in the delivery interval, licking of the latest born kitten occupied more time than either genito-abdominal self licking or licking of previously born kittens. Nor was it surprising to find that the longest acts of licking the latest born kitten occurred in the delivery intervals, with licking in the placental, contraction, and emergence intervals decreasing in that order.

The latency of licking last kitten born was significantly less ($p = .01$) for the delivery interval (mean $= 3.3$ second; median $= 2$ second) than for the contraction interval (mean $= 25$ second; median $= 10$ second) by the Mann-Whitney U test. This result we attribute to a greater variety in extrinsic stimulation (as from fluids) in the delivery interval than in the contraction interval.

Contrary to a frequent assumption, the female does not promptly lick a newborn fetus. Rather, in a total of 38 delivery intervals for which the data are subject to analysis, the neonate was licked first in only 20 cases. Moreover, the latency of licking did not differ significantly whether the female or the neonate was the first object to be licked, but general self licking occurred significantly sooner than either genito-abdominal or neonate licking. Of 58 cases, however, 52 females licked the neonate in the delivery interval.

Other behavioral shifts. On empirical grounds, we distinguished licking from chewing-and-ingesting, although, in both cases, fluids were often imbibed. The differentiation of these acts was often aided more by a shift in the female's orientation than by a change in the dominant action, as when a postural shift indicated increasing effort in mouthing and swallowing the placenta or cord.

In feline parturition highly adaptive effects often come about as incidental results. Typical is the action of severing the cord while at the same time clamping it so as to prevent hemorrhage. This is clearly an incidental outcome of other responses rather than a direct or specific action of the female with reference to the cord (Figs. 7 and 8).

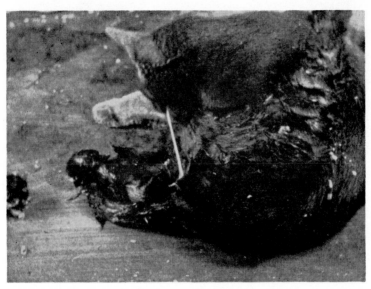

FIG. 7. *Sudsie chewing at cord of latest delivered fetus; the fetus is now free, although the placenta is still undelivered; left rear leg elevated in a common parturitive posture.*

Placenta eating involves actions that not only sever the cord more or less promptly but through an inevitable pulling and stretching have the effects both of clamping the portion that remains attached to the kitten and so weakening it as to hasten its rupture at the end of that section. Of 51 instances in which the cord remained intact after fetus and placenta had been delivered, in 35 the cord was broken incidentally as the female handled the placenta, in 1 case through pawing before placenta eating occurred, in 4 cases through her variable activities, in 9 cases by the experimenter as an emergency act.[5] One of the other two cases involved a direct response, with the female taking the placenta in her jaws and pulling it from the vulva; another was questionable because she weakened the cord through vigorous licking at frequent intervals. A binominal test of the results indicates that in a high predominance of the cases severance of the cord occurred through placenta eating.

FIG. 8. Duchess chewing at cord of a just delivered fetus whose body dangles from it; placenta still undelivered.

As a rule, the female responded promptly to the placenta when it appeared, often beginning to chew it and perhaps consuming it altogether before it had emerged completely from the vulva. Of 37 placental deliveries, in 20 the female's first reaction was to the afterbirth, either nosing, licking, or ingesting it, and in only 4 cases was there no definite response. Of the 33 cases of definite response, the placenta was completely consumed in 29. Of 20 cases in which the

---

[5] It should be noted that the figures represent groupings of the data on different bases. Thus although 51 placentas were delivered intact, the female's first reaction to the placenta was observed in only 37 cases.

female responded first to the placenta in this interval, in 19 it was eaten completely. No relationship was indicated between the sequence of births and either latency of response to the placenta or the rate or completeness of its consumption.

Cooper (1942) states that the parturient lioness, especially when primiparous, is likely to cannibalize neonate cubs by simply going on from eating the afterbirth. The case may be different in domestic cats. Under our conditions, at any rate, a total of 73 kitten births occurred without any instances of cannibalism (Tobach et al., in preparation); a very few instances were observed, however, in the postpartum resting interval and in the days immediately thereafter (Rosenblatt, Turkewitz, and Schneirla, 1962).

Variability and lack of patterning of behavioral events. To substantiate the conclusion that variability resulting from the interplay of endogenous and exogenous stimuli was an obvious feature of the parturitive behavior of the female, two aspects of the delivery process were considered for critical evaluation. The first was the question of a possible change in behavior from the birth of the first kitten to the birth of later kittens.

Both the frequency and variety of external stimulation increase necessarily with the further kitten births of a parturition; hence the character of the neonate as a stimulus object may be somewhat different when it is the fourth born (K-4) than when it is the first of the series (K-1). Furthermore, the effect of earlier kitten births might be to increase fatigue and promote satiation to new stimuli, or, on the other hand, to accelerate responses to stimuli previously experienced. It is interesting to note, however, that in an analysis of behavioral characteristics of the different intervals in succeeding kitten births, no differences of significance were found.

The second comparison was related to parity. One group of three primiparous females was contrasted with a group of three multiparous females, each cat delivering a litter of four kittens. Little difference was found between primiparous and multiparous subjects either in the repertoire or in the influence of specific activities, except that in the delivery interval the multiparous females were more likely to lick the new kitten first and to lick themselves genito-abdominally than were the primiparous females. The results indicate a somewhat greater frequency of gross bodily movements in the primiparous animals in the contraction and emergence intervals than in other intervals, perhaps indicating that inexperienced females tend to be more responsive to intraorganic sources of excitation. On the other hand, a tendency for more gross bodily movements in the multiparous than in the primiparous females during the placental interval would suggest previous experience making the placenta an attractive edible object. These results may mean that the experienced multiparous subjects tend to be relatively more relaxed and more responsive to extrinsic conditions and somewhat less disturbed by the entrance of intraorganic stimuli in the parturitive situation than the primiparous.

RÉSUMÉ AND DISCUSSION OF PARTURITION

We view the events of parturition in the domestic cat as the outcome of an interplay or at times even a competition between the stimulative effects of endogenous occurrences (such as uterine contractions and the first passage of the fetus) and of the external situation particularly as it is altered by the sequelae of such events (for example, the fluids, neonate, and afterbirth). These stimulative by-products of intraorganic processes tend to intrude upon the female's attention in an order, timing, and duration variable from case to case. Each of these occurrences, as it arises, demands a specific perceptual and behavioral adjustment.

Thus parturition in the domestic cat cannot be viewed as a regular, patterned flow of events; rather, it is a series of sporadic organic and behavioral episodes broken by activities not themselves specifically parturitive. The female thus exhibits, in a not very predictable sequence, predictable items such as self licking, squatting, licking neonate or substratum, eating afterbirth, and sitting or lying. The organic events centering on uterine contractions set off periods of intense activity indicating a high level of excitement, a condition facilitating expulsion of the fetus and delivery operations in general. Alternating with these intervals of intense activity are times of fatigue in which action is restrained, a condition facilitating the first continuous postnatal stimulative exchange between female and neonates.

Parturitive behavior in the cat may thus be characterized as a loose assemblage of functions centering on the stimulative effects of a crude succession of organic events and of their external consequences. The temporal order of behavioral adjustments and their timing thus depend upon the manner in which these internal and external occurrences may displace one another in competing for the female's variable attention. A persistent factor is an orientation to the posterior body and especially to the vaginal area, perhaps due both to earlier self experience and to currently increased stimulation from these zones. This orientation, together with the internal stimulative factors, seems indispensable for an adaptive outcome and survival of the young.

The relatively secondary differences between primiparous and multiparous females seem to involve some increase in the neonate's potency as an object to be licked and of the birth zones and objects (for example, fetus, afterbirth) as related, as well as a more relaxed condition of the multiparous females in which they are more responsive to extrinsic conditions and less to organic excitation than are primiparous females. A statement of Steyn's (1951, p. 51) that ". . . young lionesses are not always the best mothers" may have a similar basis.

The postpartum resting interval

In the events of parturition, the neonate kitten evidently participates rather passively and incidentally at first, the female in a variable and somewhat diffuse fashion depending upon outer and inner environmental circumstances. These events nevertheless intensify stimulative interactions between female and young and thus provide a broad basis for a social bond which persists and develops thereafter. The tie between mother and young, grounded particularly in actions such as licking and their gratifications, involves an elaboration of these other numerous stimulus-response processes which in time become increasingly bilateral and reciprocal. Parturition thus initiates in the female a long interval in which she deals continuously with her young as attractive entities and so becomes capable of the more complex activities constituting their care.

Directly after parturition in our cats there came an interval of several hours in which rest with the kittens superseded general activity. After the last kitten birth, decrease in the level of activity may have been somewhat slower to appear in primiparous than in multiparous subjects. In all cases there ensued an interval of about 12 hours in which the female lay nearly continuously with the kittens, encircling them.

The manner in which this resting group was formed after parturition and the manner and time at which general suckling by kittens began tended to be highly variable. Cooper (1944) noted that in one case the first actual suckling responses occurred 35 minutes after birth. Ewer (1961) reported suckling as appearing often during the first hour and in nearly all cases by the end of the second hour. In just 4 of our 17 cases, nursing of neonates began during parturition; in the others, it developed only slowly during the postpartum resting interval.

The home site, or home corner in our experimental cage situation, was established as a behavioral refuge and customary resting place and saturated chemically by the female very early in parturition and often during pregnancy. Slowness to establish such a home site and variability in using it may prove to be indications of unstable behavior in the female, impairing her adequacy as a mother. The earliest direct adjustment of the female to the kittens that promotes a feeding relationship is the reaction called "presenting," which in its first appearance may be described as simply lying down around the kittens with her ventral surface arched toward them and her front and rear legs extended to enclose them. There was wide variation in the first appearance and the early frequency of this posture.

The female's response of presenting and encircling is usually given to the main body of the litter, but on occasion it occurs with individual kittens. In the early postparturitive days she returns to the litter in the home corner at frequent intervals, each time upon her arrival making motions that might cause them to awaken and feed. In the postpartum resting interval, however, when the departures are fewer than they are later on, the kittens usually do not awaken promptly on the female's return. At times, when they fail to respond, she continues in the encircling posture, at other times she leaves and returns soon to repeat encircling.

In connection with intervals of neonate encircling, the female tends to orient the neonates not only by her movements and the little bay or functional U she forms around them, but also by attractive optimal thermal stimuli from her body and attractive (turning-to-eliciting) tactual stimuli delivered through both licking and bodily contacts. The female's behavior thus serves incidentally as well as directly through licking to guide the neonates to her and to the resting place.

After parturition, a resting group forms in a manner that varies from case to case. Suckling usually begins during female-neonate contacts within the first hour after birth (see also Ewer, 1961). Freed of its membranes, the neonate rights itself, then soon crawls slowly and irregularly forward through alternate paddlelike movements of the forelegs and uncoordinated pushing by the hind legs at intervals (Langworthy, 1929; Prechtl and Schleidt, 1950, 1951; Rosenblatt and Schneirla, 1961). In side-to-side movements of the head the neonate touches its nose variably to the floor so that a limited zone just ahead is effectively "scanned." Thus, through variable circumstances arising in connection with its own erratic actions, either during parturition or within the resting interval, the viable neonate comes into contact with the fur of the mother. Then, in response to tactual, thermal, gustatory (Pfaffman, 1936), and possibly olfactory stimuli, the young kitten begins to climb her body and promptly nuzzles in her fur. Nuzzling continues until one of many contacts with a protruding nipple elicits slow headfirst withdrawal and then nipple grasping and suckling. The female's licking of herself and of the kittens in this resting interval, a factor of importance for the first suckling, usually continues at about the same level as in the last kitten birth.

The litter period

GENERAL BEHAVIORAL CHARACTERISTICS

During the first 2 days after parturition, the mother cat rather consistently maintains her nursing group at the home site. As a rule, this situation is interrupted only at about 2-hour intervals when she rises, stretches, moves about, and feeds (or, under natural conditions, forages in the vicinity). After the first 2 days, these breaks tend to come more frequently. Then, on her return to the huddle, she stands over the group and arouses the usually sleeping kittens by licking them vigorously, then lies down encircling them; whereupon suckling resumes promptly.

The mother's encircling the kittens has the effect of quieting them, as does also (our tests show) the presence of odor cues in the home site for which the mother herself is mainly responsible. The first stage of the neonate's adjustment to this locality, thus intimately dependent upon the presence of and stimulation from the female, begins with parturition, continues for about 10 days, and develops on a tactuo-chemical (nonvisual) basis (Rosenblatt, Turkewitz, and Schneirla, in preparation).

During the parturitive period, the female appears unresponsive to the occasional crying of neonates, even passing close to a shrieking kitten or standing on one without orienting to it. Her excited condition at this time may inhibit attention, or the cue may lack perceptual meaning or, as is more likely, both factors may operate. Shortly after parturition, however, she begins to respond to the vocalizing of the young, usually of individuals away from the home corner. It is well known (Leyhausen, 1956) that the postpartum female cat does not usually retrieve her young on sight, even when they lie close to the nest, but often does so on hearing them. Usually within a day or two the mother, in response to its shrieking, will leave the nest to retrieve a marooned kitten. She behaves thus only when the sound reaches a sufficiently high level.

When the disturbance level in the litter situation rises so that the female's state of tension is increased sufficiently, she may continue for a considerable period to shift the kittens from place to place in the cage in an agitated manner. Female tigers, when disturbed, move their young to a distance, carrying them in the jaws (Burton, 1933). Causey and Waters (1936) point out that domestic cats carry their young most frequently by the nape of the neck and less frequently by the shoulders; variation is considerable, and to an appreciable extent it is a matter of convenience which part is grasped. In our subjects this act seemed somewhat random and indirect on the few occasions when it appeared during parturition and in its more frequent occurrences in early postpartum days. The act of retrieving soon improves, reaching a peak in readiness and in technique after about one week, but thereafter declines in frequency. This change may not express a lesser readiness for retrieving so much as a sharp drop in the vocalization of kittens away from the nest after the 5th or 6th day postpartum.[6] Later, however, the mother's readiness to transport her young individually to a different nesting place increases. The tendency seemed to be strongest between the 25th and the 35th days, probably because in this period the females showed a stronger susceptibility to the disturbing effects of extrinsic local conditions.

The time spent by the female in nursing the kittens typically falls off during the first 2 weeks from an initial high point related to the number of kittens in the litter (Fig. 9). In a litter of three kittens the mother at 4 days spent 70% of her time nursing the young, but a mother with two kittens spent little more than 40% of her time in this activity. Typically, after the second week, a plateau was approximated at a definitely lower level. For mothers with two or three kittens this new level approximated 30 to 50%, but for a mother with one kitten it was 15% or lower. One kitten appears to motivate the female's readiness to nurse disproportionately less than do two or more kittens (Rosenblatt, Wodinsky, Turkewitz, and Schneirla, in preparation a).

The female contributes incidentally to the development of orientation in her young to the home site and to surrounding areas. Odor cues based on the female's earlier occupancy of this area are increasingly useful to the kittens in their nonvisual returns to the nest site. Fre-

---

[6] At this time, although retrieving is much less frequent from places close to the home site, it occurs about as often as before to kittens marooned at greater distances (for example, 12 to 18 inches). Nearby, the kittens vocalize less than before and are themselves able to return; farther away their orientation is still inefficient; hence they are prone to vocalize intensely and for longer periods.

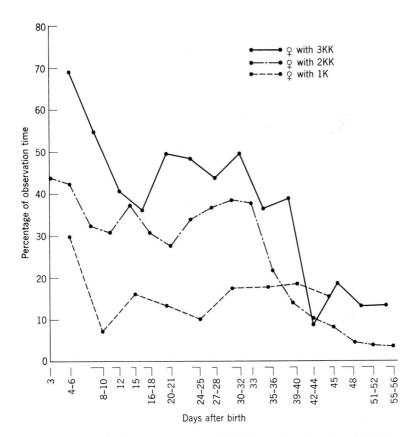

FIG. 9. *Time spent by three cats in nursing their kittens; data based on daily 2-hour observation periods.*

quently also, when the female leaves the nest, she drags some of the kittens, still attached and suckling, and after dropping off nearby they gain a further opportunity to improve their local orientation through learning. In our experimental living cages, kittens of 3 to 4 days already showed an increasing ability to return to the home corner from the adjacent corner. Frequently, a subject would stop and vocalize, whereupon the mother might intervene as described. About 12 to 15 days the kittens had begun to increase their ability to make their way to the nest across the open on the diagonal, and by the 20th day they were all proficient in this act. In the meantime, they had begun to move directly toward the female when she was seen.

The common belief that the female cat teaches her kittens to hunt seems to have some basis. Wells (1934, p. 87), experienced with lions, states that ". . . the wild lioness puts her youngsters through an intensive course of training in hunting and killing before casting them adrift. . . ." Tiger cubs begin to hunt for themselves at about 17 months, but are with the female until about 2 years of age (Burton, 1933). Because the kittens gain experience in catching and eating prey through following the female, they are on hand when she kills and thus are conditioned to become excited in the presence of such objects (Wilson and Weston, 1947). Although the maternal influence has not been shown to be specific tuition, as is often implied, it is unquestionably important for the initiation and organization of predatory behavior in the young. Kuo (1930, 1938) demonstrated that kittens reared with females that killed rodents periodically in the presence of their young later killed rodents significantly earlier and more frequently than kittens raised alone or with a small rodent. In fact, only half the kittens raised alone ever killed rodents and the others did so less frequently than did kittens raised in maternal rodent-attack situations. Notwithstanding the need for further research on this problem, in our judgment Kuo's main findings stand despite Leyhausen's (1960) criticisms.

TYPICAL DEVELOPMENT OF MATERNAL-YOUNG FEEDING RELATIONSHIPS

Through procedures yielding both qualitative and quantitative evidence we have traced the development of the normal nursing and suckling patterns of several litters of domestic cats from birth to the end of the 8th week. The general results are graphed in Fig. 10 and summarized in Table 3 in terms of how the *feeding approaches*, or behavior specifically initiating feeding, occur at different times in the course of development of a representative litter. The evidence may be summarized in the following terms.

(1) Stage 1 *(female approaches)*. In stage 1, from birth to around the 20th day, nearly all the feedings are initiated by the female. As she nears the grouped kittens, the mother lies down, arching her body around the kittens and presenting her mammary surface to them, relaxes and evidently "lets down" the milk as they begin to draw on the nipples. Her licking, and other varied stimuli presented by her, orient the kittens and facilitate their attachment and suckling. This is the basic feeding situation in which the female regularly stimulates and aids suckling by licking accessible kittens at intervals as well as by occasionally stretching and effecting slight changes in her posture. When she returns to the sleeping group after foraging, as described,

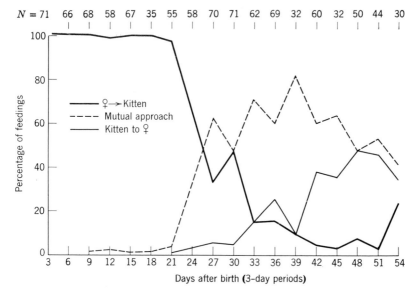

FIG. 10. *Initiation of feedings in three litters of cats, based on daily 2-hour periods of observation. N is number of feedings observed in each 3-day period. (From Schneirla and Rosenblatt, 1961, Amer. J. Orthopsychiat., 31, p. 237.)*

TABLE 3
Initiation of Feedings

STAGE I—FEMALE TO KITTENS

(1) Female approaches kittens (KK), encircles (licks); KK nuzzle, attach.

(2) Female approaches KK, sits among KK (licks); KK nuzzle, attach.

(3) Female encircling KK after nursing, arouses KK; KK nuzzle, attach.

(4) Female encircling KK in nest; KK awake, nuzzle, attach.

(5) Female sitting among KK in nest; KK crawl to female, nuzzle, attach.

(6) Female lying near KK in home area, no contact; KK crawl to female, nuzzle, attach.

(7) Female sitting near KK in home area, no contact; KK crawl to female, nuzzle, attach.

STAGE II—MUTUAL APPROACH

(8) Female lying away from home area; KK crawl to her, nuzzle, attach.

(9) Female sitting outside home area; KK crawl to female, nuzzle, attach.

(10) Female stands or sits at food dish; KK nuzzle; female leaves food, lies or sits; KK nuzzle, attach.

Maternal Behavior in the Cat 149

TABLE 3 (continued)

(11) Female stands or sits at food dish; KK nuzzle, attach; female leaves, lies or sits; KK follow, nuzzle, attach.

(12) Female stands or sits at food dish; KK nuzzle, attach; female remains at food.

(13) Female at food dish; KK nuzzle, attach; female leaves, makes self available for nursing.

(14) KK wander in vicinity of female; female lies down; KK approach, nuzzle, attach.

(15) KK wander in vicinity of female; female sits; KK approach, nuzzle, attach.

(16) Female lying or sitting, nursing KK; K wanders, turns towards her; nuzzles, attaches.

Stage III—Kittens to Female

(17) Female wanders around cage; KK follow, approach female, nuzzle; female sits or lies; KK nuzzle, attach.

(18) Female wanders around cage; KK follow, approach female, nuzzle, attach; female remains standing, then sits or lies; KK nuzzle, re-attach.

(19) Female wanders around cage; KK follow, approach, nuzzle, attach; female remains standing.

(20) Female comes down from shelf; KK immediately approach, nuzzle, attach.

(21) Female on floor; K on shelf, comes down, approaches female, attaches.

(22) Female and KK on shelf; nursing.

(23) KK vocalize towards female on shelf; female comes down; KK immediately approach and attach.

(24) KK climb to female on shelf; immediately nuzzle and attach.

---

she arouses them by licking, then "presents" and initiates another feeding episode.

In the first stage, the female's behavior changes in subtle ways in relation to developments in the behavior of the kittens. From the first postpartum hours, the kittens make gradual progress in their feeding adjustments to the mother (Wodinsky, Rosenblatt, Turkewitz, and Schneirla, 1955). At first the neonates reach the female through a slow, variable process, always with much nuzzling and fumbling in attaining her mammary surface and attaching to nipples. Adjustments of individual kittens take on an increasingly specific, individually characteristic form almost from the beginning (Rosenblatt et al., in preparation a). Usually, within the first two neonatal days, the majority of the kittens in any litter are already able to take individually specific nipple positions with appreciable regularity. With further experience, certain neonates in a litter thus come to suckle in a particular place or at a particular nipple pair in the front, the center, or the back. Some suckle alternately at either of two positions, whereas others seem to suckle at any available place. The results indicate differences in suckling specificity in more than twenty-five litters ranging from one to seven kittens. It is understandable that Ewer (1959), having worked with four litters, would be likely to emphasize the specificity of early nipple localization at the expense of individual and group variability.

The increasing involvement of the kittens in the organization of feeding situations as the first stage progresses is emphasized by the rapidity with which they advance in locating nipples so that by the fourth neonatal day most of them have become proficient in reaching the female and in attaching themselves. As Fig. 10 indicates, however, the mother holds the role of the initiator of feeding situations until near the end of the third week.

(2) Stage 2 (mutual approaches). In the second stage, which typically runs from about the 20th to shortly after the 30th day, the initiation of feeding involves active approaches by mother and kittens. The kittens, now increasingly ambulant outside the home site, begin to make feeding approaches to the female in different situations, for example, when she is resting outside the nest or crouching over the food dish and feeding. Although the nature of these situations varies increasingly, with either the female or the kittens the more active according to conditions, the initiation of feeding remains a distinctively bilateral process throughout this stage. When the kittens start the approach, the female nearly always responds appropriately, either by lying at once or, if already lying, by facilitating nipple localizations by kittens through stretching out or at least remaining in place. The kittens, on their part, respond promptly and efficiently to the mother when she presents and display an increasing adaptivity in transferring their reactions from the home site as a specific locality to the female as a focus of action.

The mother and kittens are constantly interacting, the interchanges involving subtle visual, tactual, auditory, and even olfactory cues. Although most of the auditory cues arise from movements, general reactions to vocalizing may occur. Moelk (1944) questions whether many of the vocal exchanges are direct; in her opinion one of the very few specific ones occurs after about 9 weeks when the kitten "greets" the mother upon meeting her or responds to her "murmur of greeting." "When a kitten irritates the mother by chewing and clawing her feet and tail, the irritation may find vent in growl and anger-wail" (p. 203), which, however, are doubtful as controls of kitten behavior. So far as the mother directly controls the kittens she does so behaviorally, by cuffing them, dragging them off, or turning away from one that disturbs her.

To an appreciable extent the mother thus far has accommodated her behavior to developments in the young through which they have acquired an increasingly comprehensive perceptual and motivational basis for responding to her and to littermates. She thus submits to or even joins the constantly more varied casual joint activities ("play") of the kittens including nonfeeding responses of the kittens to herself such as romping around and pouncing over her, pawing her, toying with her tail, and the like. But, near the end of the 4th week, the amount of such attentions she will tolerate at any one time seems to be on the decrease. From our results her acceptance of continued kitten encroachments would show an increasing rate of extinction between the 25th and the 35th days.

The mother, therefore, as the active center of the feeding group, through the first stage and well through the second, has provided a functional basis for the socialization of the kittens; feeding is essentially a reciprocal and social activity.

(3) Stage 3 *(kitten approaches)*. In the third stage, which generally is under way shortly after the 30th day, the initiation of suckling depends increasingly and finally almost altogether on the kittens. They now follow the mother around the cage with increasing frequency and persistency, often even pursuing her and remaining where she disappears when she evades them by leaping to the wall shelf. When the female is accessible, the kittens persist vigorously in their attempts to nuzzle. This at times results in attachment and suckling but more and more, through counteractions by the mother, may be limited to only a brief social exchange.

In many different ways therefore the kittens actively concentrate their ambulant responses upon the female and forcibly influence her behavior more and more strongly in the direction of avoidance.

Two successive types of behavioral relationship between mother and young in stage 3 are represented by the series of items 17 to 19 and 20 to 24 in Table 3. The changing attitude of the mother toward the kittens is shown by the increase in frequency and duration of her stays on the shelf (Fig. 11). But from about the 45th day, when the kittens begin to reach the shelf through their own efforts, the female avoids this place more and more as it ceases to be a refuge.

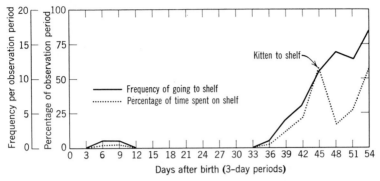

FIG. 11. *Shelf-going behavior of a female with litter of three kittens, based on daily 2-hour observation periods. Arrow indicates day when kittens first reached the shelf.*

The results point therefore to a predictable series of changes in the formation and waning of mother-young relationships; these are essential to the social bond which centers on reciprocity in the organization of the litter's social behavior (Schneirla and Rosenblatt, 1961). In stage 1 the kittens' suckling operations are gratifying to the female as are the stimulative patterns characteristic of her other meetings with them; in stage 2 these effects still predominate although the pattern of relationships is becoming complicated by occasional maternal withdrawal from the kittens; in stage 3 the withdrawal responses specialize into avoidance as the kittens' vigorous pursuits of the mother and other encroachments upon her mount. In other words, in the third stage, the strength of the social bond between female and young decreases as behavioral relationships shift from a reciprocal to a unilateral status.

It is apparent that in cats, as the litter stage advances, a basis for weaning is laid in the changing behavioral relationships of mother and kittens. At this time in domestic cats in the open, and at the corresponding time in wild cats (Wilson and Weston, 1947), the female, who now spends increasing amounts of time away from the litter, upon return usually brings slain prey to her kittens. In view of the possibility that such changing relationships occur not only in other cats but in mammals more widely, Adamson's (1960) statement that the lioness regurgitates

Maternal Behavior in the Cat 153

food to her cubs (that is, probably as nursing wanes) before they join her in hunting is suggestive. It is also significant for this point that Martins (1949) reported regurgitation by female dogs to their pups in the weaning period under conditions suggesting a basis in changing behavior relationships between mother and young (Schneirla, 1956).

Further evidence of the increasing disturbance that the kittens' relationships with the mother acquire in the third stage comes from a comparison of shelf-going behavior in females with single kittens and in females with two or three kittens. In the one-kitten situation, the female began a regular procedure of shelf climbing shortly after parturition and continued it through the litter association, with no perceptible change other than a slight rise between the 30th and 40th days. Females with two or more kittens, in contrast, exhibited a slight tendency for shelf climbing at the 3rd to 5th days, but soon lost this tendency, and such behavior did not reappear in their case until the 25th to 30th days when it became pronounced. The continuation of shelf climbing in the one-kitten females we attribute to a persistently low attraction value of the single kitten; its prompt disappearance in females with more than one kitten, to a stronger bond with the young. In Fig. 9 we see that after the first few days the one-kitten female spent a minimal part of her time in nursing, whereas two-kitten and three-kitten females spent an important part of their time thus and probably more than would be expected from the larger feeding numbers alone.

It is interesting, however, that one-kitten females, with what may be characterized as low maternal motivation, showed no indications of avoiding the one kitten at the time when mothers with litters were showing the sharp decrease in amount of nursing and increase in kitten avoidance. The distinction of three stages in the litter period is therefore less applicable to the one-kitten mother who might continue her low-level bond with the young for months. In fact, associations of a mother cat with a single kitten involving the maintenance of a stereotyped suckling pattern have been reported as lasting until sexual maturity in the young. The single-kitten mother seems to lack the behavioral disturbance, effective with litters of two or more kittens, that appears to contribute to decreased nursing and increased evasion of the young, and thereby to weaning.

The mother evidently contributes to weaning not only by incidentally emphasizing sources of solid food behaviorally, but in particular by making the infantile mode of feeding more and more difficult at a time when the young are more and more capable of getting their food independently.

Responses to strange young. Preliminary studies were made in which the kittens were removed at parturition; then at 7, 12, and 15 days the female's maternal responses were tested to *one* as against three kittens. To the introduction of one kitten the female reacted with encirclement, also by approaching the kitten at intervals and accepting its approaches as in normal litter situations. Introducing three kittens had a very different effect at 15 days postpartum. The female was very disturbed, attacked the kittens, retreated as far as possible from them, avoided contacts, and showed high excitement when they neared her. The suggestion is that a maternal motivation that is low but sufficient for the acceptance of one kitten is not equal to the task of accepting three.

Because kittens shortly after birth are able to distinguish their own mother from other littering females, and with increasing effectiveness in the course of time, a distinct initial hesitancy to suckle from the strange female may be expected. The kittens, however, soon adapt to the female, who reacts in kind. A littering female usually accepts strange kittens not too much older than her own unless an eccentricity in their behavior (as through isolation) causes a series of disturbing encounters. Then in all cases but one the female reacted by withdrawing from the situation of disturbance. Thus the difficulties had to be initiated by the kitten, with the female having to summate to the point of intolerance.

Experimental analysis through isolation studies. As another approach to studying the normal development of female-young adjustments, kittens were isolated at different times in an incubator containing a brooder or "artificial mother." Empirically, the minimal normal contributions of the female to the neonate were appraised as: (1) attractive weak tactual and optimal thermal stimulation, (2) orientative guidance in feeding (through the "functional-U"), and (3) a stable food supply. The brooder as first used in 1951 is shown in Fig. 12. This situation supplied female-factor one through its optimal temperature and cover of soft toweling, factor two through its U shape with either arm furnishing tactual guidance to the base, and factor three through the nipple at the base with its temperature-controlled synthetic food supply. To complete the initial situation, as a female substitute, regular manual guidance in feedings was given all neonates during the first 3 days, also brief daily manipulative stimulation during the first two neonatal weeks to facilitate the onset of defecation and urination.

Maternal Behavior in the Cat   155

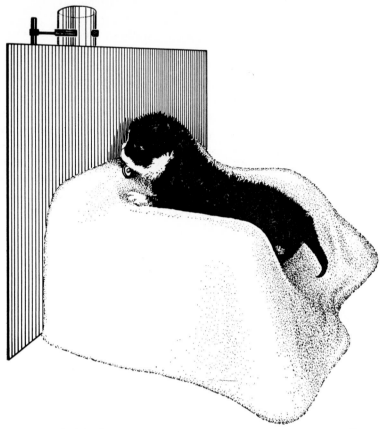

FIG. 12. *Week-old isolate kitten in suckling position at the brooder. The milk supply is indicated behind the rear guard panel. (From Schneirla and Rosenblatt, 1961, Amer. J. Orthopsychiat.,* **31,** *239.)*

The variety of stimulation normally supplied by the female to the neonates, although initially incidental to her role, has cumulative psychological effects far beyond those of the active guidance and stimulation supplied by the experimenter with the brooder. The "artificial female" was thus no mother substitute as was found when the isolates were tested by being returned to the litter situation after different intervals.

First, a striking difference appeared in the results for kittens segregated in pairs in the brooder as against single isolates (Rosenblatt, Wodinsky, Turkewitz, and Schneirla, in preparation b). The brooder adjustments themselves were very different in these cases. Although two nipples were available to each pair of kittens segregated in the brooder, virtually always when one kitten held one nipple, the other kitten, instead of taking the second nipple, left this food source unused while it nuzzled its mate then in the act of suckling. The mate is attractive not just because it presents a soft, warm surface but because this object emphasizes these stimulative properties by being motile and reactive. As further results of the isolation experiments show, these characteristics are basic to the female's normal attraction for the young and to her potent effect upon their feeding and other normal activities.

Following their isolation periods in the incubator, the kittens held there as single occupants for scheduled intervals were returned to the female and litter to test their individual reactions to the female, littermates, and situation. Although suckling appeared in all the kittens isolated from birth to the 7th day, from the 6th to the 23rd day, and from the 18th to the 33rd day, it did not appear immediately on any of the returns. Instead, suckling required up to 3 hours in the birth-to-7-day group, 20 hours in the 6 to 23rd day group, and 15 hours in the 18 to 33rd group. Analysis of the results shows that the delay in female suckling centers on two different adjustments to the female: an initial general adjustment, "contact latency," scored when the kitten made its first sustained contact with the female; and a more specific adjustment through which suckling appeared after a "suckling delay."

Attainment of a sustained contact with the female, although only a preliminary and partial adjustment in itself, depended upon adaptations both to the living situation and to the female. In the cage orientation tests, isolates returned from the brooder at 7 days were significantly inferior to the litter-raised kittens in their ability to orient spatially to the home corner and return to it even from close by. Hence these kittens soon became marooned away from the home corner and, consequently, the initial contact with the female had to occur by chance and was greatly delayed. When one of them happened to brush the female, the initial contact was followed by the kitten's turning towards her and then by a pushing against her body and nuzzling persistently into her fur. In their cruder orientative reactions, and especially in the low efficiency of their nipple-locating actions as compared with normal subjects, the isolate kittens revealed the handicap of having lost the first week of experience with the female.

The nuzzling reactions of these kittens differed significantly from those of normals. One-week-old female-reared kittens locate an abdominal area very soon after having reached the female, and thereupon nuzzle very little before achieving an attachment, with this nuzzling confined to the immediate nipple area. Any littermate touched in the preliminary orientative process is never nuzzled, although this response is common in 3-day-old neonates with litter experience. The 7-day isolates, in contrast, reached the female through much wandering, which brought them to the home corner accidentally, if at all, or perhaps through a retrieval elicited by their squealing. If an isolate happened to wander close to the female while she was lying down, she would lick it; this licking then would cause the isolate to turn toward her and push, as described, against whatever part of her body was touched. This was a crude reaction; the isolate would nuzzle over the female's entire body including even paws, neck, and back, although somewhat more frequently around her genital area. Thus the isolate's proximal orientation to the female was initially quite generalized and not more efficient than that of a neonate kitten. Female and incubator were equivalent to the extent that each furnished attractive tactual and thermal stimulation, but localizing a nipple was clearly a very different problem in the two cases, requiring specific experience with the main object involved.

In their adjustments to the female, the birth-to-7-day isolates clearly behaved differently from the neonates. They took longer for the first suckling engagement than did neonates. Analysis of the protocols discloses that they had a special difficulty, absent in the relatively simple and invariable situation of the initial postpartum resting group. The female's nursing pattern had changed progressively in the first week in relation to the behavioral development of the kittens that had been with her since parturition. These kittens, now specifically attractive to her as a group, began their suckling promptly when she encircled them in the home corner, and often held her there for some time. This condition greatly lowered the chances that the female would respond to the isolate's crying and retrieve it from a distance. Consequently, the first week isolates were at a distinct disadvantage in comparison with neonates as to factors in female behavior facilitating the first suckling.

The female, as an active agent with complex potentialities for reciprocal stimulative relationships with young, was thus hardly equivalent to the brooder to which the isolates had adjusted. But it is interesting that kittens isolated from the 6th to the 23rd day also were clearly inferior to normal littermates in the return tests, notwithstanding their early experience with the female. Although they also soon achieved their first contacts with the female, being attracted to her visually, the latency of their first suckling reactions was much greater than that for the first week isolates. Although littermate controls suckled twice in each hour, each of the 6 to 23rd day isolates continued for more than 20 hours in a persistent orientation to the female's face and anterior body. These kittens also, as with the first week isolates, were generalized in their nuzzling, spending long intervals nuzzling over the bodies of other kittens and the furry nonmammary surfaces of the female before nipple localization occurred. Visual attraction to the female did not seem to help them much in their main task nor did early suckling experience in the litter situation noticeably help them in localizing a nipple on return. We conclude that the deficiencies were due to their having been deprived of the opportunity to advance their feeding and social adjustments to cope with modifications that had occurred in the female's behavior during their absence.

The deprivation differed for kittens isolated from the 18th to 33rd day. Although they were also slow in localizing the female's mammary region, they had less difficulty in localizing nipples than the others. Their main drawback lay rather in adapting to the female as an object from which to suckle. A similar difficulty occurred in the kittens isolated from the 34th to 44th day; they needed even more time for their first suckling adjustments. The deprivation seems to have handicapped them in effecting an appropriate suckling orientation to the female rather than in the specific operations of localizing a nipple and suckling.

In the five isolate groups in which suckling finally appeared, the principal difficulty lay not in the preliminary adjustments to the female, although these were deficient, but in the more intimate adaptation required by suckling. In the two isolate groups that failed to suckle in the tests, the data indicated a special difficulty in making any sustained contact with the female, with a considerable degree of tension and excitement when near her, so intense and lasting as to exclude any suckling adjustment. Responses in the female's presence involved hissing and other indications of marked disturbance up to overt withdrawal in three of four 23rd to 44th day isolates and in all of the 2nd to 44th day isolates. Also, the 34th to 49th day isolates, the one other group in which disturbance signs appeared, showed the longest latency of all accomplishing the suckling adjustment. Although their disturbance with the female decreased sufficiently within 2 hours to admit a suckling relationship, their responses to the female still showed withdrawal tendencies and signs of "fright" differing only in degree from those in the two nonsuckling groups. It is quite likely that the members of all three of these groups would have left the litter situation altogether had this been possible.

To examine the deficiencies of the brooder as a substitute for the female, readjustment to the brooder was tested in kittens that had suckled at the female for several weeks, and readjustment to the female was tested in kittens that had just completed lengthy periods at the brooder. Three kittens that had initial periods with the female in which all had suckled were placed in the brooder at the 25th day. When, after 2 weeks they were retested in the litter situation, they had great difficulty in readjusting to the female. One had a suckling latency of more than 3 days and the other two did not suckle at all. By way of contrast, the two kittens that spent an early period (day 6 to 24) at the brooder, equivalent to that spent with the female by the others, but then had been placed with the female on the 24th day to remain with her in a suckling relationship while the others were at the brooder, reinstated brooder suckling almost at once on their terminal tests at 49 days. The sixth kitten, similarly prepared and transferred from the female to the brooder for a test on the 47th day, needed only 10 minutes to reinstate suckling at the brooder. But the last three kittens, taken from the brooder at times preceding the 25th and 35th day respectively, when tested with the female, needed periods of from 12 to 23 hours to reinstate female-suckling—much longer suckling latencies than those obtained either in female-return tests at later ages or in brooder-return tests at any age.

The length of the intervening period has a very different effect on suckling adjustments according to whether the tested kitten has been with the brooder or with the female. After intervals in the brooder of from 8 to 17 days, 11 kittens averaged 31 hours in their suckling latency when tested with the female. But in tests with the brooder after intervals with the female ranging from 10 to 36 days, 9 kittens scored a minimal suckling latency of only 12 minutes. In female tests after brooder isolation the shortest latency was 33 minutes and followed an isolation of 8 days; the longest was 93 hours, with 1 kitten not suckling at all after 66 hours in the brooder. The shortest latency in brooder tests after an intervening period with the female was 3 minutes after 17 days with the female, the longest was 25 minutes after 24 days with the female, but one kitten suckled at once after having been away from the brooder for 36 days spent partly with the mother and partly alone and feeding from a dish.

These results show clearly that the brooder suckling pattern was reinstated far more readily than was the pattern of female suckling in kittens that had fed from one or the other during equivalent periods in early development. The kitten's capacity to recall an earlier suckling adjustment therefore depends on the conditions under which it developed in relation to conditions prevalent in the test. The difficulties or the failures of subjects to reinstate the female suckling pattern under certain conditions must have been due to specific differences in the circumstances prevalent in the litter situation at the time of the test as against those prevalent there before the subject's absence. As the investigations of normal litter conditions have shown, during the time of these absences from the litter situation important changes were occurring in the female's behavior with respect to the kittens which affected the entire relationship of mother and kittens. In contrast, the brooder situation, which had not changed in the meantime independently of the kitten, presented no such difficulties in the tests.

Summary

In the domestic cat, the specific processes antecedent to maternal behavior begin during pregnancy, with a reconditioning and reorientation by the female to her own changing organism marked by intensified self licking and by fixation of a resting place. The entire pattern involves a complex progressive organization depending on the intervening variables of physiological change in the female and the young, the developmental changes in the perception of both, and upon complex and changing reciprocal relationships between female and young.

Basic factors in the female introduced essentially by neurohormonal changes are: secretory process (for example, prolactin) specific to stages; raised metabolic level; local tumescence; direct reproductive changes (for example, contractions, expulsion of fetus); sequelae of reproductive changes such as release of fluids; and in both female and young, stage-conditioned factors of sensitivity and action. These factors provide the basis for the rise of a specialized pattern of mutual adjustment in which the female is, of course, the primary active agent.

The female's changing organic status and physiological condition facilitate her habituation to a resting situation prior to parturition; the events of parturition such as uterine contractions hold her to this situation; licking fluids and eating placenta fix first the situation and then the young as attractive and initiate a behavioral bond with the neonates. There is no unitary, template basis for the patterning of behavior. Behavioral processes of different types become dominant and change in the parturitive situation according to the interplay or competition of stimuli arising from internal organic function with external stimuli from fluids, neonate, and afterbirth, sequelae of the birth-processes.

From the time parturition begins, the consequences of events such as licking fluids, fused with associated gratifications such as those from cutaneous stimulation and from eating afterbirth, dominate the female's behavior. These occurrences, in a continuous and changing succession, focus the female first on her own body and then on the young when they appear. These sources of satisfaction are an excellent basis for a perceptual attachment to the young which intensifies in time and which is essential for the normal status of caring for the young.

The strength of the social bond as a function of the extent to which an adequate pattern of reciprocal stimulation can develop between mother and young is clearly indicated by the differences found in the motivation of one-kitten and of multi-kitten mothers. Cues from the female are essential for the socialization of the young, for in the early postpartum situation the female's licking is an important guide in the first suckling adjustments of the neonate, and later in the litter stage her behavior influences the young in getting solid food. Thus relationships of feeding normally are basic to the female's role in the socialization of the young, furnishing a center of organization for the reciprocal stimulative processes maintaining the social bond.

Maternal motivation and the neurohormonal conditions maintaining it remain high in the feline mother through both the stage in which she makes the approaches and the stage in which overt approaches are mutually initiated, but weaken and change in the further stage in which increasingly vigorous approaches of the young often verge on harrying or pursuit. It is possible that her increasing avoidance of the young represents a behavioral condition appropriate for changes in hormonal secretions necessary for the waning of maternal behavior and favoring sexual receptivity. Maternal behavior is often long continued in the one-kitten litter in which the sequelae of disturbed relations do not arise as they do between mother and more than one offspring. But normally in the domestic cat the changes of the third stage promote weaning and the dissolution of the bond between mother and young. A waning attachment to the litter and the rise of physiological and behavioral changes favoring mating are evidenced by the frequency with which fertilization occurs in female cats before the actual end of the litter period.

Appendix 1. Abbreviated protocol of typical behavior just preceding parturition in the domestic cat

CASE MABEL, 31 JULY 1953, 10:25:00 A.M. TO 7:08:35 P.M. Reddish discharge at vulva. Feeds, lies, licks self generally; pronounced fetal movements; cries and pants; digs at sawdust; scratches floor; digs, lies, cries repeatedly; digs; sits down slowly elsewhere; crouches. 1:30 P.M.: drinks milk, lies on side panting; salivates heavily; digs in sawdust; digs on bare floor; licks meat but does not feed. 4:50 P.M.: mounts to shelf for first time today, cries and pants. 4:54 P.M.: down and to food dish without feeding, lies, digs in sawdust, twice; vulvar discharge thinner and increasing in quantity; digs; lies and half-rolls into genital-licking position but without any licking; palpation of nipples shows that female is lactating; licks self generally, also genitally; drinks milk; feeds briefly; digs, four times; general self licking. 5:31 P.M.: onto shelf; vocalizes; general self licking. 5:32 P.M.: down from shelf; urinates and covers; vaginal discharge; digs on bare floor and in sawdust with increasing speed and intensity; defecates and covers. 5:37 P.M.: lies. 6:25 P.M.: female assumes genital-licking position but does not lick. 7:08:35 P.M.: first contraction.

Appendix 2. Abbreviated protocol of typical behavior in the domestic cat in parturition

CASE DELLA, 3 MAY 1951. This case, in which four kittens were born, has been selected as the most representative with respect to parturitive behavior and related events, although labor was overlong for the second kitten.

FIRST KITTEN (K-1). *Contraction interval* (4:26:34 to 4:37:10): Contractions; female lifts hind leg; contractions; rolls; scratches bare floor; crouches; contractions; lifts rear leg; rolls; contractions. *Emergence interval* (4:37:10 to 4:56:10): Female shifts onto hip; licks food; lifts rear leg; contractions; lifts rear leg; licks self generally; lifts rear leg; shifts position; contractions; shifts position; contractions; shifts position; stands; contractions; licks fetus. *Delivery and placental intervals combined* (4:56:10 to 5:04:28): Neonate and afterbirth delivered together; female eats afterbirth to completion; chews cord; licks neonate; noses neonate; licks floor; noses floor; licks neonate; neonate gets covered with sawdust, female sits on it; female licks self generally.

SECOND KITTEN (K-2). *Contraction interval* (5:04:28 to 5:31:26): Contractions; female licks K-1; braces rear legs; lordosis; retrieves K-1 and licks it; retrieves K-1, licks it; grips K-1 in jaws; licks K-1; grips K-1 in mouth; paws K-1; licks K-1; lies down on K-1; stands; pants; braces; licks K-1; lies, curled around K-1; licks K-1; contractions; lies on side, K-1 at head; contractions; K-1 nuzzles female's foreleg and vocalizes; female shifts position; lifts rear leg; contractions; lifts rear leg; lies on K-1; stands; braces; stands; circles; licks K-1; gets up; sits and licks K-1; licks self generally; licks K-1. *Emergence interval* (5:31:26 to 6:26:18): Fetus visible in vulva; female circles; licks K-1; licks self generally; K-1 vocalizing steadily; female stands; shifts position; noses floor; vocalizes; circles; braces; sits down; licks K-1; shifts position; nuzzles K-1; licks self generally; licks K-1; licks self generally; licks own abdomen; contraction; licks K-1; braces; K-1 inspected by *E;* female mouths K-1 as *E* holds it; contraction; female noses floor; *E* weighs and tags K-1; female stands and vocalizes; contraction; female lies on side; braces; circles; retrieves K-1; licks K-1 while sitting on K-2 (fetus); contractions; scratches floor; lies on K-1; licks K-1; licks self generally; licks fluids on floor; licks K-1; licks floor. *Delivery interval* (6:26:18 to 6:27:20): As female licks floor and circles, K-2 emerges; free of sac, vocalizing promptly and continually; female continues licking fluids on floor, circling, and then licks K-2 while K-2 clings to her tail; female continues to lick both fluids on floor and K-2 (the floor was licked for 40 seconds in four bursts of licking, and K-2 was licked in three bursts lasting 40 seconds). Female licks floor; circles; licks K-1. *Placental interval* (6:27:20 to 6:46:22): Afterbirth delivered; female licks K-2; licks afterbirth; chews cord; eats placenta; licks K-2; licks self generally; retrieves K-2; licks K-2; licks K-1; licks K-2 at length; licks K-1 briefly; licks self abdominally and generally for extensive period during which she retrieves K-2 three times; licks K-1 and K-2 briefly; alternately licks K-2 and self generally; licks K-1 and K-2 briefly; licks floor; female mouths K-1; circles; lies down in presenting position; *E* tags K-2.

THIRD KITTEN (K-3). *Contraction interval* (6:46:22 to 6:56:46): Contractions; female licks self generally; licks K-1; licks self abdominally; squats; licks K-1; licks self genitally; licks self generally; licks K-1; licks K-2; contractions; squats; licks self generally; licks self abdominally; contractions. *Emergence interval* (6:56:46 to 6:58:04): Fetus visible; female stands; strains; defecatory crouch; licks self genitally; contractions. *Delivery interval* (6:58:04 to 7:02:40): K-3 born; female licks self abdominally; licks K-3; paws K-3; eats sac; licks self generally; licks K-3 and K-2; stands up dangling K-3; female drags K-3 as she moves about. *Placental arrest interval* (7:02:40 to 7:10:18): Placenta of K-3 visible in vulva; female licks self generally; licks K-3; licks self genitally; licks cord; licks K-1 and K-2; circles several times dragging K-3. *Placental interval* (7:10:18 to 7:14:40): Afterbirth delivered as female stands; female eats placenta; retrieves K-2 and sits on K-3; licks K-2 briefly.

FOURTH KITTEN (K-4). *Contraction interval* (7:14:40 to 7:28:44): Contraction; licks K-3; licks K-1; licks self generally; licks self abdominally; licks K-3; drags K-3 by cord; mouths K-3; retrieves K-3; steps on K-2; licks K-2; licks floor; shifts; stands; lies down; contraction. *Emergence interval* (7:28:44 to 7:29:14): Fetus visible; contraction; female lies on side; licks floor. *Delivery interval* (7:29:14 to 7:40:18): K-4 delivered; female licks K-4 and cord; stands with fetus dangling from vulva; licks self generally; licks abdominal area and cord; licks self generally; licks K-4; circles, dragging K-4; lies down; rises. *Placental interval* (7:40:18 to 8:00:00): Afterbirth falls out; female eats afterbirth; licks K-4; licks K-2; licks floor; retrieves K-3; licks K-4; retrieves K-3, dragging K-1; licks K-4; licks self generally; retrieves K-1; licks K-1 and K-2; E palpates female, weighs kittens; female licks K-1, K-2, K-3, K-4 and self generally; licks K-3; protocol ends.

References

Adamson, Joy (1960), *Born Free,* New York: Pantheon.
Asdell, S. A. (1946), *Patterns of Mammalian Reproduction,* Ithaca, N. Y.: Comstock.
Bard, P. (1936), Oestrual behavior in surviving decorticate cats. *Amer. J. Physiol.,* **116,** 4–5.
Barelare, B. Jr., and C. P. Richter (1938), Increased sodium chloride appetite in pregnant rats. *Amer. J. Physiol.,* **121,** 185–188.
Beach, F. A. (1948), *Hormones and Behavior,* New York: Hoeber.
Beach, F. A. (1958), Neural and chemical regulation of behavior. In H. F. Harlow and C. N. Woolsey (Eds.), *Biological and Biochemical Bases of Behavior,* Madison: University of Wisconsin Press. Pp. 263–284.
Burton, R. G. (1933), *The Book of the Tiger,* London: Hutchinson and Co.
Causey, D., and R. H. Waters (1936), Parental care in mammals with especial reference to the carrying of young by the albino rat. *J. comp. Psychol.,* **22,** 241–254.
Clegg, M. T. (1959), Factors affecting gestation length and parturition. In H. H. Cole and P. T. Cupps (Eds.), *Reproduction in Domestic Animals,* New York: Academic Press. Pp. 509–538.
Cooper, J. B. (1942), An exploratory study on African lions. *Comp. Psychol. Monogr.,* **17,** 91, 1–48.
Cooper, J. B. (1944), A description of parturition in the domestic cat. *J. comp. Psychol.,* **37,** 71–79.
Eckstein, P., and S. Zuckerman (1956), The oestrous cycle in the mammalia. In A. S. Parkes (Ed.), *Marshall's Physiology of Reproduction,* Vol. 1, Part I., 3rd ed. London: Longmans, Green and Co. Pp. 226–398.
Ewer, R. F. (1959), Suckling behaviour in kittens. *Behaviour,* **15,** 146–162.
Ewer, R. F. (1961), Further observations on suckling behaviour in kittens, together with some general consideration of the interrelations of innate and acquired responses. *Behaviour,* **17,** 247–260.

Günther, S. (1954), Klinische Beobachtungen über die Geburtsfunktion bei der Katze. *Arch. Exp. Vet.-Med.,* **8,** 739–743.

Hain, Annie M. (1935), The effect (a) of litter-size on growth and (b) of oestrone administrated during lactation (rat). *Quart. J. exper. Physiol.,* **25,** 303–313.

Hall, Kathleen (1957), The effect of relaxin extracts, progesterone and oestradiol on maintenance of pregnancy, parturition and rearing of young after ovariectomy in mice. *J. Endocrin.,* **15,** 108–117.

Harris, G. W. (1955), *Neural Control of the Pituitary Gland,* London: E. Arnold and Co.

Kuo, Z. Y. (1930), The genesis of the cats' responses to the rat. *J. comp. Psychol.,* **11,** 1–35.

Kuo, Z. Y. (1938), Further study on the behavior of the cat toward the rat. *J. comp. Psychol.,* **25,** 1–8.

Labriola, J. (1953), Effects of caesarean delivery upon maternal behavior in rats. *Proc. Soc. exper. Biol. Med.,* **83,** 556–557.

Langworthy, O. R. (1929), A correlated study of the development of reflex activity in fetal and young kittens and the myelinization of tracts in the nervous system. *Contr. Embryol., Carneg. Instn.,* **20,** 114, 127–171.

Leblond, C. P. (1937), L'Instinct maternel. Nature et relations avec la glande mammaire, l'hypophyse et le système nerveux. *Rev. franc. Endocr.,* 15, 457–475.

Lehrman, D. S. (1956), On the organization of maternal behavior and the problem of instinct. In P.-P. Grassé (Ed.), *L'Instinct dans le Comportement des Animaux et de l'Homme,* Paris: Masson et Cie. Pp. 475–520.

Lehrman, D. S. (1961), Hormonal regulation of parental behavior in birds and infrahuman mammals. In W. C. Young (Ed.), *Sex and Internal Secretions,* Baltimore: Williams and Wilkins. Pp. 1268–1382.

Leyhausen, P. (1956), Das Verhalten der Katzen (Felidae). *Hand. Zool., Berl.,* **10** (21), 1–34.

Leyhausen, P. (1960), Verhaltensstudien an Katzen. *Z. Tierpsychol.,* Beiheft 2.

Lindemann, W. (1955), Über die Jugendentwicklung beim Luchs (*Lynx L. Lynx Kerr*) und bei der Wildkatze (*Felis S. Silvestris Schreb*). *Behaviour,* **8,** 1–45.

Martins, T. (1949), Disgorging of food to the puppies by the lactating dog. *Physiol. Zoöl.,* **22,** 169–172.

Meites, J. (1959), Mammary growth and lactation. In H. H. Cole and P. T. Cupps (Eds.), *Reproduction in Domestic Animals,* Vol. 1, New York: Academic Press. Pp. 539–593.

Michael, R. P. (1958), Sexual behaviour and the vaginal cycle in the cat. *Nature, London,* **181,** 567–568.

Moelk, Mildred (1944), Vocalizing in the house-cat; a phonetic and functional study. *Amer. J. Psychol.,* **57,** 184–205.

Nicoll, C. S., P. K. Talwalker, and J. Meites (1960), Initiation of lactation in rats by nonspecific stresses. *Amer. J. Physiol.,* **198,** 1103–1106.

Pfaffmann, C. (1936), Differential responses of the new-born cat to gustatory stimuli. *Ped. Sem. and J. genet. Psychol.,* **49,** 61–67.

Prechtl, H., and W. M. Schleidt (1950), Auslösende und steuernde Mechanismen des Saugaktes. I. Mitteilung. *Z. vergl. Physiol.,* **32,** 257–262.

Prechtl, H., and W. M. Schleidt (1951), Auslösende und steuernde Mechanismen des Saugaktes. II. Mitteilung. *Z. vergl. Physiol.,* **33,** 53–62.

Racadot, J. (1957a), La thyroïde de la chatte durant la gestation et la lactation. *C.R. Soc. Biol.,* **151,** 5, 1005–1007.

Racadot, J. (1957b), Neurosécrétion et activité thyroïdienne chez la chatte au cours de la gestation et de l'allaitement. *Ann. Endocr., Paris,* **18,** 628–634.

Riddle, O. (1935), Aspects and implications of the hormonal control of the maternal instinct. *Proc. Amer. phil. Soc.,* **75,** 521–525.

Riddle, O., E. L. Lahr, and R. W. Bates (1935), Maternal behavior induced in virgin rats by prolactin. *Proc. Soc. exp. Biol. Med.,* **32,** 730–734.

Riddle, O., E. L. Lahr, and R. W. Bates (1942), The rôle of hormones in the initiation of maternal behavior in rats, *Amer. J. Physiol.* **137,** 299–317.

Rosenblatt, J. S., and L. R. Aronson (1958), The influence of experience on the behavioural effects of androgen in prepuberally castrated male cats. *Anim. Behav.,* **6,** 171–182.

Rosenblatt, J. S., and T. C. Schneirla (1962), Behaviour of the cat. In E. S. E. Hafez (Ed.), *The Behaviour of Domestic Animals,* London: Baillière, Tindall and Cox. Pp. 453–488.

Rosenblatt, J. S., G. Turkewitz, and T. C. Schneirla (1961), Early socialization in the domestic cat as based on feeding and other relationships between female and young. In B. M. Foss (Ed.), *Determinants of Infant Behaviour,* London: Methuen. Pp. 51–74.

Rosenblatt, J. S., G. Turkewitz, and T. C. Schneirla (1962), Development of suckling and related behavior in neonate kittens. In E. L. Bliss (Ed.), *Roots of Behavior,* New York: Hoeber. Pp. 198–210.

Rosenblatt, J. S., G. Turkewitz, and T. C. Schneirla (in preparation), Analytical studies on maternal behavior in relation to litter adjustment and socialization in the domestic cat. II. Development of orientation.

Rosenblatt, J. S., J. Wodinsky, G. Turkewitz, and T. C. Schneirla (in preparation a), Analytical studies on maternal behavior in relation to litter adjustment and socialization in the domestic cat. III. Maternal-young relations from birth to weaning.

Rosenblatt, J. S., J. Wodinsky, G. Turkewitz, and T. C. Schneirla (in preparation b), A study of individual isolates and segregated pairs of kittens in relation to normal adjustments in the litter situation.

Rothchild, I. (1960a), The corpus luteum-pituitary relationship: the association between the cause of luteotrophin secretion and the cause of follicular quiescence during lactation; the basis for a tentative theory of the corpus luteum-pituitary relationship in the rat. *Endocrinology,* **67,** 9–41.

Rothchild, I. (1960b), The corpus luteum-pituitary relationship: the lack of an inhibiting effect of progesterone on the secretion of pituitary luteotrophin. *Endocrinology,* **67,** 54–61.

Schneirla, T. C. (1951), A consideration of some problems in the ontogeny of family life and social adjustments in various infrahuman animals. In M. J. E. Senn (Ed.), *Problems of Infancy and Childhood,* (Trans. 4th Conference, 1950), New York: Josiah Macy, Jr. Foundation. Pp. 81–124.

Schneirla, T. C. (1956), Interrelationships of the "Innate" and the "Acquired" in instinctive behavior. In P.-P. Grassé (Ed.), *L'Instinct dans le Comportement des Animaux et de l'Homme,* Paris: Masson et Cie. Pp. 387–452.

Schneirla, T. C., and J. S. Rosenblatt (1961), Behavioral organization and genesis of the social bond in insects and mammals. *Amer. J. Orthopsychiat.,* **31,** 223–253.

Scott, Patricia P., and M. A. Lloyd-Jacob (1955), Some interesting features in the reproductive cycle of the cat. *Studies on Fertility,* **7,** 123–129.

Steyn, T. J. (1951), The breeding of lions in captivity. *Fauna and Flora, Transvaal,* **2,** 37–55.

Tobach, Ethel, M. L. Failla, R. Cohn, and T. C. Schneirla (in preparation), Analytical studies on maternal behavior in relation to litter adjustment and socialization in the domestic cat. I. Parturition.

Wells, E. F. V. (1934), *Lions Wild and Friendly,* New York: Viking Press.

Wilson, Charis, and E. Weston (1947), *The Cats of Wildcat Hill,* New York: Duell, Sloan and Pearce.

Wislocki, G. B. (1935), On the volume of the foetal fluids in sow and cat. *Anat. Rec.,* **63,** 183–191.

Wodinsky, J., J. S. Rosenblatt, G. Turkewitz, and T. C. Schneirla (1955), The development of individual nursing position habits in newborn kittens. Paper read at Eastern Psychol. Assoc., New York.

5

maternal behavior in the DOG

Harriet L. Rheingold

The purpose of this study was to identify and quantitatively describe the activities performed by the dog while caring for its young. Activities of the pups which seemed relevant to the mothers' caretaking activities were also recorded. Mothers and infants were observed day by day according to a prearranged schedule, and records made of what they were doing. The main data of the study are frequency data abstracted from the records. Material from the records has also been used to describe details of the chief activities, to present findings on infrequent activities, and to suggest relationships between the activities of mothers and young.

Method

SUBJECTS

During the spring of 1959 five mothers and their litters were observed at the Hamilton Station of the Roscoe B. Jackson Memorial Laboratory

I wish to thank J. P. Scott and W. C. Stanley of Hamilton Station, Roscoe B. Jackson Laboratory, Bar Harbor, Maine for providing subjects and facilities, Geraldine C. Keene and Marian B. Sherman for assistance in organizing the data, and D. W. Hayne for advice on the design and analysis of the study.

(Table 1). The sample of mothers was composed of a cocker spaniel, a beagle, and three Shetland sheep dogs (Shelties). Their litters varied in size from two to seven. Observations were started on different days in the lives of the litters and carried out for varying numbers of days. Choice of subjects and periods of observations were set by the availability of animals during the period of the investigator's stay. Parturition was not observed. Excellent accounts are presented in Bleicher (1962) and Harrop (1960).

TABLE 1

Subjects and Duration of Study

Subjects	Age (Year)	Ordinal N of Litter	N of Pups	Days Ob-served	N of Observa-tion Periods
Cocker spaniel	2	2	7	1–66†	174
Sheltie* (brown)	5	6	4	6–68	169
Sheltie (black)	2	2	5	5–19	51
Sheltie (merle)	1	1	2	1–42	132
Beagle	4	4	6	1–29	86

* Shetland sheep dog.
† Day 1 is day litter was born.

Each mother, with her litter, was housed in an individual indoor pen, approximately 9 × 8 feet, separated from an adjoining pen by a wall, approximately 4 feet high. In the corner of the pen was a wooden box, 45 inches long, 30 inches wide, and 28 inches high, called the whelping box. In addition, each pen contained a low bench, a small ramp (for climbing), two containers of dry food, and a water pail. The floor of the pen was covered with wood shavings, the floor of the whelping box with straw. The pens were cleaned early in the morning and shortly thereafter the animals were fed a wet mash, an extra pan of which was provided for the pups on the 30th day. Water, dry meal, and dry pellets were always available.

The subjects of the study were cared for by laboratory employees in accordance with their general practices. Mothers, when 4½ weeks pregnant, were washed, clipped, and brought into the nursery wing; when 8 weeks pregnant, they were given extra feedings, and straw was spread on the floor of the whelping box. The pups were weighed shortly after birth and thereafter at weekly intervals, wormed at 2 weeks, and given distemper inoculations at 8 weeks. The only change made in standard laboratory practice for the study was the removal of one side of the whelping box to facilitate the observations; otherwise, the side would not have been removed until the litter was two weeks old.

The pups were apparently normal and healthy. Birth weights and weight gains were comparable to those reported by Scott and Marston (1950) with one exception: a brown Sheltie pup weighed 30% less than the average pup in its litter at birth and 50% less at 63 days of age.

PROCEDURE OF OBSERVATION

Observations were made on each mother and her litter during four 15-minute periods a day, distributed at random between 8:00 A.M. and 6:00 P.M. A day without observations intervened between 5-day blocks of observations. To measure the temporary effect of the observer's entrance, some periods of observation were doubled, with the observer staying in the pen for 30 minutes. Data from the second 15-minute period have not been included in the main report.

The observer entered the pen and sat on the bench about 3 feet from the whelping box. (When the pups began to direct their activities to the observer, at one month of age, the observer took a post on the other side of a wire fence but still within the dog's room.) The observer did not handle, feed, pet, or play with the dogs except for a word or two to the cocker spaniel and beagle to quiet their greetings. The Shetland sheep dogs did not exhibit greeting behavior.

Directly upon entrance into the pen the observer began to record the behavior of mother and pups in a running account, minute by minute. In the first minute, the observer recorded the position of the animals as well as those with whom they were in contact and what they were doing. Then, minute by minute, as they changed position, vocalized, nursed, played, etc., their behaviors were noted until the end of the period of observation.

From the handwritten accounts, activities of mothers and pups directly or indirectly related to maternal care were identified, coded, and tallied; these constitute the frequency data. Descriptive data were also abstracted from the accounts to supply details of the activities and to suggest relationships among them. For the convenience of the reader, definitions and measures of the activities will be given as the data on each activity are presented.

TREATMENT OF DATA

Depending on the nature of the activity, frequency measures were of two main kinds: number of minutes out of the 15 which made up an observation period in which the activity was present for at least 30 seconds, and the number of occurrences of the activity during the 15-minute period of observation. Less frequently used measures will be described in the appropriate places.

The data were averaged over successive 3-day intervals and plotted on ordinal number of days in the life of the litter. For each activity, the curves for the individual mother or litter were plotted, as well as a mean curve based on all subjects. As a result, not only can the main trend of each activity be seen but also the variability between subjects; in addition, the number of subjects for whom there are data at any 3-day interval is made clear. Curves of pup behavior have been corrected for litter size; values were calculated as average activity per pup in the litter. The mean curves were based on the unweighted average of litter averages. The curves for maternal activities, in contrast, were not corrected for litter size; each curve shows how much activity was characteristic of the mother regardless of litter size. (With 24 pups in the sample, the average litter was 4.8 pups.)

Interpretation of the data is based on inspection of the curves. The runs test (Siegel, 1956) was used with certain curves to confirm that their fluctuations were not chance oscillations. With the curves for mothers' going away from pups, for mothers' punishing pups, and for the number of minutes pups and mothers were asleep the test did not detect nonrandomness; nonrandomness was indicated, however, with minutes of contact, number of pups in contact, minutes of nursing, number of pups suckling, duration of licking, number of times mothers went to pups, and number of times pups went to mothers.

Maternal activities

CONTACT

Contact was defined as physical contact of any sort between mother and pups. The first measure of contact was number of minutes out of 15 in which contact lasted for more than 30 seconds. The second measure was the number of pups in contact with mother on each minute of observation (sum of number of pups in contact on each minute divided by 15).

Contact between mother and young occupies a central place among the activities to be considered. In addition to positioning mother and pups for other activities (for example, for the mother to lick the pups, for the pups to suckle), it also provides warmth for the young who are poikilothermic during the first few weeks of life (Jensen and Ederstrom, 1955).

Mother and young were in contact with each other for almost the entire 15 minutes of observation during the first 3 days of litter life (Fig. 1); by days 43 to 45, contact amounted to only 2 minutes in any period of observation. Inspection of the composite curve suggests that four time segments may be distinguished.

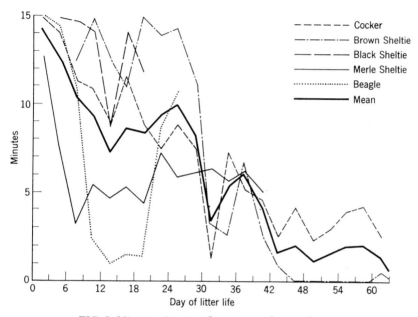

FIG. 1. Minutes of contact between mothers and pups.

During the first segment, days 1–3 to 13–15, contact between mother and pups fell off fairly rapidly as the mothers left the litter more and more often (Fig. 7). They might continue to stay in the box but not in contact with the litter or they might leave the box entirely. The young during this period cried when the mothers left, but soon became quiet as they huddled in a heap on each other. During the second segment of time, days 13–15 to 31–33, contact between mother and pups began to increase as the pups, which could now move more readily, went to the mother. Mothers, in contrast, seldom went to their young. Contact between mother and pups increased until it reached a peak of 10 minutes on days 25 to 27; thereafter, it fell off sharply. Nursing was coming to an end: the mothers more and more often walked away from the pups, and punishment of pups by mother had begun. In the third segment, days 31–33 to 43–45, another, although smaller, peak of contact appeared. Nursing had all but dis-

Maternal Behavior in the Dog 173

appeared, and contact was now mostly playful. But even at the end of the observations, a pup might, on occasion, still sleep in contact with some part of a mother's body.

The number of pups in contact with the mother decreased over time in a fashion similar to that for amount of time in contact (Fig. 2). From a mean of 4.6 pups on days 1 to 3 the number dropped to a mean of one pup around day 36, and thereafter only occasionally was even one pup in contact with the mother. Number of pups as a measure of contact yields data different from amount of time, but they are correlated data and their course is therefore similar.

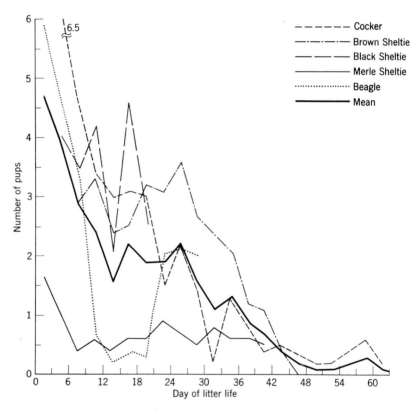

FIG. 2. Number of pups in contact with mothers.

Contact, in summary, was at a maximum in the first few days of litter life, but by 60 days occurred infrequently and for very short durations. During the first 2 weeks it was initiated almost entirely by the mother. As the pup acquired vision and locomotory skills, it was he who initiated contact. Thereafter, the mother's activities reduced contact more and more as the pup's activities tended to increase it.

Nursing is an activity closely related to contact; contact is a necessary condition for it. It is a somewhat equivocal item of maternal care because although the mother can permit nursing, it is the young who execute the activity. The mother's contribution will be called nursing, the pups' suckling, to follow the terminology recommended by Cowie et al. (1951).

Nursing was defined as including only times of active suckling by the pup and excluding those times when a pup simply held a nipple in its mouth. The measures were, first, the number of minutes in a 15-minute period of observation during which one or more pups suckled for longer than 30 seconds and, second, the number of pups suckling on each of these minutes.

Suckling was a complex activity; even at the beginning it was composed of several components and the nature of each component changed with time. The components were: finding a nipple, maintaining the grasp, pushing in of forelegs, pulling up of head, and disposing of rear legs so that head and foreleg activities continued.

Of the three litters observed on day 1, the entire sequence of activities labeled suckling was present in two, although not yet well coordinated; in the third litter, the merle Sheltie's, both infants stayed between the mother's rear legs and were not observed to suckle on day 1. Early suckling was characterized by fumbling in locating a nipple and by the prominence of first one component, then another. The pup rooted here and there over the heads, backs, and legs of the mother and of other pups. Since the pup's eyes did not begin to open until day 12, vision could not be employed in the search. If smell were the cue, it seems likely that success would have occurred without so much rooting. It is proposed therefore that the cues employed were tactile. When a nipple was finally found, the pup's mouth closed around it, the body quivered, and the head bobbed rapidly.

By day 3 the separate acts were better coordinated. The pull-up on the nipple was a sharp, high jerk. Paws, extended on each side of the nipple, pushed in as the head pulled up. The hindlegs, used for holding the rest of the body in place, often slipped out from under the pup as he pushed in with his front legs and pulled out on the nipple. Often the harder he worked, the more he tended to slip away and lose contact.

At least two sets of events in the environment complicated the infant's suckling; one concerns the mother, and one the other pups. The con-formation of the mother's body and especially her posture made his suckling easier or more difficult. The flat chest and belly cavity of the cocker spaniel made her nipples more easily available than the rounded cavity of the Shelties. The sitting mother was more difficult to suckle than the mother who lay on her side. The activity of the other pups in the litter on occasion also interrupted or interfered with a pup's suckling. When a pup lost a nipple, a great increase in his activity occurred. In thrashing about he was apt to dislodge a littermate; within a moment the whole litter was intensely active, pushing and shoving, each in the way of the other. Minutes might pass until each again had a nipple in its mouth and suckling was resumed. A change in the mother's position produced the same flurry of activity.

These statements suggest that the pup expends a considerable amount of energy in suckling and that suckling is not without its frustrations. The image one might have of the contented infant at the breast was not often verified. Throughout the records such terms as furious, aggressive, voracious, impatient, excitement, haste, and mad scramble may be found. The mothers, on the other hand, whose bodies were the ground of the pups' battle for a nipple, did not protest. Instead, they often closed their eyes and apparently slept.

By day 17, the pups nursed with greater precision and with fewer extraneous efforts. Their hindlegs held them in place more efficiently; they more often lay on their sides, with their eyes closed. Instead of the strong downward thrust with both forelegs, one on either side of the nipple, they tapped the mother's belly lightly with one paw. Sucking and swallowing were now clearly audible.

A new pattern of suckling behavior appeared about days 20 to 22. Suckling now began with noisy sucks. The pups nursed vigorously for 2 or 3 minutes, then ceased. The nipple was held with body taut and unmoving while swallowing could be heard. Then suddenly and simultaneously each shifted to another nipple with rapid, jerky move-ments, protests and grunts, and much noisy sucking. This was followed by vigorous nursing for a couple of minutes, only to be followed by the same sequence of acts. Similar behavior has been described in the pig, of whom it is characteristic from the first (Gill and Thomson, 1956). It apparently indicates an intermittent flow of milk.

During the last few days of suckling, pups sucked very rapidly and for short periods. Suckling was noisier. The sound of one pup's sucking aroused the others, whether asleep or not, all running to join the first one.

Figures 3 and 4 present the frequency data which the foregoing descriptive material elucidates. On the mean curve, nursing was observed on 6 of the 15 minutes during days 1 to 3, rose to 9 minutes on days 4 to 6, and fell off gradually, disappearing by day 45.

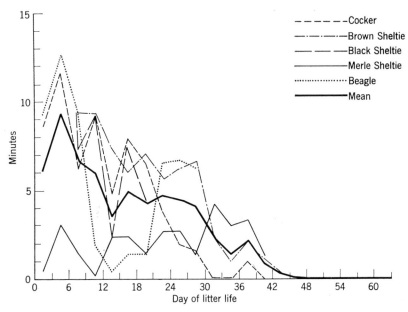

FIG. 3. *Minutes of nursing.*

The number of pups suckling at any minute of observation also decreased across the course of the study. That the curve (Fig. 4) resembles that for minutes during which mother is nursed is to be expected, for they are related data. What is remarkable is the small number of pups nursing on any minute, the mean number at the peak of the curve being only 1.5.

Other activities associated with nursing on which some information was gained are rate of suckling, nipple preference, pups' eating of dry food and wet mash, mother's regurgitation of wet mash, and mother's adjusting of position during nursing.

The tempo at which pups suckled was not recorded systematically. Scattered notes, however, show that on day 4 the number of pulls during 5 seconds was 2.5; on day 8, it had increased to 4; and on day 25, seven pulls in 5 seconds were recorded for a beagle pup.

Preference for a particular nipple or pair of nipples was observed

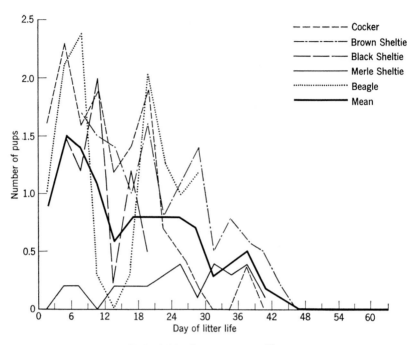

FIG. 4. Number of pups suckling.

in only the merle Sheltie litter: the larger of the two pups more often nursed at the rearmost nipples, the smaller at the next forward ones. The rear mammae in the dog appear to be larger and to have more milk. Some nipple preference may exist in the dog—it was after all not consistently recorded in this study. But had it been as specific as Ewer (1959) reports for the kitten, one might have expected it to be more apparent.

Pups began to supplement their diet by eating wet mash between the 3rd and 4th weeks of life (day 21 in the cocker, day 26 in the beagle, and day 27 in the brown and merle Shelties). Dry food was first consumed on day 23. No marked drop in nursing occurred during these days.

Scott (1950) suggested that wild dog mothers would supplement their pups' diet by foraging afield, eating, and then disgorging the partly digested food for the pups upon their return. Martins (1949) observed regurgitation in three dogs, but among the Jackson Laboratory population of dogs it was not a common phenomenon (Scott and Marston, 1950). It was observed in two of the five dogs in this sample, once in the cocker spaniel and several times in the brown Sheltie.

The sole observation for the cocker occurred on day 42 as follows: "Pup goes to mother, jumps on her head, pulls mother's ear, mother regurgitates, pup eats, mother covers vomitus with sawdust." (It should be noted, however, that the cocker began on day 21 to regularly cover the pan of wet mash and the tins of dry food with sawdust.)

Entries on the brown Sheltie are fuller. On day 28 at 10:00 A.M., she regurgitated, but the pups paid no attention to the vomitus. Twenty days later, on day 48, at 10:30 A.M., regurgitation was observed, and again on days 51, 52, 54, 62, and 64, on each occasion between 11 A.M. and 12 noon. (She may, of course, have regurgitated on other intervening days as well.) Preliminary to regurgitation the mother paced, walked, and whined. The pups followed closely, appeared excited, jumped at mother, ran after her, and fell over each other. After she regurgitated, the pups ate the vomitus at once. On the second occasion, day 48, the pups were sleeping in the box and the mother pawed the floor near the box. They awoke, stood up, followed her as she left the box, as she walked and ran, and as she finally regurgitated. Thus, the mother aroused the pups; it was not they who gave the initial stimulus.

During nursing, mothers on occasion changed their postures in response to pushing or crying by pups. They might lie down, roll further over on their sides, stretch their bellies, or raise or extend a leg. As a result the pups found access to a nipple. This activity was labeled adjusting position, and all occurrences were tallied. Although impressive when observed, it proved to occur infrequently (highest mean value, on days 1 to 3, was 0.7), and to decrease gradually over the course of nursing. In general, the mothers seemed not to be aware of much of the pups' striving to reach her. Most of the pups' crying, even loud and insistent crying, seemed to go unheeded. And many a pup "swam" into a mother's leg or head or back, in an apparent effort to get to her belly, with no change in mother's posture.

LICKING

Each occurrence of the mother's licking of the pups was timed in seconds (note difference from other measures) and summed to obtain a measure of duration of licking during a 15-minute period of observation. Licking was present on the first day of the litter's life, reached a peak during days 4 to 6, decreased over the course of the study, and occurred infrequently after day 42 (Fig. 5).

Licking appeared to serve several functions, a conclusion based on the results it seemed to produce. In order of frequency, the functions were: to take care of the excreta of the pups, to arouse the pups from sleep, and to retrieve them.

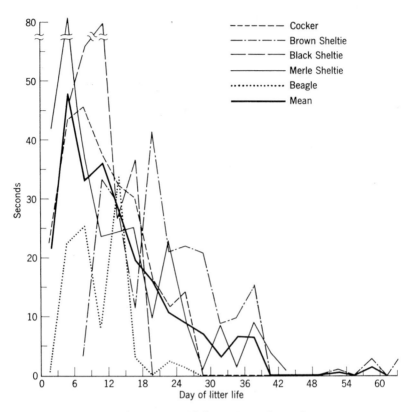

FIG. 5. Duration of licking of pups by mothers.

Licking of the pups' perineal region was common. In the early days the actual excretion of urine and feces and their ingestion by the mother could not be seen. Her tongue was large, the pup was small, and the product was probably correspondingly minute. By day 7, and increasingly thereafter, urine or feces could sometimes be observed as they emerged from the pup and were consumed by the mother. Licking became increasingly vigorous, the pup's body was often lifted into the air as the mother licked under it, and pups sometimes protested as they were licked, especially if they were suckling. Even after the pups were out of the box and away from the mother, she not only kept the pen free of excrement but regularly caught it as the pup began to urinate or defecate by himself. The mothers were surprisingly quick to notice a pup's squatting or to hear a pup's grunting as he began to defecate. The first time a cocker pup urinated by himself without bringing the mother to his side was on day 17; the corresponding day for the beagle was 25. On day 39 the merle Sheltie was still catching the pup's urine as it was voided. Feces, however, were caught until a later date; day 26 was the first day on which a pup's feces were seen in the cocker's pen. The beagle was still catching the pup's feces on day 29, the last day of observation for this animal. The merle Sheltie stopped on day 35, but the brown Sheltie on day 67 was still catching urine and feces. Although variability was considerable, the length of time the mothers carried out the activity is noteworthy.

Of interest was the voiding behavior of pups beginning about day 23. Upon awakening they would walk out of the box or away from the mother or litter, depending on where they had been sleeping, to a distance of 3 or 4 feet, and then urinate or defecate, at first in any spot, then more and more often in the spot characteristically used by the mother.

A mother also licked the pups when she went to them after being away. Sometimes she licked their perineal regions as above, but at times she also briefly licked their heads and backs. The litter then became intensely active, moved to her, turned their heads to her belly, and attempted to suckle. The mother frequently lay down, continued to lick for a while, the pups suckled, and the mother ceased to lick. In these instances licking appeared to arouse the litter and to result in nursing.

Lastly, licking was used by the mothers to retrieve pups. During the 3 months of observations, only twice was a dog seen to retrieve a pup by carrying it in its mouth, and one of these dogs was not a subject of this study. Both occasions occurred in the first week of life: the mother carried the dog for a few inches, dropped it, grasped it in her mouth again, carried it for a few inches, repeating the process until she got the pup into the box. Usually, however, a mother licked the pup in any region. Then he turned to face her, she backed up, and he followed her nose, until step by step, he was retrieved. It appeared that more often the cue for mother's retrieval was not the cries, no matter how loud, but the sight of the pup away from the box or litter.

The Shelties retrieved their pups for a longer period of time than the other dogs. Retrieval by licking a pup 3 feet from the litter was noted as late as day 22 for the brown Sheltie. For them, licking was only one form of retrieving; the brown Sheltie punished pups which ventured too far afield and the merle Sheltie kept pups close to her and away from the observer by a herding-type of maneuver, to be described later.

Maternal Behavior in the Dog   *181*

Record was kept of the part of pup's body licked by the mother. In general, the perineal region, a category including the areas of anus, urinary opening, belly, and rear, was licked more often than the head and back. But during the 1st week and again during the 5th and 6th weeks the differences between the number of times the perineal region was licked and the head-and-back, taken as another category, were small. For example, during the first week, the perineal region was licked a mean of eighteen times during a 15-minute period of observation; the head and back, combined, fifteen times. During the 2nd, 3rd, and 4th weeks, however, the perineal region was licked two to three times as often as the head and back.

Smelling and nosing were activities related to licking. They were systematically recorded and, because of the difficulty of always distinguishing between them, were combined in one item. The data reveal that they were low-frequency behaviors occurring, on the average, less than once in each period of observation, with no major change during the course of the study. Smelling and nosing often preceded perineal licking. Nosing by itself also both aroused the litter and retrieved a "lost" pup, in these respects resembling licking.

PLAY

The behavior of some of the mothers with their pups appeared to be playful. It was observed infrequently, especially in light of the frequent playful overtures of pups to mothers. Only 21 occurrences of playful maternal behavior were observed, 3 in the cocker spaniel, 6 in the brown Sheltie, and 12 in the merle Sheltie. First day of occurrence was 53 in the cocker, 43 in the brown Sheltie, and 14 in the merle Sheltie. Playful behavior was not observed in the black Sheltie or the beagle; the last day of observation for each was day 19 and day 29, respectively, and therefore perhaps too early for its appearance.

Play took several forms. In the cocker spaniel it consisted only of rubbing her face against the face of a pup which approached her. This behavior was observed on days 53, 55, and 62. In the brown Sheltie, play consisted of rubbing noses, mouthing a pup's mouth, gentle biting, putting a paw on pup, and, once, while lying on her right side, of pawing, mouthing, and nibbling the runt who climbed over her. The merle Sheltie was the most playful of the three. Early play consisted of rolling the pup over, nosing, nudging, licking, and catching head in mouth. An entry on day 32 is as follows: "Mother leaps at black pup, then gets down on her belly. Pup rolls over. Mother goes to gray pup, catches her, paws and mouths her. Mother leaps high in air and circles pups. Licks black pup. Catches gray pup with her paw. Rolls black pup over with her nose; holds him between her front legs as she lies on her belly and he on his back. Mother nibbles at his neck (elapsed time, 2 minutes)."

It must be concluded that although the pups were playful and invited play, play between mother and pups was not frequent. On the other hand, both the cocker spaniel and the beagle mothers invited the observer to play with them.

MOVEMENTS OF MOTHERS TO AND AWAY FROM PUPS

Record was kept of each time the mother separated herself by at least 12 inches from the litter or from individual pups, and of each time she went to the litter or to individual pups from a distance of at least 12 inches. During the first 2 or 3 weeks the pups tended to stay together and then it was the litter which was left or approached.

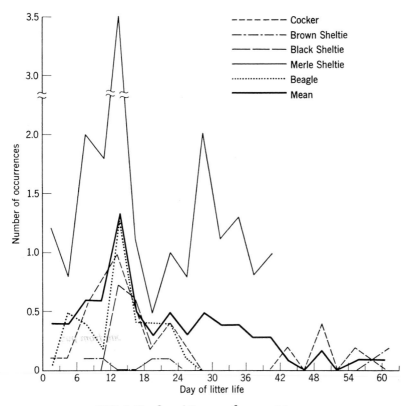

FIG. 6. Number of times mothers went to pups.

Maternal Behavior in the Dog 183

Later the object might be the litter or only part of it. In the first few days the mother might move only a short distance but by day 9 and increasingly thereafter she was often several feet distant.

During the first 3 weeks the mother's movements to and away from the litter were few and balanced each other in frequency (Figs. 6 and 7). During the first nine days of the litter's life she left them seldom but returned to them as often as she left them. Movements to and away reached a peak at days 13 to 15, and at least once in each session the mother departed and returned. After day 16 mothers went to the litter less and less often, but left them more and more often. Despite variability in the behavior of individual mothers, the drop in going to the litter and in leaving it from days 16 to 21, roughly the third week of litter life, is clear in each animal. Each mother, also, after day 19 went away from the pups more often than she went to them.

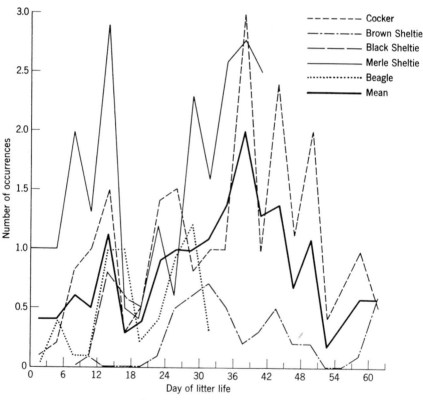

FIG. 7. Number of times mothers went away from pups.

184   Maternal Behavior in Mammals

The approaches and departures of the mothers become comprehensible when the behavior of the pups is examined. Records were made of the number of times pups went to their mothers, with the stipulation that at least several inches must be traversed (thus eliminating such activities as just moving the head to make contact with mother).

Beginning on days 13 to 15 the pups, now capable of locomotion, went to the mother (Fig. 8). Day by day, as they progressed for greater distances and as vision guided their movements, they went to the mothers more and more often.

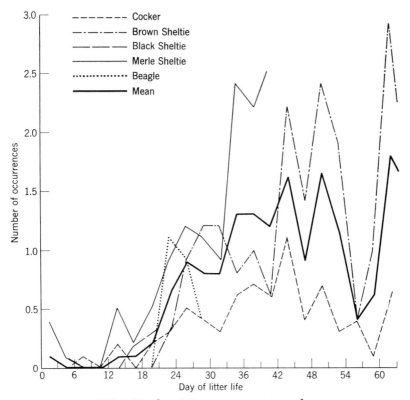

FIG. 8. Number of times pups went to mothers.

Although many objects in their environment attracted the pups, the mothers were objects of considerable attraction throughout the entire period of study. The loci of attraction in the mother during the first month were her belly and inguinal region, the first for nursing and the second as a favored place for sleeping. Pups jockeyed for position in the mother's groin, sleeping there with their heads up on the mother's body. After the first month, however, the pups increasingly transferred their attention to the mother's head.

As in the early days when there was a relationship between the mother's movements to and from the litter, later there was a relationship between the movements of the mother and the pups. As she left them, they followed her; as they made contact with her, she left them. Going away from the pups may be seen as the first separating behavior which the mothers showed. When pups did make contact with the mother, they sought out the nipples and suckled. The number of departures reached a peak on days 37 to 39 (Fig. 7). From days 31 to 39 the behavior of pups and mothers resembled the chase, with the pups the pursuers and the mother the quarry. Running from the pups was the mother's first, but not her only, defense, and by itself did not deter the pups from their activity, although it reduced the number of occasions during which they could suckle. Mothers did not climb or jump to the top of the whelping box or the ramp to elude the pups, a maneuver certainly within their powers.

The maneuvers employed by the mothers are illustrated in the merle Sheltie's record for day 32. "Mother ends nursing by getting up and pacing while pups try to hang on. They cry when they cannot reach a nipple. They hang on the nipples again. Mother walks in and out of whelping box. Pups fall off nipples as they trip over (2-inch high) ledge of box. Mother continues to walk." On day 40 an entry reads, "Pups go to mother and suckle. Mother raises rear legs and shakes them off. Pups go to mother again. She moves back fast, and they fall off nipples. Pups pursue, mother moves back fast again."

Not all the pups' approaches to the mother were to her nipples. Beginning on day 21 some of them were to the mother's head, and later after nursing had dropped out, most of them were to her head. An individual pup would go to the mother's face, whine and cry, and raise a paw to her as in play. This sequence of behavior resembled begging. If it was a begging for food (Scott and Marston, 1950), regurgitation followed it only once—in the cocker; where regurgitation did occur regularly, in the brown Sheltie, the act appeared to originate with the mother. Begging at the mother's head might be an invitation to play, an invitation to which the cocker spaniel did respond on rare occasions and the merle Sheltie regularly. Increasingly the approaches to the mother were playful. Pups mouthed the mother's mouth, pawed her ears, eyes, mouth, licked the mother's head, often with low vocalizations. Pups also mouthed, chewed, and pulled on the mother's tail, belly, back, and legs. Mothers, with the exception of the merle Sheltie, made no response to this behavior or averted their heads or moved away or punished it. A typical entry, on the brown Sheltie, day 32, is as follows: "Pup begs mother to play. Lies so that his back is next to her, turns head so his mouth catches her fur, puts paws to her mouth, vocalizes little begging sounds and looks at her face. She sits up."

PUNISHING

Punishing was defined as the mother's growling or barking at a pup, snapping or baring her teeth to it, catching its head in her mouth and shaking it, holding it down with a paw, or pouncing on it, but in distinction to the same acts in apparent play. Often a mother executed more than one of these separate acts; for example, she might growl, snap, and pounce on a pup. The measure was the number of punishment episodes, whether the activity consisted of only a growl or a series of punishing acts.

Punishing appeared relatively late, increased rapidly to a peak at days 43 to 45, when an average of four punishings was observed in a 15-minute period of observation, fell off irregularly thereafter but even on the last days of study was still occurring at the rate of two per period (Fig. 9). Considerable variability was apparent. The first punishing act was observed in the cocker spaniel on day 17, in the brown Sheltie on day 28, and in the merle Sheltie on day 40. Furthermore, no punishing behavior was observed in the black Sheltie or in the beagle, even though observations continued on the first until day 19 and on the second until day 29, days which fall within the range of first appearance for the other three animals.

Various puppy acts preceded punishment. Mothers punished pups when they suckled or tried to suckle. The brown Sheltie and the cocker also punished pups which came near them. In addition, the brown Sheltie twice punished pups which had gone to a far corner of the pen. Following punishment, nursing and contact decreased and the mothers set up a space around themselves free of pups. For the brown Sheltie this space was the whelping box in which she stayed and from which she excluded the pups; a common occurrence was the lining up of the four pups along the periphery of the box, bodies parallel and heads facing her. For the cocker spaniel the space was wherever she chanced to be. The cocker spaniel alone punished pups which ate from the wet mash pans, pups which approached her, or even faced in her direction, while she ate.

The mothers' punishing appeared only to check, but not to elimi-

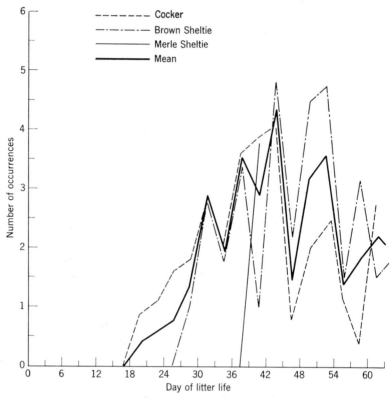

FIG. 9. Number of times mothers punished pups.

nate, the behavior. The pups persisted in trying to nurse, to make contact and to play with the mother. A cocker pup might flee from the mother's punishment, yelping and dragging its rear as though in pain, then, shortly, return to the activity. On the last day of observation, pups were still being punished upon approaching the mother, but they no longer tried to suckle.

The pups' persistence should be weighed against the inconsistency of punishment, for the same act would be followed with punishment one moment but not the next. At times mothers seemed distracted by outside noises; at times they dozed. Then, especially, the brown Sheltie pups would try to enter the whelping box from the side or in back of the mother. Sometimes individual pups were indulged; the brown Sheltie, for example, occasionally permitted the runt of the litter to sleep in the box with her while the other pups were kept outside.

Herding was observed only in the merle Sheltie. On five occasions, the first on day 24, the last on day 40, she circled the pups, wove in and out and around them, held them down with a paw, and pushed them under her. The stimulus appeared to be the pups' wandering too far afield or coming too close to the observer. As a result of her activities, the pups were kept together on the side of her body away from the center of the pen and restricted to the corner where she herself usually stayed. In effect, then, herding was similar to retrieving.

A similar effect was produced by the brown Sheltie who was twice observed, on days 52 and 61, to punish her pups when they had gone to a far corner of the pen on the opposite side of which the cocker spaniel mother spent most of her time. (From day 41 on, the cocker cried, yelped, and barked at this corner—there was a small crack here through which presumably she could see the brown Sheltie pups.)

Breaking up fights between pups was observed only in the merle Sheltie. On days 27, 28, and 32 she responded to their fighting by walking between them. Fighting, to be discussed later, occurred in the cocker spaniel and brown Sheltie pups but brought no response from their mothers.

Relations between maternal activities

A sharper picture of the relationships among various maternal activities may be obtained by plotting several activities in the same figure (Fig. 10). Contact, nursing, licking, going away from the pups, and punishing were selected for study, and the curves were smoothed by the use of three-point moving averages.

Contact, unlike nursing and licking, was highest at first. Nursing, except for the slightly later appearance of its maximum and its always lesser amount, resembled contact in pattern; both decreased in a similar manner. Licking followed a course similar to nursing in the early days of the litter's life but thereafter resembled the course for contact as well. Generally, these were activities which decreased as the litter grew older, apparently in orderly fashion. Opposed to this trend were the other maternal activities: moving away from the pups and punishing the pups. They resembled each other in pattern of increase and decrease, although moving away began earlier and did not occur as frequently.

Maternal Behavior in the Dog   189

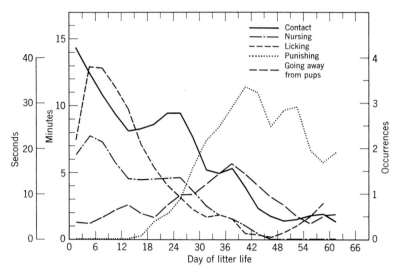

FIG. 10. Relations between maternal activities. Contact and nursing were measured in minutes; licking, in seconds; punishing and going away from pups, in number of occurrences.

Other activities of mothers and pups

ASLEEP

A mother was recorded as asleep if her eyes were closed and she did not move. The measure was number of minutes in which she was asleep for more than 30 seconds. Mothers slept during only a small fraction of a 15-minute period of observation (mean = 2.8 minutes, s = 0.96). The amount did not vary markedly for individual mothers and its relative constancy over the course of study suggests that sleep was not affected by the age of the young (Fig. 11).

The pups, in contrast, slept approximately twice as long during observation periods as the mothers (Fig. 12). Here, too, variability among animals was small. The curve, although irregular, showed no general trend. During the first days, the pups' eyes were closed and the only usable criterion was the absence of movement, except twitching.

Twitching, noted by Scott and Marston (1950) and Fredericson et al. (1956), occurred only when the pup was asleep, and was a prominent activity not so much for its frequency as for the regularity with which it appeared and the violence of the jerks often apparent. On occasion the jerk was so extreme that the pup's head bounced on the

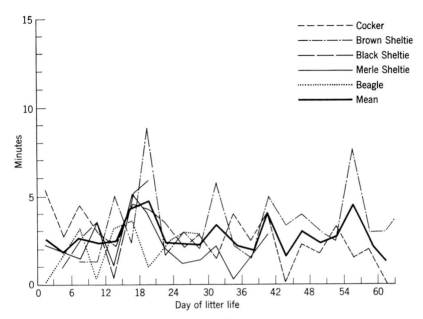

FIG. 11. *Minutes mothers were asleep.*

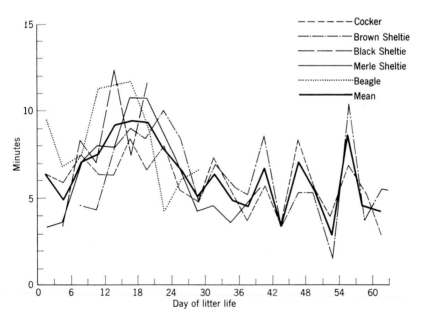

FIG. 12. *Minutes pups were asleep.*

Maternal Behavior in the Dog 191

floor. Twitching was more frequent when the pups had no contact with the mother and, in agreement with the findings of Jensen and Ederstrom (1955), all but disappeared during days 21 to 23 (Fig. 13).

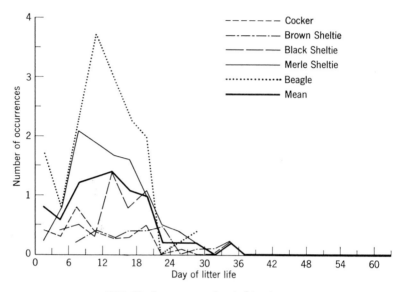

FIG. 13. *Occurrence of twitching in pups.*

Although the item "in box" tells only of the mothers' and pups' physical position in the pen, it nevertheless yields some information about maternal care.

"In box" measured the amount of time the animals spent in the whelping box (that is, number of minutes during the 15-minute period of observation). No mean curve was drawn either for mother or pups because the behavior of the brown Sheltie subjects differed so markedly from the others.

The mothers generally stayed in the box during the first week of the litter's life (Fig. 14); thereafter they gradually spent more and more time outside the box. The pups stayed in the box about a week longer than the mothers and then left it more abruptly (Fig. 15).

The brown Sheltie mother, in contrast to the others, seldom left the box during the first 6 weeks. The pups stayed with her during the first 3 weeks. Thereafter she began to exclude them from the box by growling and snapping at them as they returned from eating, exploring, or playing outside the box.

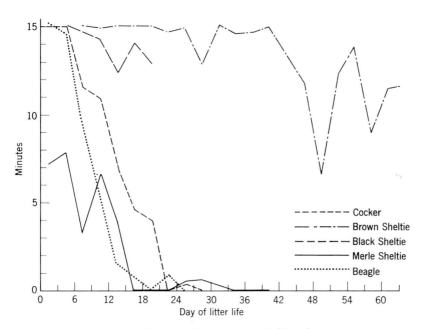

FIG. 14. *Time mothers spent in whelping box.*

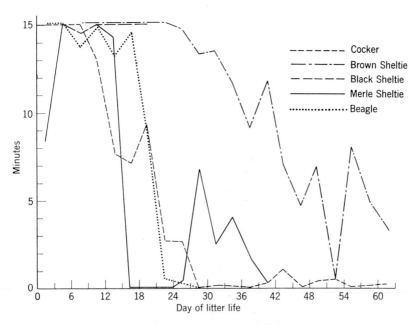

FIG. 15. *Time pups spent in whelping box.*

Maternal Behavior in the Dog   193

The posture assumed by the mother was recorded for each minute of observation. Lying on side, the predominant posture during days 1 to 3, was, by days 31 to 33, the least often observed posture (Table 2). All other postures increased in frequency, with walking and standing showing the greatest change. By the time the young were a month old, the mothers spent only 2 out of the 15 minutes on their sides, an amount of time roughly equivalent to that spent in nursing. The distribution of postures at two months was similar to that at one month. These findings supplement and corroborate the other measures of maternal care: lying on side occurred frequently when contact and nursing were high. This position, which maximally exposes the nipples, facilitates nursing.

TABLE 2
Postures of Mothers
*Measure Is Number of Minutes Posture Was Assumed
during 15-Minute Period of Observation*

	Days		
	1 – 3	*31 – 33*	*61 – 62*
Lying on side	11.3	1.8	1.1
Lying on belly	2.4	5.3	5.8
Sitting	0.5	2.9	2.0
Standing	0.2	2.9	3.6
Walking	0.7	2.0	2.5

ADDITIONAL PUP ACTIVITIES

The development in the pup of certain behavior patterns, not specifically related to maternal care, is traced here in brief with little attention to individual differences. The patterns are those of vision, locomotion, vocalizations, litter contacts in the absence of the mother, play and exploratory behavior, fighting, and sex behavior.

Vision. The pups' eyes opened gradually. Eye slits were first observed between days 12 and 15; the eyes were completely open between days 18 and 20. There was clear evidence that at least one pup walked *to* his mother on day 15, which suggests that the pup may see before his eyes are completely open.

Locomotion. From the first day of life the pups were observed to cover distances of several inches (see also James, 1952). With body flat on the floor and forelegs held back along the side of the body, the pup progressed by moving the hind legs alternately. Or he pivoted in circles by swinging the head around. By day 5, the head was raised a fraction of an inch above the floor; day 8, the legs were held under the body; day 9, the pup was trying to stand; day 11, the head was held an inch above the floor for a second or two. The pup progressed now by placing forelegs in front and pulling the hind legs under the body. By day 14, the pup was almost walking, although losing balance often—the legs sliding out to the side—or rolling over on his back. He righted himself and repeated the attempt often. On day 15, he could cover a distance of 2 feet, unsteadily, step by step with belly dragging, always correcting for a tendency to go sideways rather than ahead. On day 20, he walked 6 feet, gait still ataxic, slow, and weaving. Although gait was still unsteady on day 25, prancing appeared. Three days later there was a bouncing, waddling run which ended in a slide and fall. On day 32, pouncing was observed. Hopping and running in leaps and bounds appeared on day 37. On day 41, the pup climbed to the top of the ramp. Throughout this period the pup appeared not daunted by falls and spills; he repeated each new skill over and over, and seemed always to be attempting the act just beyond easy competence.

Vocalizations. Four classes of vocalizations were distinguished and counted. Murmurs—nonprotest vocalizations, low in volume—included squeals, squeaks, and clucks, and were heard on day 1, becoming most frequent between days 4 to 9, then decreasing gradually until day 39, when they were no longer heard. Whimpers were protest vocalizations, also low in volume, and included whines, protests, complaints, and fussing. They were heard on day 1, reaching a maximum between days 7 to 9, and disappearing at days 25 to 27. Cries and yelps were louder protest vocalizations. Present on day 1, they remained relatively constant in number throughout the study, and were still heard on the last day of observation. Growls and barks, the fourth class, first appeared on days 16 to 18 and, in contrast to the other classes, increased to reach a peak on days 61 to 63.

Litter contact. In the absence of the mother, the pups usually attained contact with their littermates (see also Welker, 1959). During the first few days the pups cried when the mother left them, milling around, pivoting, and eventually making contact with each other. They pulled themselves toward one another until large parts of their bodies were in contact, their heads over the bodies of others. Pups in such a heap quieted and apparently fell asleep. While the mother stayed away, there was a tendency for the pups on the periphery to climb over other pups and burrow into the center. The heap thus became more and more compact but was never stable for more than a few minutes at a time.

By the end of the first week the pups did not always cry when the mother left. They more quickly formed a heap and settled in sleep. The shift of those on the periphery into the center continued. More prominent now were movements to the periphery of pups at the bottom of the heap and movements of all pups to get their heads over the bodies of others. By the end of the second week the pups sometimes slept with their bodies parallel, no longer in a heap. At the end of the fourth week pups slept in groups of two or three. In the sixth week a pup might sleep alone, but usually against something, a wall or the whelping box.

Play and exploratory behavior. The first apparently playful response of pup to pup was mutual mouthing. Occurring at 20 days of age, this was followed in a day or two by mouth biting. Thereafter mouthing and biting increased rapidly as the pups mouthed and bit other parts of each other's bodies and the mother's ears, tail, leg feathers, or the fur on her back. On day 24 occurred the first record of pups' biting objects in the pen; a beagle pup bit a splinter of wood projecting from the whelping box, and a merle Sheltie pup chewed on a wood shaving. On day 27, the pups rooted over the observer's shoes, mouthed them, and bit the laces. Day by day, in rapid succession, other items were bitten—the ramp, the food tins, the water pail, the fence. Biting was still a prominent activity on the last day of observation.

A day or two after mouthing and biting appeared, the pups began to put a front paw out to another pup (day 23). At first this gesture cost them their balance and they fell. Soon it was a frequent gesture and resulted in contact. Its later form was boxing (day 25). Tumbling over each other's body appeared around day 25. On day 27, tossing the head while holding in the mouth some part of another pup's body, head, neck, or back, was observed. On the same day, too, crouching of the forepart of the body appeared as a prelude to play. Pouncing on and lunging into each other followed within a few days. These activities were freely combined, often accompanied by mouthing and biting, and they increased in frequency and vigor. During the second month, rough and tumble play with much biting, running, and chasing was observed whenever the pups were not eating or sleeping. Often the play involved the whole litter, at times only a part of it, and occasionally a pup would play by himself, prancing, charging, twirling, and shadow boxing.

One other kind of play deserves mention. Pups sometimes reached for inaccessible objects like water pipes, nails, and other hardware. They would jump toward them and cry. Similar behavior was directed toward the observer after the post of observation was outside the pen. Especially at her entrance, but also at other times, the pups would run to the fence, stand on their hind legs, paw at the mesh with their forefeet, and cry, yelp, or bark.

Fighting. Fighting, although similar to some forms of play, was a term restricted to tussling marked by growling, snarling, biting and tossing of head, and sometimes by the crying of the attacked pup. The first instance was observed on day 26 in the cocker spaniel pups and on day 27 in the merle Sheltie and brown Sheltie pups. The numbers of times fighting was observed in these three litters were 15, 6, and 9, respectively, and thus it qualifies as behavior of low frequency. The brown Sheltie pups showed a kind of conquering behavior—the vanquished pup rolled over on his back, the winning pup stood over him—and a tendency to "gang up" on the runt.

Sex behavior. Sex behavior was also observed. A merle Sheltie pup mounted and clasped another pup on day 28 and again on day 38. Similar behavior was not observed in the brown Sheltie pups until day 52 and in the cocker spaniel pups until day 53. Mounting, clasping, and thrusting were observed in a cocker pup on day 66. In every instance the behavior was exhibited by a male pup; the object was both male and female, and on two occasions among the cockers it was the mother.

Effect of observer's entrance into the pen

If the entrance of the observer changed the activities of the mother and pups, an extended period of observation might result in a return to their undisturbed state. Therefore some periods of observation were doubled and the results of the second 15 minutes were compared with those of the first. On 20% of the observation periods the observer stayed in the pen and continued to record behavior for 30 minutes. These periods were distributed at random when other activities permitted. The results of the second half of these periods were not included in the results reported earlier.

Four maternal activities which might be affected by the observer's entry were sleeping, contact, nursing, and licking. An examination of 123 differences between first and second 15-minute periods showed few instances where the mean difference could be statistically distinguished from zero (Table 3). On 8 of the 16 comparisons, the means for the second half were greater than for the first, on 8 they were less. But all four mothers slept more during the second 15 minutes, and for three of these the differences were statistically reliable.

TABLE 3
Measures of Reliability

	Cocker Spaniel	Brown Sheltie	Merle Sheltie	Beagle
Number of Measures	34	33	45	10
Days of litter life	17–62	28–68	1–16	2–6
Mother asleep (min)				
Mean 1st 15 min	3.0	4.5	2.0	0.2
Mean 2nd 15 min	5.8*	7.8*	6.1*	1.5
Contact (min)				
Mean 1st 15 min	4.4	3.8	6.1	14.3
Mean 2nd 15 min	5.3	4.7	5.5	14.0
Nursing (min)				
Mean 1st 15 min	1.8	1.6	1.3	10.9
Mean 2nd 15 min	1.4	0.5	1.8	13.3
Licking (occurrences)				
Mean 1st 15 min	0.3	0.8	2.8	1.3
Mean 2nd 15 min	0.0	0.5	1.1	0.5

* t test of difference between 1st and 2nd measures significant at the .01 level (two-tailed test).

These results suggest therefore that, except for the number of minutes the mothers slept during a period of observation, the observer's entrance into the pen did not have a consistent effect on the activities selected for study.

Discussion

The main conclusions of the study are as follows:

1. The maternal activities of the dogs changed markedly during the first two months of the pups' lives. The pups' activities also changed, and there appeared to be a systematic relationship between maternal and pup behavior.

2. During the first week of the pups' lives, when they were blind and deaf organisms which sought only to be in contact with the mother and to secure a nipple, the major maternal activities were staying in contact with the pups and licking them.

3. Contact included not only the mother's staying with the pups but also appropriate positioning of her body. Her availability provided the pups with the opportunity to obtain warmth and nourishment. It also set the occasion for her licking of them.

4. Licking cared for the pups' excretory functions, aroused them, and brought them back when they strayed.

5. During the second week of the litter's life, contact between mothers and pups, nursing, and licking decreased as the mothers spent more and more time away from the litter.

6. During the third week pups went to the mothers when the mothers left them. As a result, contact and nursing increased but did not reach the frequency characteristic of the first few days.

7. During the fourth week the mothers began to punish the pups as they approached or began to suckle. Punishing and leaving the litter were termed separating activities.

8. During the second month, licking and nursing disappeared as major activities, and contact was markedly reduced. Punishment was frequent; at times it appeared severe, at other times, inconsistent. Generally it seemed to check rather than to eliminate the behavior it followed.

9. In some mothers, regurgitation, play, and herding were observed.

Some maternal activities seemingly within the capability of the dog were not observed. Nest building was not seen; some mothers in fact scratched the straw away from where they lay. On only a few occasions did the mothers respond even by looking to a pup's cries; rather, retrieving by nosing or licking followed the mother's *seeing* a pup away from the litter. [The sight of the moving pup, and not its vocalizations, attracted the mother during parturition also, according to Bleicher (1962).] Nor did mothers adjust their postures when pups wormed their way in at their heads, backs, or legs, although they occasionally did so when pups were at their bellies and trying to secure a nipple. The mother did not call the young to nurse, as do cat mothers according to Ewer (1959). The only vocalizations mothers were heard to make to their pups were growls and barks in punishing them. No defense of the young (nor any apparent threat in the environment) was observed; two Sheltie mothers did on occasion interfere with their pups' going to the far end of the pen.

The capability of the young was an important factor in maternal care. It was the pup which burrowed into the mother's fur, found the nipple and grasped it, and which went to the mother when she left him.

As impressive was the activity of the pups in relation to their littermates. Although the mother constituted an object of great attraction—witness the pups' numerous approaches to her—in her absence, littermates were approached, perhaps first as substitutes but later clearly in their own right. Thus, in the beginning, when the mother left the pups, they cried until they established contact with each other. Later, play with each other was their commonest activity. They might sleep alone but awake they turned to each other.

The mother and the littermates were not the only objects to which the pups paid attention. Long before they could walk steadily they were on their feet and going—to the ramp, to the food pan, and to the observer. They cried to objects seen but not accessible. By 2 months of age they were active, independent organisms with keen sensory powers.

Many of the findings reported here are limited to the conditions obtaining in this study. The subjects were kennel-raised dogs and the mothers and pups were confined within a pen. The number of subjects was small, and during the second half of the second month only two litters were observed. Variability of behavior was great, both among animals and for any animal from day to day. No statements can be made about the effects of breed, number of pups in the litter, age of mother or her parity, since with so small a sample each variable was confounded with the others.

The method of the study was simple narrative description of events occuring during scheduled periods of observation. It is a method which permits the immediate recording of data and seems especially useful when the varieties of behavior to be observed are unknown. Yet it presents a serious hazard in that very area in which it seems to possess great advantage. Because the record offers a chronological account of events, minute by minute, it is easy to assume not only that the events are related but also that they bear a cause and effect relationship. Much of what has been said about the relationships between various maternal and pup activities should therefore be regarded as speculative. Now that some of the elementary variables in maternal behavior in the dog have been quantitatively described, it should be possible to study them with greater precision and control.

Summary

The purpose of this study was to identify and quantitatively describe the activities performed by the dog in caring for its young. Activities of the pups which seemed relevant to the mother's caretaking activities were also recorded.

Five mothers and their litters were observed, the longest span of observation covering two months. The dogs were kennel-raised and observations were made in the animals' pens. Observations were made on each mother and litter during four 15-minute periods a day, distributed at random. Narrative descriptions of events were recorded minute by minute. Frequently occurring activities were identified, coded, and tallied, and the data averaged over successive 3-day intervals. Descriptive data were also abstracted from the records to give details of the chief activities, to present findings on infrequent activities, and to suggest relationships between the activities of mother and young.

It was found that the maternal activities changed markedly during the first two months of the pups' lives. The pups' activities also changed, and there appeared to be a systematic relationship between maternal and pup behavior.

During the first week of the pups' lives the major maternal activities were staying in contact with the pups and licking them. Contact provided the pups with the opportunity to obtain warmth and nourishment. Licking aroused the pups, took care of their excreta, and retrieved them when they left the litter. During the 2nd week contact, nursing, and licking decreased as the mothers spent more and more time away from the litter. In the third week, however, the pups went to the mothers; as a consequence, contact, nursing, and licking increased. A week later, mothers began to punish pups as they approached them or began to suckle.

During the second month, licking and nursing disappeared as major maternal activities, and contact was markedly reduced. Punishment was frequent and often severe, but did not result in suppressing the behavior it appeared to follow. During this month, play, herding, and regurgitation were observed in some mothers.

The capability of the pups was an important factor in maternal care. When the mother was in contact with the pups, they burrowed into her fur, found and grasped a nipple; when she was not in contact with them, they went to her. Even after nursing had ended, the mother remained an object of great attraction. Play with each other and interest in other objects in their environment were also frequently observed. By two months of age they were active, independent organisms with well-developed sensory powers.

References

Bleicher, N. (1962), Behavior of the bitch during parturition. *J. Amer. vet. med. Ass.*, **140**, 1076–1082.

Cowie, A. T., S. J. Folley, B. A. Cross, G. W. Harris, Dora Jacobsohn, and K. C. Richardson (1951), Terminology for use in lactational physiology. *Nature*, **168**, 421.

Ewer, R. F. (1959), Suckling behaviour in kittens. *Behaviour*, **15**, 146–162.

Fredericson, E., Nancy Gurney, and Edna Dubois (1956), The relationship between environmental temperature and behavior in neonatal puppies. *J. comp. physiol. Psychol.*, **49**, 278–280.

Gill, J. C., and W. Thomson (1956), Observations on the behaviour of suckling pigs. *Brit. J. anim. Behav.*, **4**, 46–51.

Harrop, A. E. (1960), *Reproduction in the Dog*, Baltimore: The Williams & Wilkins Co., 204 pp.

James, W. T. (1952), Observations on behavior of new-born puppies: method of measurement and types of behavior involved. *J. genet. Psychol.*, **80**, 65–73.

Jensen, C., and H. E. Ederstrom (1955), Development of temperature regulation in the dog. *Amer. J. Physiol.*, **183**, 340–344.

Martins, T. (1949), Disgorging of food to the puppies by the lactating dog. *Physiol. Zoöl.*, **22**, 169–172.

Scott, J. P. (1950), The social behavior of dogs and wolves: an illustration of sociobiological systematics. *Ann. N. Y. Acad. Sci.*, **51**, Art. 6, 1009–1021.

Scott, J. P., and Mary-'Vesta Marston (1950), Critical periods affecting the development of normal and maladjustive social behavior of puppies. *J. genet. Psychol.*, **77**, 25–60.

Siegel, S. (1956), *Nonparametric Statistics*, New York: McGraw-Hill, 312 pp.

Welker, W. I. (1959), Factors influencing aggregation of neonatal puppies. *J. comp. physiol. Psychol.*, **52**, 376–380.

6

maternal behavior in
SHEEP AND GOATS

Leonard Hersher, Julius B. Richmond, and A. Ulric Moore

In the development of a general theory of maternal behavior each species selected for experimental investigation in a comparative study should exhibit a unique aspect or degree of mothering behavior. Maternal care in sheep and goats is characterized by the rapid and early development of strongly individual-specific maternal bonds: care limited to the mother's own offspring with rejection of other young who may approach. Mothers of many species distinguish in some degree between their own and alien young during the period of nursing, but sheep and goats are consistently violent in their rejection of all young other than their own. This highly discriminating behavior results in stable mother-young units even within a freely mixing herd. The examination of the antecedents of this type of mothering and the investigation of the effect such upbringing may have on the young provide the background for the study of the experimental manipulation of the normal mother-young relationship.

Many mammals show much less discriminating individual-specific care (Kahmann and v. Frisch, 1952). Lactating rats, for example, retrieve their own young preferentially, and yet frequently will care for

The research studies conducted at the Behavior Farm Laboratory of Cornell University were supported, in part, by grants from the Josiah Macy, Jr. Foundation, the Ford Foundation, and the National Institutes of Health.

strange rat pups, mice, and even infant animals larger than themselves (Beach and Jaynes, 1956a; Wiesner and Sheard, 1933). During the first postpartum month, rhesus monkeys show maternal responses to young not their own (Harlow, 1961). Sheep and goats, however, will vigorously attack any alien young, from parturition onward, often with a violence comparable to that popularly attributed to maternal protection of young threatened by a predator.

Fortunately for the experimenter, both wild and domestic sheep and goats show individual-specific care. The study of domestic sheep and goats is affected by the well-known advantages and disadvantages inherent in all work with domestic animals. However, the relative inaccessibility of wild, newborn sheep and goats and dams, resulting from the extreme seclusiveness of the parturient mother, presents a severe obstacle to study not encountered in a flock of cooperative domestic animals. Maternal behavior in domestic sheep and goats, including parturition, is easily observed and readily manipulated experimentally, since the animals are accustomed to the presence of man.

Breeding

The average age of puberty in the female dairy goat, *Capra hircus*, is 5 months. Sheep generally reach sexual maturity at about the same age, although Spencer (1943) reported that wild Rocky Mountain sheep do not become mature until 2½ years old. Buck kids reach puberty between 3½ to 4 months of age, although sexual play is seen before that age, in some cases even shortly after birth.

Length of estrus and of the estrous cycle varies over the world and possibly for different breeds. Although most does and ewes come into heat every 2 to 3 weeks, Arriola (1936) reported an average of 18 hours for estrus and an average interval of 10.2 days between estrous periods for Philippine goats. For goats raised in Puerto Rico, Nadel-Grau (1956) found that estrus lasted 33.8 ± 8.95 hours, with a range of 8 to 72 hours, and that the estrous cycle was 25.3 ± 12.12 days. Williams, Garrigus, Norton, and Nalbandov (1956) reported that, for ewes, the majority of estrous cycles deviating from the range of 14 to 19 days occur either very early or very late in the breeding season.

Breeding seasons also vary over the world and for different varieties. In the Northern hemisphere sheep and goats usually breed from June to November, with September the month of greatest sexual activity, whereas in the tropics sexual behavior may appear in January and February, the wet, hot summer season. The Merino, Rambouillet,

Tunis, and especially the Dorset varieties and their grades and crosses may breed in the spring (Willman, Brannon, and Hogue, 1960).

Changes in the ratio of daylight to darkness hours may have an effect upon the onset of the breeding season. Bissonnette (1941) found that although unbred does usually show their last heat period not later than the middle of March, fertile mating may be induced in July when day length is artificially shortened during the preceding 2 months. Sykes and Cole (1944) produced unseasonal sexual behavior and reproduction by modifying the amount of light per day. However, a definite annual breeding period may exist even in tropical countries where annual variation in the length of the day is relatively small (Jardim, Peixoto, and Silveira, 1956).

Environmental temperature also affects sexual physiology and behavior of sheep. Dutt and Simpson (1957) found that the semen quality and the fertility level of Southdown rams were improved early in the breeding season by keeping them in an air-conditioned room during the summer months. Lowering the environmental temperature during the summer significantly hastened the onset of the breeding season in ewes (Dutt and Bush, 1955).

Ewes treated with chorionic gonadotropin were capable of fertile mating during the period of normal anestrum (Cole and Miller, 1933). Hammond (1944) also evoked normal estrus in anestrous sheep by injections of exogenous estrogen and with stilbestrol (Hammond, 1945). Warwick and Casida (1943) found that follicle-stimulating hormone lengthens the normal estrous cycle in ewes. In a review of hormonal effects on estrus and ovulation in sheep and goats, Phillips, Fraps, and Frank (1945) concluded that while follicle growth and ovulation are reliably stimulated by gonadotropins, the induction of estrus is less reliable.

It is difficult for observers (although evidently not for rams) to tell when a ewe or doe is in heat. Some females in heat may eat less; others stand apart from the flock (Young, 1941). Male mountain sheep chase ewes in estrus for long distances, usually with several rams after one ewe. Females will sometimes wait for a tired ram to rest, or lie down themselves, only to resume their flight upon arising. Eventually the ewe stands still for mounting. Rams generally ignore each other during the breeding season, although they will joust occasionally (McCann, 1956). Frequently, several male sheep or goats succeed in mounting the female, although she may show a preference for one particular animal. Wilson (1957) reported an average of 2.3 services per live kid born for the East African Dwarf goat.

Maternal Behavior in Sheep and Goats 205

Gestation

With the onset of pregnancy the estrous cycle generally disappears, although an occasional ewe may come into heat after she has been bred. Adequately fed pregnant ewes and does gain weight throughout gestation, sheep carrying more than one lamb tending to graze longer than nonpregnant ewes or ewes carrying only one lamb (Tribe, 1950). Length of gestation is generally between 140 and 150 days, although somewhat longer for wild mountain sheep, and is not affected by the mother's age or the number of offspring carried.

Parturition and the newborn period

PARTURITION

Isolation from the herd. Expectant dams tend to separate themselves from the herd as parturition becomes imminent. Domestic ewes are likely to seek shelter indoors and parturient bighorns tarry on the mountain ranges, often seeking out highly inaccessible spots protected by steep cliffs (Davis, 1938; McCann, 1956; Spencer, 1943). Wild sheep may remain in these places for days, often without food or water. Domestic hill sheep appear to become more sensitive to weather exposure at this time, frequently seeking shelter under conditions to which they would not have reacted a month earlier (Hunter, 1954).

Shortly before parturition there is rapid distension of the udder and belly and full swelling of the vulva. Some dams betray their condition by a marked interest in the young of other mothers, even butting away the real mother in an attempt to steal her offspring.

Birth. The first sign of approaching parturition is a general restlessness. The dam rises and moves about fitfully, lies down again, chews her cud, nibbles hay, gasps, blows through her nostrils, paws the ground, grunts, often pawing out a hollow in the straw and lying in it. The bag of waters protrudes, bursts and, shortly afterwards, the newborn is forced out. As a rule the birth process is smooth and seemingly free from extreme distress, although an occasional dam makes known her pain by a piercing scream. During labor, the dam often turns her attention to the anal area and licks the protruding amnion and fluid. The final delivery of the young may take place while the mother is standing or lying down; the newborn appears with head and forefeet forward, and collapses into a wet, generally motionless heap on the ground.

The data in Table 1 demonstrate the wide variation in duration of the various birth processes in sheep. Older ewes generally have shorter labors than young ewes. Births are distributed randomly throughout a 24-hour period (in spite of the fact that many farmers and research workers are convinced that most lambs arrive at night). Although final expulsion usually follows within one-half hour after the lamb becomes visible, Wallace (1949) reported several instances of lambs remaining only partly expelled for 2 to 3 hours. These lambs, with assistance, were born alive. In one unassisted birth, the lamb was born alive even after being visible for 1 hour, 40 minutes.

MULTIPLE BIRTHS

Multiple births occur in 45 to 65% of pregnant animals. Between 40 to 50% of births are twins, 5 to 11% triplets, and 1% quadruplets (Nadel-Grau, 1956; Villegas, 1939). Older does tend to be more prolific than young does. There are on record quintuplet lambs and kids (Cook, 1941; Nordby, 1928), and one fertile Romney ewe is reported to have delivered successfully six live lambs in one pregnancy (Wilson and Gregory, 1931). Attempts to increase total births by interbreeding fecund dams have not been successful (Cook, 1941). Multiple births are probably much less frequent among the bighorn sheep (Spencer, 1943).

Some difference of opinion exists on the sex ratio at birth. For sheep, Rasmussen (1941) reported a ratio of 1:1 in single births, slightly more females in twin births; for sheep and goats, Villegas (1939) suggested a sex ratio of 114 males to 100 females.

Single and male offspring are heavier at birth. For single lambs this weight advantage disappears after a year, but for males the weight difference increases with time. Twin lambs survive as well as singles for the first 3 months, but males and all early spring lambs generally have better survival records than females and late lambs (Phillips and Dawson, 1938; Dawson, 1940). That heavier mothers tend to have heavier young is supported by a correlation of .52 ± .081 reported by Arriola (1936).

Ewes experimentally subjected to high temperatures (112°F., daily for 7 hours each day) during their pregnancies produced lambs having a mean birth weight significantly lower than that of the lambs of eight unheated control ewes (Yeates, 1956).

LICKING THE NEWBORN

The mother begins licking the neonate almost immediately after the delivery. Most frequently she starts with the head, working gradually over the body until the newborn animal is completely dry and free of birth membranes. An occasional mother (especially a poorly fed one

TABLE 1
Normal Time Variation in Parturition

Interval between onset of uneasiness and birth of lamb (hr)	0–1	1–2	2–3	Over
% of 2,3,4-year-old ewes ($N = 116$)	34	32	18	16
% of 5- and 6-year-old ewes ($N = 96$)	47	28	12	13
% of all ewes ($N = 212$)	40	30	15	15

Interval between bursting of "waterbag" and birth of lamb (hr)	0–½	½–1	1–2	Over
% of all ewes ($N = 186$)	36	27	22	15

Interval between onset of labor and birth of lamb (hr)	0–½	½–1	1–2	Over
% of all ewes ($N = 173$)	36	36	18	9

Interval between first appearance of lamb and final expulsion (min)	0–15	16–30	31–60	Over
% of all ewes ($N = 112$)	37	28	22	13
% of ewes requiring assistance ($N = 86$)	20	40	54	79
% of ewes rated "poor" and "fair" as mothers ($N = 80$)	38	43	39	52

Time of day	12–4 A.M.	4–8 A.M.	8–12 Noon	12–4 P.M.	4–8 P.M.	8–1 Midn
% of all ewes ($N = 230$)	22	15	14	18	15	16

Interval between birth of lamb and lamb's first standing on 4 feet (min)	0–15	15–30	Over 30
% of all ewes	30	40	30

Interval between birth of lamb and first sucking of teat (hr)	0–½	½–1	1–2	Over
% of singles ($N = 165$)	24	39	27	10
% of twins ($N = 83$)	18	40	26	16

Interval between birth of lamb and voiding of placenta (hr)	0–1	1–2	2–3	3–4	Over
% of all ewes ($N = 184$)	6	11	50	24	9

Adapted from Wallace, L. R., 1949, Observations of lambing behavior in ewes, *Proc. N. Z. Soc. Anim. Prod.*, 9, 85–96.

with delayed milk flow) will pay little attention to her young until some time after birth, or even ignore it completely. Wallace (cf. Table 1) found that many of these "poor" mothers had experienced especially difficult labors.

During this drying-off process the newborn begins to wriggle about and to bleat feebly, especially in response to a call from the mother. The mother's motivation to lick off the kid seems to be strong, since she will even push down with her foot a young animal struggling to rise but not yet licked entirely dry. Although the dam appears attracted primarily to the newborn, her appetite for the birth membranes (it is not uncommon for dams to eat the placenta) probably plays some role in the licking process. Collias (1956) successfully attracted a ewe for short distances with a rag rubbed in fresh birth membranes. Gibson and Collias (reported in Collias, 1956), however, found that kids and a lamb washed off with strong detergent were nevertheless accepted by the mother.

Licking of the newborn probably facilitates development but is not necessary for the vitality of the young. Barron (reported in Blauvelt, 1955) found that dried-off lambs rise on all 4 feet before lambs not dried off, but Collias (reported in Blauvelt, 1955) observed a lamb which was separated from its mother for 4½ hours immediately after birth that was able to breathe, vocalize, stand, and walk, even though the birth membranes had not been rubbed off. Many newborn, however, left without stimulation for as little as 1 hour, fail to stand and subsequently die (unpublished data, Cornell Behavior Farm).

Drying of the lamb is likely to be more vital under cold, wet, and windy conditions, when the lamb may expend up to 70 kg cal each hour. Much of this energy is utilized to maintain body temperature, which drops at birth and normally rises within a few hours. After 2 or 3 hours the total energy used may amount to a substantial proportion of the estimated initial energy reserves (600 to 900 kg cal) according to Alexander (1958). Alexander found in the population he studied that most of the lambs that died did not obtain milk when they reached the udder, possibly because they lacked the vigor to suck.

BLEATING

Parturient dams are highly sensitive to the bleating of the young, responding to the cries with a series of low-pitched short bleats (goats) or low-pitched gurgling calls (sheep), moving over to the young at the same time. Many dams will answer the call of any young lamb or kid, including those not their own or of the other species even though they will reject the bleating alien young if it attempts to suck. The young seem stimulated to bleat when they hear the mother call or when they see her move a short distance away.

The parturient mother attempts to butt away any other animal that approaches her, regardless of age or sex. Under normal circumstances, when her young is near her, this butting behavior appears to be maternal defense of the young. When the mother is separated from her own young and approached by other young animals, however, she vigorously pushes them away. What appears as defense of the young, therefore, may rather be the mother's isolation of herself. Similar behavior is seen in mothers who have rejected their own young—they butt away all young who approach them, including their own (Fig. 1).

FIG. 1. Mother butting alien young kid.

A dam may sometimes concentrate much of her butting behavior on one kid or lamb, chasing the young animal about long after it has ceased trying to suckle and merely stands shivering in a corner. Mothers have been observed to continue their attacks against individual young for long periods, ignoring other alien kids standing much closer to the maternal milk supply.

Preparturient mothers who steal the young of other dams will often, if able, drive off the true mother from her own young. The real, frustrated mothers in these circumstances might not be permitted to raise their own kids. Baby-stealing dams are very persistent and will attempt the same behavior year after year. After their own young arrive, however, they no longer show interest in the young of other mothers (Fraser, 1954).

FILIAL BEHAVIOR AND NURSING

A kid or lamb spends the first hour of its life trying to stand on all four feet. Most neonates manage to stand within a half hour from birth, after much struggling and sudden sprawling, but some stand within a few minutes of birth and others take as long as 80 minutes.

Like most other precocial mammals (Hess, 1958), the newborn kid and lamb move toward any large object in view, preferring a moving object to a stationary one and an object with which it has already made contact to an untouched one (Blauvelt, Richmond, and Moore, 1960). The young lamb or kid will continue moving until stopped by obstruction, sucking and nibbling on anything with which its mouth comes in contact, normally first on the mother's hair. This forward movement of the kid or lamb, combined with the mother's tendency to turn her body about so that she can continue licking it as it moves, eventually brings the newborn's mouth into contact with the udder and teats. Contact with the udder itself seems to have stimulus value, since the neonate's next approach to the udder is usually much more direct even when unsuccessful on the first try. The approach to the teat and sucking become efficient very rapidly.

The time needed from birth to first sucking varies among individuals from a few minutes to 3 hours, and differs also among breeds (Alexander, 1958). Feeding periods are generally frequent at first and last from 1½ to 3 minutes. Later, young are seldom permitted to nurse for more than 20 seconds.

The ewe or doe sometimes makes it easier for the young to nurse by lifting the hind leg on the side on which the young is sucking. She often breaks off nursing abruptly, sometimes in order to continue licking the newborn. Occasionally a young kid will fail to receive milk for hours after birth because of its mother's enthusiasm for licking. Sometimes the udder is too full, making the teat too small and wobbly for the young to grasp it. Occasionally the teat of an ewe may be jammed against her leg and inaccessible to the lamb. A young animal frequently wags its tail as it nurses, a movement that appears to stimulate the mother to sniff under the wagging appendage. This sniffing seems to serve as a primary mechanism for recognition of the young since the mother will frequently accept the approach of a strange kid or lamb if it is similar in appearance to her own until she sniffs at it. Then she will move away quickly or butt it from her.

Newborn kids and lambs are very precocious, standing without assistance, walking within hours of birth, and rapidly and efficiently learning the source of food. It is not surprising, therefore, that they can be conditioned at a very early age. Moore (1958) conditioned both lambs and kids under 4 hours of age, using a classical conditioning procedure: sudden dimming of lights was the CS and a mild electric shock to the leg the UCS. Some of the animals showed a conditioned response to the second signal.

DEVELOPMENT OF THE MATERNAL FILIAL BOND

Not long after birth, the bond between a single mother and her own offspring becomes permanently established. Two principal conditions, neither necessarily independent of the other, contribute to the development of this bond: the mother's licking of the fetal membranes and the "critical period" timing of the postpartum period.

Licking the fetal membranes. A method popular among sheep and goat raisers attempting to induce a mother to adopt an orphan kid or lamb is to drape the skin of the mother's own dead lamb or kid over the orphan's back or to rub the orphan with the mother's afterbirth. Other similar methods include squirting the young with kerosene or with the mother's milk (especially the anus and back). Lamond (1949) reported skin-draping not a particularly successful device although milk-spraying generally worked.

Gibson (1951) rubbed the placenta of one female goat on a 1-day-old kid not the mother's own and found that the mother accepted it immediately even though she had rejected it previously. Collias (1956), however, repeating the experiment with a 2-day-old kid, found the adoption to be short-lived; the mother rejected the kid by the following morning.

A special sensitivity or lack of sensitivity to her own scent may attract the dam to the kid carrying that odor, as suggested by Moore (reported in Blauvelt, 1955). Yet mothers will adopt young bearing the scent of another dam, and dams will accept newborn washed thoroughly in strong detergent. Collias (1956) concluded that "the birth membranes facilitate but are not essential to the formation of the maternal-filial bond" (p. 236).

The critical period. Immediately after (and for some females shortly before) giving birth, the motivation of the dam to "mother" a young animal is very strong.[1] This maternal drive fades rapidly within a few hours after parturition, however, if the maternal-filial bond is not cemented within that time and it can be established only with difficulty at a later time.

Collias (1956) separated newborn kids and lambs from their mothers at or shortly after birth for periods ranging from 15 minutes to 4½ hours. He found that in five of six cases in which the newborn was separated from the mother for 2 to 4½ hours, the young one was rejected upon its return, at least for the first hour after restoration. In six of six cases in which the newborn was separated for only 15 to 45 minutes, it was accepted at once upon its return. Eight twins were left with their mothers and were all accepted.

The effect of early separation appears to be enduring. Hersher, Moore, and Richmond (1958) separated twenty-four newborn kids from their mothers for ½ hour to 1 hour, after permitting 5 to 10 minutes of contact immediately after birth. The kids were then returned to their mothers. Two and 3 months later all the kids as a group were isolated from the flock for 6 to 10 hours, and then each mother was placed in a room with her own and two other kids for a short observation period. Half the mothers refused to nurse any young, including their own, whereas the other half nursed indiscriminately, giving milk to other young kids as much as they nursed their own. None of these mothers butted their own kids, however, although alien kids were butted frequently. Some evidence of rejection of the young (but no indiscriminate nursing) was found among a group of similarly observed control mothers in the same flock that were not separated from their young at birth. This rejection was apparently a result of the association between the control and experimental animals, since no rejection of the young was seen during the same observation procedure among another group of nonseparated control mothers in a different flock.

The results of this study suggest that as little as 5 to 10 minutes of contact during the critical period (perhaps only if licking is permitted then) is sufficient for the mother to establish the identity of her own kid. A longer period of contact immediately after birth may be necessary for the development of the individual-specific nursing bond. For half the group at least, lack of contact with a newborn for the hour

---

[1] Maternal behavior is rare, though not unknown, among barren females (Scott, 1945).

following birth (after the initial 5 to 10 minute contact) was not sufficient to submerge general maternal responsiveness.

Why some animals respond to early separation by refusing to nurse all young during the experimental procedure, whereas others nurse indiscriminately, is unknown. The factors of maternal age, parity, sex, and weight of the kid at birth do not distinguish the two groups of mothers. Casual observation, however, suggests that less dominant animals, uncertain in the nursing relationship with their own kids, may be less able to resist the importunate advances of other hungry kids. (Hungry kids will attempt to nurse any dam, even if they are accustomed to receiving individual-specific care from their mothers.)

The "critical period" is probably not critical in the sense that particular experiences must occur during that time span or certain responses are permanently lost to the mother's behavioral repertoire, but rather that during this period the dam is maximally sensitive to particular stimuli. Long after the sensitive postpartum period has passed, dams can be induced to accept strange young as their own, even young of a different species (doe-lamb, ewe-kid), if the dam is forcibly prevented from butting off the young animal until acceptance occurs. The formation of the mother-young bond through enforced contact between mother and young at this later time generally requires much more time than during the period immediately after birth.

Modifiability of the critical period for the development of maternal behavior. In a recent study at the Cornell Behavior Farm Laboratory (Hersher, Richmond, and Moore, 1963) sheep and goat dams were separated from their lambs and kids within 12 hours after parturition and placed in a restraining harness attached to a wall. If the mother had delivered twins, only one twin was taken from her while the other twin remained by the mother's side. Wooden partitions were then placed around the mother to form a small cubicle closed on all sides except the top. A lamb or kid, strange to her, was placed within that cubicle. The age of the foster young varied from a few hours to several days. Some of the kids were placed with sheep mothers and some of the lambs with goat mothers.

The above procedure resulted in the formation of four different adoptive groups: goats adopting lambs (N=5), sheep adopting kids (N=3), sheep adopting lambs (N=4), and goats adopting kids (N=4).

Once a day the mother was released from restraint for a few minutes and observed. Most mothers reacted aggressively toward the foster young at first, but gradually began to accept them. The mothers were permanently removed from the stanchions when they no longer butted off the young animal and when they permitted it to nurse. Mothers reached these criteria of adoption at various times, from a few minutes to more than one month of enforced contact. The median period was 10 days. Eventually, all adoption attempts were successful.

After the mothers were released from restraint, members of each of the four groups were housed together, the groups separate from each other and from the rest of the flock.

When they were 2 months old, each kid and lamb was separated from its foster mother for an observation period of several hours. Each adopted young was taken from the mother, as she watched, and placed on the other side of a screen door, a procedure which permitted mother and young to see and hear each other but prevented physical contact. Three measures of the mother's response to the separation were rated on four-point scales (from 0 = no response to 3 = extreme response).

(Scale 1) *Alerting:* any response in which the mother ceased her ongoing behavior and looked in the direction of the separated kid or lamb.

(Scale 2) *Pacing:* agitated walking near the door.

(Scale 3) *Bleating:* rated in terms of frequency.

The ratings, made independently by two observers, showed considerable agreement (reliability coefficient = .88); when the two ratings differed, the mean rating was used.

Following the end of the test, mother and kid remained separated from each other for several hours. Each mother in turn was then led into the room containing her adopted kid and the other kids in her adoptive group. The experimenter observed from behind a one-way vision glass, and recorded the following behaviors for a 10 minute period, using electric counters and electric clocks activated by finger switches: (1) number of attempts to nurse the mother made by foster young and by all other young; (2) time in seconds that the mother nursed her foster young; and (3) number of times the mother butted her foster young and all other young. Both tests were repeated a month later when the young were 3 months of age. The final score for each test was the average of the two sets of measures.

The most significant results may be summarized as follows.

1. There were no differences between natural young—and foster young—mother pairs in the dam's reaction to separation and in nursing time.

2. There were no differences in any of the measured variables between dams that reared both their own and a foster young and dams that reared foster young only.

3. Cross-species foster mothers reacted more vigorously to separation and nursed less than same-species foster mothers.

4. There was a positive correlation between the length of time necessary for an adoption to be established and maternal reactions to separation, but no relationship between adoption time and amount of nursing.

5. No relationship was found among the three areas of maternal care studied: (a) reaction to separation from the young, (b) amount of nursing, and (c) mother-young isolation behavior (butting the young). There has been some discussion of this problem in the research literature, and some investigators have reported positive correlations among various measures of maternal behavior (Denenberg, Sawin, Frommer, and Ross, 1958) but the results of this adoption study fail to support the concept of a general factor of maternalism in sheep and goats.

6. The three measures of reaction to separation—alerting, pacing, and bleating—however, did vary positively with each other.

The results of this study suggest that, although the development of individual-specific maternal behavior in goats and sheep normally takes place shortly after birth and very rapidly, the effective period for that development may be prolonged by enforced contact between dam and young long after birth. This in turn suggests that the development of individual-specific maternal care rests upon both contact behavior and maternal isolation (butting away other young). Maternal isolation behavior, of course, prevents contact between mother and young. Experimentally preventing isolation behavior therefore permits continued contact and the eventual development of maternal care behavior. The process, however, takes time since the mother's butting behavior (toward the foster young) is only slowly extinguished. The development of individual-specific maternal care takes hours for normal relationships, but days for foster mother-young pairs.

No ready explanation exists for the differences between the cross-species groups and the same-species groups although it is clear that species-differences between dam and young differentially affect the thresholds for different maternal behaviors. The results, however, may be related to the additional finding that the longer the dam resisted accepting the foster kid, the greater her reaction when separated later.

There was a tendency for the cross-species adoptions to require a longer time to become established.

Not only can goat mothers be induced to adopt lambs, but there is at least one observation that they may adopt human babies as well. Montaigne in the sixteenth century recorded such adoptions to buttress his opinions on human frailty.

> . . . it is ordinary around where I live to see village women, when they cannot feed their children from their breasts, call goats to their aid; and I have at this moment two lackeys who never sucked woman's milk for more than a week. These goats are promptly trained to come and suckle these little children; they recognize their voices when they call out, and come running. If any other than their nursling is presented to them, they refuse it; and the child does the same with another goat. I saw one the other day whose goat they took away because his father had only borrowed her from a neighbor of his; he never could take to the other that they presented to him, and doubtless died of hunger. Animals alter and corrupt their natural affection as easily as we. (Montaigne, 1957, pp. 290-291).[2]

Environmental circumstances during the postpartum sensitive period also affect the length of time over which maternal acceptance is possible. Recent studies at the Cornell Behavior Farm Laboratory (Moore and Moore, 1960) suggest that goats separated from their newborn kids for as long as 8 hours after birth will accept their kids upon reunion with them provided the mothers are isolated during that time and not in contact with other animals. Collias (1956) found, moreover, that of two does separated from their newborn for 2 hours, the mother who had contact with one of her twin kids during the separation rejected the separated twin upon its return, whereas the mother remaining without any young to care for during the 2-hour period accepted the returned kid at once. Blauvelt (1956) reported an experiment in which an alien kid was rejected by a mother when *added* to the mother's own twins, but was accepted by the same mother when *substituted* for one of the twins.

The rapid development of differential maternal responsiveness to a young animal during a sensitive period in the dam's life suggests that there is a similarity between the development of maternal care in goats and sheep and "imprinting" in precocial neonatal birds and mammals (Scott, 1958a; Hersher, Richmond, and Moore, 1957). Whether the development of maternal care in sheep and goats will be found to show any of the other properties characteristic of imprinting is an interesting question.

---

[2] I am indebted to Professor Earle Lipton for the discovery of this quotation.

Other factors. Vision also plays some role in the mother's recognition of the young. Dams spend much more time smelling strange young that approach them when the young are similar to their own in size, color, and general appearance than when the strange young and the mothers' own young are markedly different in appearance. Mothers will also accept other young for adoption more readily if the foster young are similar in appearance to their own, although the adoption of young that look very unlike the mother's own is possible.

Auditory aids to recognition are probably not very significant, since it has frequently been observed that several mothers will respond to the bleats of a young animal they cannot see. Some dams are particularly responsive to the bleating of the young, answering almost any call of distress from any young; other dams almost never show vocal responsiveness. It has been suggested, on the other hand, that lambs (of Dall sheep) may be able to recognize the call of their own mothers (Murie, 1944). Older domestic kids and lambs may also recognize the bleating of their own mothers.

By shearing time in May or June, when the young lambs are about 4 or 5 months old, they seem to use sight as well as sound to identify their mothers. It has been observed repeatedly at the Behavior Farm that lambs will run to the bleat of their newly sheared mother but, failing to recognize her new shape and color, will run past her and not be able to find her. This is a common observation among farmers. There have been two exceptions: a lamb whose mother had brown legs and a kid raised by a sheep. They both found their mothers at once.

HIDING THE YOUNG

After the newborn kid or lamb has nursed sufficiently, it lies down and sleeps. The mother then may leave it to graze, either alone or with the rest of the herd. The tendency for the kid, but not for the lamb, to remain immobile until the mother returns is one of the few characteristics that distinguish the behavior of the two species, and serves as the basis for a theory of the difference in leadership between sheep and goats (Scott, 1945; Scott, 1958a).

Collias (1956) described a newborn kid that remained motionless, almost lifeless, for 4 hours while its mother was gone, even though the kid was handled repeatedly by humans during that time. Sheep frequently leave their young to graze, too, but lambs have less tendency to remain still and frequently will wander off when they awaken, much to the distress of the ewe (Minor, 1950). There is some difference of opinion as to whether wild sheep show a greater tendency to cache their lambs.

Still other behavior traits are worth noting. McCann (1956) observed a mother which had been startled. She gave a snort and the lamb, which was following her, at once dropped to the ground and remained motionless. At times one or two ewes will act as "nursemaids" to as many as nine resting or playing lambs while the other ewes are off feeding by themselves (Spencer, 1943).

Maternal care after the newborn period

Kids and lambs begin to graze by the side of the mother within a few weeks of birth, then wander farther and farther from her as the amount of grazing increases, but run back (usually to attempt to nurse) when frightened. Dams become agitated and look for their young when they are separated, but may run off without the young if disturbed (Blauvelt, 1956). Ewes exposed to severe cold, wind and rain or to extreme heat may desert their lambs permanently (Spencer, 1960).

The onset of grazing and browsing seems to depend upon the age, rather than the weight, of the young. The proportion of hours grazing to hours idle or playing increases steadily from 1:3 at 3 weeks of age to the normal adult ratio of 1:1 at 11 weeks (Wilson, 1957). Bighorn lambs follow their mothers to the alpine summering grounds, arriving there in early July when they are about 1 month old.

Weaning occurs when the young are 3 to 6 months old and is gradual. Mothers tend to lose interest in the young after weaning, and the young then may be separated from the flock and caught by predators. Survival of the 1933 lamb crop on Mt. Washburn, Yellowstone National Park, was only 46.7%, the lambs presumably dying over the winter (Davis, 1938). Wild lambs in other areas have a comparably low rate of survival (Sheldon, 1932).

Effect of maternal care on later behavior

CONDITIONING AND STRESS

Although relatively mature and independent early in life, goats and sheep are not resistant to prolonged stress during infancy. Moore (1958) found that six of seven kids conditioned to raise a foreleg to a signal when they were less than 4 hours old died within a few months, even though none of twenty nonconditioned kids of comparable age were lost.

The pattern of conditioning in adults is affected by early and prolonged separation from the mother. Liddell (1956) separated four kids from their mothers at birth and bottle-fed them, leaving their twins (controls) with the mother. The males were castrated. At 3 weeks of age all the kids were given twenty conditioning trials per day for 50 days. Signals (dimming lights) were 10 seconds in duration and were terminated by a mild electric shock to the foreleg. Trials were separated by intervals of 2 minutes. The separated kids received the conditioning trials alone and the nonseparated were conditioned with the mother present in the same room. Liddell reported that during this training period the separated kids were lethargic and lost muscular tone, whereas the nonseparated did not.

The separated kids remained isolated for 1 year, at which time they joined the flock. They were reconditioned with the same method at 2 years of age, for 2 hours a day for 24 days. Interval between trials was increased to 6 minutes. Liddell found that during these later trials the nonseparated goats showed "fidgety" or "fretful" movements during the rest interval for the entire 24 days as contrasted to the orphaned goats which ceased making fretful movements shortly after the start of the conditioning trials. Mothered goats failed to respond to approximately 25% of the signals throughout the testing period, but separated goats, missing 25% of the signals at the start of the 24-day period, increased their percentage of failures to respond to 45% by the end of the training period. Liddell suggests that these results may be attributed to the lack of protection from violent contact with other kids in the separated group.

Kids and lambs adopted by foster mothers and kids and lambs reared by hand at the Cornell Behavior Farm showed a pattern of conditioning different from the conditioning of controls reared by their own mothers. Adopted and bottle-fed kids and lambs conditioned earlier, had more vigorous conditioned responses, and responded to a greater number of signals than did their controls. The mother-deprived, bottle-fed animals also were more active but spent less time near the wall in an "open-field" test, had higher heart and respiration rates, and were low in dominance (Moore, 1962; Hersher et al., 1962). Figures 2, 3, and 4 illustrate the method of recording movements. Furthermore, Moore and Amstey (1962; in press) report that none of these adopted or bottle-fed animals was susceptible to tonic immobility, whereas all normally reared lambs and kids were readily "hypnotized."

FIG. 2. *Goat attached to tracking cable for measuring amount and pattern of activity, and to apparatus for applying electric shock to foreleg.*

SOCIAL BEHAVIOR

Scott (1945) found that sheep reared by humans showed a sense of familiarity with enclosures, a tendency to follow humans without fear, and some tendency toward independence of other sheep. When he separated a female lamb at birth and returned it to the flock at 9 days of age, the lamb tried to join the other sheep but was butted off by the ewe. She never developed social behavior, returning to the flock only for a short period when in heat, and at 1 year of age was still independent. When she had lambs of her own, the orphaned ewe (1) did not butt strange lambs in the normal manner, although she permitted none to nurse, (2) showed lessened maternal care of her own lambs, and (3) reacted only mildly to frequent separation from the lambs. The lambs showed tendencies of independence mixed with fearfulness.

Maternal Behavior in Sheep and Goats   221

FIG. 3. Lever-operated pens trace path of animal and counters record distance traveled.

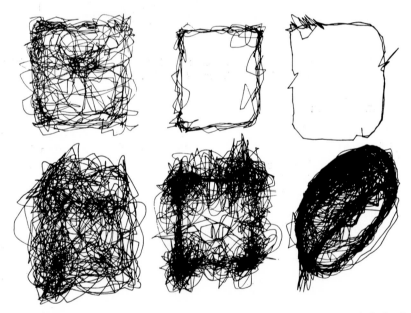

FIG. 4. Sample tracings of animal movements. (From A. U. Moore, 1962. In J. Wortis, Ed., Recent Advances in Biological Psychiatry, Vol. IV. Pp. 58–66. Plenum Press, New York.)

A male lamb, isolated from the 4th to the 12th day of life, was also driven off by the ewes when he tried to rejoin the flock, but he successfully returned during the rutting season. His later sexual behavior, however, was not as aggressive as normal male sexual activity.

LEADERSHIP

Adult sheep tend to follow a single leader consistently, generally the oldest ewe.[3] They often follow in single file, imitating the turning and jumping of the leader. Goats show much less tendency to follow a single leader. Scott (1958a) attributes the species difference in leadership-following behavior to the greater tendency of newborn kids to "freeze" while separated from their mothers, so that the habit of following the mother in sheep is more strongly established early in life and continues throughout adulthood. But different breeds vary in gregariousness; the Merino and Rambouillet breeds are highly gregarious, the Cheviot and Blackfaced Highland breeds are less so (Willman et al., 1960). Thus more frequent instances of early freezing behavior might be found among lambs of the less gregarious breeds, further substantiating Scott's hypothesis.

INTERSPECIES REARING

The behavior of sheep adopted in infancy by goats and of goats adopted by sheep has been observed at Cornell Behavior Farm for the past 4 years (Fig. 5). In general, living with a mother (and the social group) of the other closely related species does not permanently change the basic behavior patterns of the adopted animals. Goats do not behave like sheep nor sheep like goats. The behavioral differences between the two species of adopted animals are approximately the same as one finds between normally reared sheep and goats (Scott, 1958b).

Any behavior of the adopted animals similar to the behavior of the fostering social group is likely to be short lived. Although occasionally an adopted lamb will climb onto elevated objects as kids characteristically do, most of the time it will not. A kid raised with lambs may tend to be slightly less active and more subdued than kids raised with other kids, but the change is only fleeting. Infrequently, a lamb living with kids will return a butt rather than submit to the greater aggressiveness and activity of its kid foster siblings. However, kids reared by sheep and lambs reared by goats grow faster, gain weight more rapidly, and appear healthier than kids and lambs reared by their own mothers (Blauvelt, Richmond, and Moore, 1959).

---

[3] An instance has been reported, however, of a flock following a sheep that was trained to be led by a human (Dunn, 1946).

FIG. 5. *Goat nursing adopted lamb; her own kid, hidden behind lamb, is also nursing.*

Year-old male goats that have lived with sheep all their lives rear up on their hind legs to fight, as do normally reared bucks. However, a male goat living with rams for several years and experiencing the body blows of charging rams may learn to fight with its feet on the ground. For, staying on the ground in their charge, rams can easily knock over a rearing buck. On the other hand, hornless rams living with such an infighting animal as the goat soon learn to respect its sharp horns.

Unspecies-like behavior often appears among the foster mothers of lambs and kids, presumably as a result of the maintenance of species-specific behavior among the young and the mothers' inability to adjust to it. Experienced ewes are, of course, accustomed to having their young follow close behind and become disturbed when the young fail to do so. Since kids tend to wander away, ewes rearing kids are often in a high state of disturbance, spend much time seeking the kid, and therefore tend to separate from the flock more than ewes rearing lambs.

Goats rearing lambs, on the other hand, spend less time seeking out their young, since the lamb tends to stay close to the foster mother. In those families in which a doe is rearing both her own kid and a foster lamb, the mother's own kid frequently is cut off from the mother by the closely following lamb.

Kids and lambs adopted into the flock of the other species also adopt the foster flock, and even when mature will prefer to associate with the species with which they were reared. Goats reared as kids in a flock of sheep show signs of extreme fear if placed with their own species.

The influence on other aspects of behavior of being reared in a foster group of a different species is still to be investigated. Once the influence of the foster group is known, it may be possible to isolate further the influence of the maternal behavior itself on the behavior of the young.

Problems for future research

Freud's emphasis on the role of childhood in the development of personality and psychological studies of the acquisition of behavior by learning have stimulated popular interest in the effect of early experience upon later behavior. But few research workers interested in the effects of early experience have organized the problem around the concepts of any particular learning theory, presumably because they structured their task as one of establishing empirical relationships before attempting to analyze the intervening variables between early experience and later behavior.

Learning theorists and research workers in general have shown little interest in long-term behavior changes. Although the literature on the acquisition of behavior is now voluminous, research on retention over long periods is virtually nonexistent (Brogden, 1951). Learning theorists, in fact, pay so little attention to problems of retention that learned behavior which continues for a considerable length of time has been referred to as abnormal fixation (Maier, 1949).

Many research workers, however, are concerned with more permanent changes in behavior, for example, in stable changes in the habit family hierarchy and in the development of individuality. If such permanent behavior patterns are learned, it is likely that their acquisition follows the laws of learning already discovered. The investigation of this likelihood offers a large area of research for the future.

The mother, of course, is part of the early environment of the young mammal. She is one of the stimuli frequently impinging upon the organism in the stimulus-response formula of learning, and her behavior presumably may be a constant source of learning opportunities for her young. Maternal behavior, then, may be seen as an early experience or a stimulus. How this behavior affects the behavior of the young is a field begging for investigation.

Social objects other than the mother also interact with young sheep and goats and may affect the learning process as well as what is learned. Social objects that represent almost constant sources of stimulation to the young are the other adults in the flock (including the males during the rutting season), the yearlings, and the other young.

The effects on behavior of various kinds of social stimuli, however, need not be exclusively social effects. Differences in early social environments may influence learning ability or style, motivation, activity, or other behaviors, as well as those acts, like sexuality or aggression, more commonly classified as social. The effect of differing maternal behaviors on the development of subsequent maternal behavior of the offspring is a problem of obvious interest.

What are some of the most significant problems in understanding maternal behavior in sheep and goats? Research problems come primarily from two sources. One series of questions arises as a result of the occurrence of "odd" or unexpected behavior which does not fit our current theoretical scheme or point of view. An example is the appearance, in one of our studies, of indiscriminate mothering. If discriminating mothering is a species-characteristic of sheep and goats, a factor setting them apart from many other mammals, what is the significance of the development of indiscriminate maternal behavior? Clearly, normal, discriminating maternal behavior is learned, but why do some mothers, prevented from maintaining contact with their young for the first few hours after birth, reject their young, whereas others accept all young, including alien kids? Neither mother's age, parity, sex, nor weight of the kid distinguishes the two groups, but observation suggests that dominance may be a significant factor. Dominance, of course, varies normally within a herd, and its effect upon indiscriminate mothering may be studied by the correlational method. Enough is understood about dominance behavior, moreover, to make its experimental manipulation possible. Its effect on indiscriminate mothering could be studied, at the same time controlling for the possibly confounding effects of the mother's size or milk production.

A second series of problems arises from the perception of gaps in our understanding. The gaps may be due to our ignorance of the behavior determinants we observe in experimental animals: *why* does the animal behave as it does? *How* does the animal acquire certain habits? Or we may wish to fill in gaps in our understanding based on what is known of the behavior of other animals, or on a general theory of behavior, much as one searches for elements to fit the periodic table. Thus a problem of the future, suggested by the research on the sensory cues used by the mother rat to recognize her young (Beach and Jaynes, 1956b), is: which cues are used by sheep and goats?

Any behavior in which animals consistently differ invites investigation. Of practical importance to animal husbandry is the difference between good mothering and poor mothering (in terms of the mortality and growth of the young). It will be recalled that Wallace (1949) attributed some of the difference to difficulty in labor. Will physical trauma of other kinds—or emotional trauma—similarly affect mothering? Is mothering learned? Little difference has been found to date between primiparous and multiparous mothers in mothering behavior, but if more careful research does reveal differences between them, how does the animal learn the distinguishing behavior?

A further source of experimental problems is the suggestion that maternal behavior in sheep and goats normally develops as does filial behavior in precocial birds and many other animals, a process known as imprinting. The existence of similar critical periods for the appearance of attachment behavior, on the behavioral side, and the common occurrence of marked physiological changes (from fetal to neonatal physiology for the imprinted young bird and from prepartum to postpartum physiology for the mother goat), on the physiological side, suggest the bases for the analogy. For the student of behavior development imprinting is a challenge, since it probably borders between gene- (or prenatally) determined and environment-determined behavior. If the analysis of maternal behavior in sheep and goats helps to foster the broadening of the concept of imprinting from a definition limited to filial behavior to a more general definition of the learning phenomenon, that analysis should have heuristic as well as substantive value.

The question of the gene-determination of behavior introduces still another important area of research. The study of strain differences in maternal behavior in sheep and goats is relatively unexplored, although there is considerable inbreeding, especially of sheep, for commercial purposes. It is not unlikely that studies of changes in maternal behavior as a result of inbreeding sheep and goats, like those of Hodgson (1935) on inbreeding in swine and Dilger (1961) on crossbreeding in birds, would yield rich research data.

Summary

The study of maternal care in sheep and goats provided a unique opportunity for the analysis of maternal behavior characterized by the rapid and early development of strongly individual-specific maternal bonds (care limited to the mother's own offspring and rejection of other young who approach her). This highly discriminating behavior results in the early formation of stable mother-young units even within a freely mixing herd and offers research workers the chance to study a type of mother-young relationship different from the relationships more commonly found among mammalian species.

Sheep and goats generally breed only during a definite annual season, although these seasons vary with breed, geography, environmental temperature, and changes in the ratio of daylight to darkness hours. Estrous periods commonly last several days, and the estrous cycle 2 to 4 weeks. Females in estrus are usually chased and mounted by several males, who most often ignore, but who will occasionally fight, each other. Estrous cycles disappear after a female has begun her pregnancy, which lasts between 140 and 150 days.

Shortly before and during parturition the dam isolates herself from the flock and seeks shelter. The mother begins licking the newborn immediately after it is born, probably facilitating the development of vitality in the young, especially under adverse weather conditions. Newborn kids and lambs are very precocious, standing and walking shortly after birth and rapidly and efficiently learning the source of food.

A highly sensitive period exists immediately after birth during which the motivation of dams to mother any young animal is very strong. This maternal drive toward all young fades rapidly within a few hours after parturition, and the mother remains strongly attached only to her own young and strongly aggressive toward all other young. However, long after the sensitive postpartum period has passed, dams can be induced to accept strange young as their own if contact between mother and young is forced, and the mother is prevented from butting the strange young animal. Sheep and goats can be induced to adopt young of the other species, and these cross-species foster mothers react more vigorously to separation from their foster young but nurse less than same-species foster mothers.

Kids and lambs begin to graze by the side of the mother within a few weeks after birth, wandering farther and farther from her side as the amount of their grazing increases, but running back to her (usually to attempt to nurse) when frightened. Dams become agitated and look for their young when separated, but may run off without the young if disturbed. Weaning occurs when the young are 3 to 6 months old and is gradual. Mothers tend to lose interest gradually in the young after weaning.

Kids reared by humans and isolated from other goats, and kids and lambs reared by foster sheep and goat mothers, show a pattern of conditioning different from normal, as well as different social, aggressive, and maternal behaviors.

There is much still unknown about the antecedents and consequences of maternal behavior in sheep and goats, and ideas sure to contribute to a better understanding of mammalian maternal behavior in general can reasonably be expected from further study of these individual-oriented, family-centered mothers.

References

Alexander, G. (1958), Behaviour of newly born lambs. *Proc. Aust. Soc. Anim. Prod.*, **2**, 123–125.

Arriola, G. C. (1936), A study on the breeding habits of goats. *Philipp. Agric.*, **25**, 11–29.

Beach, F. A., and J. Jaynes (1956a), Studies of maternal retrieving in rats. I: Recognition of young. *J. Mammal.*, **37**, 177–180.

Beach, F. A., and J. Jaynes (1956b), Studies of maternal retrieving in rats. III. Sensory cues involved in the lactating female's response to her young. *Behaviour*, **10**, 104–125.

Bissonnette, T. H. (1941), Experimental modification of breeding cycles in goats. *Physiol. Zoöl.*, **14**, 379-383.

Blauvelt, Helen (1955), Dynamics of the mother-newborn relationship in goats. In B. Schaffner (Ed.), *Group Processes* (Transactions of the first conference, 1954), New York: Josiah Macy, Jr. Foundation. Pp. 221–258.

Blauvelt, Helen (1956), Neonate-mother relationship in goat and man. In B. Schaffner (Ed.), *Group Processes* (Transaction of the second conference, 1955), New York: Josiah Macy, Jr. Foundation. Pp. 94–140.

Blauvelt, Helen, J. B. Richmond, and A. U. Moore (1959), The influence of a difference in species between mother and young on the protection and vitality of the offspring. *Anat. Rec.*, **134**, 536–537. (Abstract)

Blauvelt, Helen, J. B. Richmond, and A. U. Moore (1960), The development of contact between mother and offspring in ungulates (domestic sheep and goats). *Bull. ecol. Soc. Amer.*, **41**, 91. (Abstract)

Brogden, W. J. (1951), Animal studies of learning. In S. S. Stevens (Ed.), *Handbook of Experimental Psychology*. New York: Wiley. Pp. 568–612.

Cole, H. H., and R. F. Miller (1933), Artificial induction of ovulation and oestrum in the ewe during anoestrum. *Amer. J. Physiol.*, **104**, 165–171.

Collias, N. E. (1956), The analysis of socialization in sheep and goats. *Ecology*, **37**, 228–239.

Cook, R. C. (1941), Quintuplet-bearing goats back to normal. *J. Hered.*, **32**, 5–6. (Editorial)

Davis, W. B. (1938), Summer activity of mountain sheep on Mt. Washburn, Yellowstone National Park. *J. Mammal.*, **19**, 88–94.

Denenberg, V. H., P. B. Sawin, G. P. Frommer, and S. Ross (1958), Genetic, physiological and behavioral background of reproduction in the rabbit: IV. An analysis of maternal behavior at successive parturitions. *Behaviour*, **13**, 131–142.

Dilger, W. C. (1961), Changes in nest-material carrying behavior of F₁ hybrids between *Agapornis roseicollis* and *A. personata fischeri* during three years. *Amer. Zoöl.*, **1**, 350. (Abstract)

Dunn, Alta B. (1946), Sheep are funny that way. *Breed. Gaz.*, **111**, 18–19.

Dutt, R. H., and L. F. Bush (1955), The effect of low environmental temperature on initiation of the breeding season and fertility in sheep. *J. Anim. Sci.*, **14**, 885-896.

Dutt, R. H., and E. C. Simpson (1957), Environmental temperature and fertility of Southdown rams early in the breeding season. *J. Anim. Sci.*, **16**, 136–143.

Fraser, A. (1954), *Sheep-farming*, 6th ed., London: Crosby Lockwood and Son, Ltd.

Gibson, E. J. (1951), Maternal behavior in the domestic goat. *Anat. Rec.*, **111**, 483. (Abstract)

Hammond, J. (1944), Control of ovulation in farm animals. *Nature, London*, **153**, 702.

Hammond, J. (1945), Induced ovulation and heat in anoestrous sheep. *J. Endocrinol.*, **4**, 169–180.

Harlow, H. (1961), Messenger Lectures, Cornell Univer.

Hersher, L., A. U. Moore, and J. B. Richmond (1958), Effect of postpartum separation of mother and kid on maternal care in the domestic goat. *Science*, **128**, 1342–1343.

Hersher, L., A. U. Moore, J. B. Richmond, and Helen Blauvelt (1962), The effects of maternal deprivation during the nursing period on the behavior of young goats. *Amer. Psychologist*, **17**, 307. (Abstract)

Hersher, L., J. B. Richmond, and A. U. Moore (1957), Critical periods in the development of maternal care patterns in the domestic goat. *Amer. Psychologist*, **12**, 398. (Abstract)

Hersher, L., J. B. Richmond, and A. U. Moore (1963), Modifiability of the critical period for the development of maternal behavior in sheep and goats. *Behaviour*, **20**, 311–320.

Hess, E. S. (1958), "Imprinting" in animals. *Sci. Amer.*, **198**, 3, 81–90.

Hodgson, R. E. (1935), An eight generation experiment in inbreeding swine. *J. Hered.*, **26**, 209–217.

Hunter, R. F. (1954), Some notes on the behaviour of hill sheep. *Brit. J. Anim. Behav.*, **2**, 75–78.

Jardim, W. R., A. M. Peixoto, and S. Silveira (1956), Estudo sôbre o comportamento de ovinos mestiços Romney-Marsh em Piracicaba. *Rev. Agric., S. Paulo.*, **31**, 93–106.

Kahmann, H., and O. v. Frisch (1952), Über die Beziehungen von Muttertier und Nestling bei kleinen Säugetiern. *Experientia*, **8**, 221–223.

Lamond, H. G. (1949), Mothering a lamb. *Sheep and Goat Rais.*, **29** (9), 36–38.

Liddell, H. S. (1956), *Emotional Hazards in Animals and Man*. Springfield, Illinois: Charles C Thomas.

McCann, L. J. (1956), Ecology of the mountain sheep. *Amer. Midl. Nat.*, **56**, 297–324.

Maier, N. R. F. (1949), *Frustration: The Study of Behavior Without a Goal*. Ann Arbor: University of Michigan Press.

Minor, W. C. (1950), Sometimes they're not so dumb! *Nat. Wool Gr.*, **40** (4), 10–11.

Montaigne, M. E. (1957), *Complete Works*. Trans. by D. M. Frame. Stanford, California: Stanford University Press.

Moore, A. U. (1958), Conditioning and stress in the newborn lamb and kid. In W. H. Gantt (Ed.), *Physiological Bases of Psychiatry*. Springfield, Illinois, Charles C Thomas. Pp. 270–297.

Moore, A. U. (1962), Early trauma as revealed by performance during initial conditioning. In J. Wortis (Ed.), *Recent Advances in Biological Psychiatry*, Vol. IV, New York: Plenum Press. Pp. 58–66.

Moore, A. U., and M. S. Amstey (1962), Tonic immobility: Differences in susceptibility of experimental and normal sheep and goats. *Science*, **135**, 729–730.

Moore, A. U., and M. S. Amstey (in press), Tonic immobility: Effects of mother-neonate separation in sheep and goats. *J. Neuropsychiat.*

Moore, A. U., and Frances Moore (1960), Studies in the formation of the mother-neonate bond in sheep and goats. Symposium on Mechanisms of Primary Socialization. *Amer. Psychologist*, **15**, 413. (Title)

Murie, A. (1944), *The Wolves of Mount McKinley*. Washington: U. S. Government Printing Office (U. S. Dep. Interior Fauna Series No. 5).

Nadel-Grau, R. A. (1956), Reproductive behavior of the dairy goat, *Capra hircus*, under Puerto Rican conditions. *Dissertation Abstr.*, **16**, 423.

Nordby, J. E. (1928), Quintuplet lambs—an unusually large family. *J. Hered.*, **19**, 384.

Phillips, R. W., and W. M. Dawson (1938), The relation of type and time of birth and birth weight of lambs to their survival, growth and suitability for breeding. *Proc. Amer. Soc. Anim. Prod.*, **30**, 296–305.

Phillips, R. W., and W. M. Dawson (1940), Some factors affecting survival, growth, and selection of lambs. *Circ. U. S. Dep. Agric.*, No. 538, 1–17.

Phillips, R. W., R. N. Fraps, and A. H. Frank (1945), Hormonal stimulation of estrus and ovulation in sheep and goats. (A review). *Amer. J. vet. Res.*, **6**, 165–179.

Rasmussen, K. (1941), A note on the effect of multiple births on the sex ratio in sheep. *Sci. Agric.*, **21**, 759–760.

Scott, J. P. (1945), Social behavior, organization and leadership in a small flock of domestic sheep. *Comp. Psychol. Monogr.*, **18**, 1–29.

Scott, J. P. (1958a), *Animal Behavior*, Chicago: Univer. Chicago Press.

Scott, J. P. (1958b) Social behavior of domestic goats and sheep: a comparative study. *Anim. Behav.*, **6**, 247. (Abstract)

Sheldon, W. G. (1932), Mammals collected or observed in the vicinity of Laurier Pass., B. C. *J. Mammal.*, **13**, 196–203.

Spencer, C. C. (1943), Notes on the life history of the Rocky Mountain bighorn sheep in the Tarryall Mountains of Colorado. *J. Mammal.*, **24**, 1–11.

Spencer, C. J. (1960), Help those lambs to live. *J. Dep. Agric. W. Aust.*, 1 (4th series) 621–624.

Sykes, J. F., and C. C. Cole (1944), Modification of mating season in sheep by light treatment. *Quart. Bull. Mich. agric. Exp. Sta.*, **26**, 250–252.

Tribe, D. E. (1950), Influence of pregnancy and social facilitation on the behaviour of the grazing sheep. *Nature, London*, **166**, 74.

Villegas, V. (1939), Multiple births in goats and sheep. *Philipp. Agric.*, **28**, 5–14.

Wallace, L. R. (1949), Observations of lambing behaviour in ewes. *Proc. N. Z. Soc. Anim. Prod.*, **9**, 85–96.

Warwick, E. J., and L. E. Casida (1943), Effects of pituitary gonadotropins on estrual phenomena in ewes. *Endocrinology*, **33**, 169–173.

Wiesner, B. P., and Norah M. Sheard (1933), *Maternal Behaviour in the Rat*, Edinburgh: Oliver & Boyd.

Williams, S. M., U. S. Garrigus, H. W. Norton, and A. V. Nalbandov (1956), Variations in the length of estrus cycles and the breeding season in ewes. *J. Anim. Sci.*, **15**, 984–989.

Willman, J. P., W. F. Brannon, and D. E. Hogue (1960), *Sheep Production*, Cornell Ext. Bull. 828, New York State College of Agric.

Wilson, P. N. (1957), Studies of the browsing and reproductive behaviour of the East African dwarf goat. *E. Afr. agric. J.*, **23**, 138–147.

Wilson, J. F., and D. W. Gregory (1931), Sextuplet lambs: An example of exceptional fertility in sheep. *J. Hered.*, **22**, 229–230.

Yeates, N. T. M. (1956), The effect of high air temperature on pregnancy and birth weight in Merino sheep. *Aust. J. agric. Res.*, **7**, 435–439.

Young, W. C. (1941), Observations and experiments on mating behavior in female mammals. *Quart. Rev. Biol.*, **16**, 135–156, 311–335.

7

naturalistic studies
of maternal care in
MOOSE AND ELK

Margaret Altmann

Most animal studies of maternal care and mother-young relationships have been carried out on confined or restricted animals. The study of such animals has a number of advantages; the most important are the ease with which observations can be made and the degree to which environmental conditions can be controlled and standardized.

It has become increasingly apparent, however, that the more subtle types of behavior, in particular social behaviors involving mutual re-action chains and signal systems operating over distance, are frequently inhibited, reduced, or altered in captivity (Scott, 1950). This is of particular importance in the wide-ranging, grazing, larger mammals. Furthermore, the conditions of confinement add a rather serious limita-tion to the activities of such wild animals since ground cover, natural spacing, olfactory cues, choice of climatic gradients (sun angle, tem-perature, humidity, etc.), and food selection (browse) cannot easily be provided in an enclosure or cage.

For these reasons, techniques of naturalistic observation have been developed for the long-term study of social dynamics in free-ranging

The studies reported here were sponsored by the New York Zoological Society, the National Science Foundation, and by Grant M-2599 from the National Institute of Mental Health, United States Public Health Service.

wild ungulates. These techniques also serve to overcome limitations and alterations of behavioral expression imposed by human observers.

Methods

Once the difficulties of locating, approaching, and observing the various animal populations were overcome, definite and consistent patterns of behavior were revealed. In the case of mother-young relationships, sequences of behavior were observed which would not occur among confined representatives of the species. As work proceeded from year to year, methods of observations were revised and more powerful tools, such as spotting scope and binoculars, were utilized. It was discovered that in most cases it was not advantageous to approach the animal groups closely. Observation at greater distances (300 feet to 1½ miles) not only did not interfere with social interactions among animals that lived in such widely spaced patterns but also permitted return visits to the same area and additional observations of the same animals. Close stalking was occasionally employed, as needed. A staggered time schedule of observation and the use of different observation points made it possible to get a more complete picture of the animal's life. Hill slopes and overlook points were located from which observations could best be made. Identification of the observed individuals was recorded manually on prepared sheets or vocally on a transistorized tape-recorder (Mohawk 400). Color markings with paint blobs shot from a crossbow on a buffered bulb or a description of natural markers (antler shape, bell in moose, pelage, etc.) were used. A sociometric sketch, using standardized symbols for sex and age groups, was made of each observation.

Although daily observations at dawn and dusk were most frequently used, daytime and moonlight night observations were also made, when high altitude or special seasonal events (rutting season, hunting season, parturition) demanded them. The length of uninterrupted observation periods varied from 15 minutes to 5 hours. On occasion a continuous day-and-night schedule of observations was carried out in 2 to 3 hour shifts of two observers. Evaluations of findings were based on several years of observational results in order to recognize typical and exceptional cases. The bulk of the observations was gathered from June to November, during the years 1948 to 1962. Additional observations during March, April, and May were conducted for 2 years to obtain material on premigration and parturition periods. The areas selected for study and used in consecutive years were major parts of the Teton

National Forest, the Grand Teton National Park, and the southern areas of Yellowstone National Park.

The two wild ungulate species dealt with in detail in this chapter are the Wyoming elk or Wapiti, a highly social animal, and the Wyoming moose, a representative of a highly solitary species. Most of the descriptions are based on my own long-range observations, although I am indebted to other workers for reports of their observations.

Maternal care in the elk

Preparation for maternal care in elk *(Cervus canadensis)* begins with the approach of the impending parturition of the calf in late May or June. If the pregnant elk cow is still accompanied by last year's young about 2 weeks before parturition, as is the rule, she will show increasingly hostile behavior toward the yearling and enforce a separation by chasing it from her side. Threat by gesture (ears folded back and head held high, front feet stamping) is usually sufficient to initiate and maintain a definite spacing, but in some cases the mother elk forces the

FIG. 1. *Half-hour-old calf with its dam. (Reproduced with permission from Kodachrome slide by J. R. Simon.)*

Naturalistic Studies of Maternal Care in Moose and Elk   235

stubborn yearling to a distance by actually beating it with her front hooves.

The elk cow remains in visual, auditory, or olfactory contact with her band, but seeks a marginal retreat for the actual event of birth. Shrubs and undergrowth shield her and the newborn calf during parturition and for a few hours or a day after the birth (Fig. 1). During this period careful screening of noises as auditory cues to the safety of the nearby elk group is employed as a means of protection. At birth the elk cow licks the calf and when it rises, stimulated by this contact, she nurses it. After nursing, the calf is gently pushed down with her head to remain there alone until the mother returns from grazing with the rest of the group. The intervals between nursing visits increase from 20 minutes to several hours. Safety checkups by the elk cow are also spaced. At night the elk cow stays with the calf. Sometimes a group of several elk calves is deposited close together in a favorable location, wind protected and well secluded. The elk mothers visit these "calf pools" at intervals, each one keeping the yearling at a distance as shown in Fig. 2.

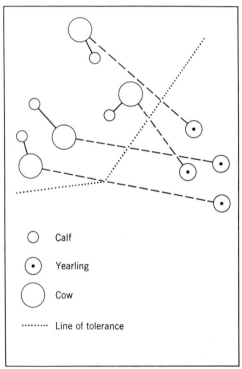

FIG. 2. Elk cows with calves keeping yearlings at a distance (Altmann, 1956a).

In the event of a disturbance, the elk mother creates a distraction by a noisy break into flight away from the calf's hiding place. If the calf is attacked while the cow is near (for example, by a coyote), defense patterns are at times swift and relentless, but in most cases flight will result. When the calf is less than 3 weeks old, it remains hidden while the mother flees alone. A calf's distress call is answered by any mature elk cow which rushes up to find it. When "mothered up," that is, when joined by its own dam, the other rescuers no longer pay attention to it.

At first, olfactory identification by the mother elk is the most crucial test of recognition. Observations (Altmann, 1952) agree with O. Murie's (personal communication in Jackson Hole, 1950) that, although there may be a lesser amount of scent in a calf than in a mature elk, the elk cow clearly and slowly smells the tracks and the calf itself in selecting and recognizing her own offspring (Fig. 3). (The scent is so light, however, that coyotes and dogs often miss an elk calf at close distance.) De Vos (1960) reported the same for caribou mothers. Auditory cues gradually also become significant and eventually even visual recognition is effected. Each elk cow knows her calf, although the calves make many errors in their approaches to various cow elk during the first 2 weeks. Thereafter mutual recognition is more definitely established.

FIG. 3. Elk cows testing calves.

Naturalistic Studies of Maternal Care in Moose and Elk   237

At 18 to 20 days of age the elk calf begins to follow the elk cow into the grazing elk group, although it often drops down for rest while the group is feeding.

The unique vocal expression of "bugling" by the elk mother in the early weeks after parturition has been described by O. Murie (1932) and by Altmann (1952). The bugling sound, universally known as the male expression of challenge in the rutting season, thus reappears for a limited period as a warning and challenge in the female wapiti when with her calf. Bugling was never heard in female elk at other stages.

Infantile sex patterns such as mounting their dams (Altmann, 1961) appear early in some calves. Directed at times toward other elk calves, mounting appears to urge the one mounted to change places or to begin play.

A widening pattern of activity and play emerges in the elk calves' daily routine, punctuated by nursing and rest. The games are mostly rush-and-flight (Meyer-Holzapfel, 1949; Meyer-Holzapfel, 1956), some, for example, the high-step warning gait or the freezing posture which indicates surprise, contain elements of the species-specific elk signal and communication system. Elk mothers sometimes participate in the games.

Shallow bodies of water seem to be favored locations for play. Here elk mothers have been observed to initiate splash and run games with the calves. The elk calves at first show fear and are reluctant to enter the water, but after a few play experiences become eager to rush and splash in the water. Vocalization between mother elk and calf is evident at such times, with continuous chiming of calls back and forth, any interruption of which becomes a warning signal.

Water games, which precede the spring migration to the higher summer ranges, prepare the elk calves for the many crossings of swollen streams which have to be made in reaching higher elevations. As a special protective pattern (Fig. 4), elk cows with calves enter the water downstream from the calves and swim in bodily contact with them to keep them from being swept away. Stream crossings take place most frequently in the early dawn hours when streams are less swollen than later in the day. In entering the stream, the calves sometimes are gently nudged into the upstream position by their dams. The "heeling response" of the calf apparently cannot function properly in the face of the tremendous deflecting power of a swollen river.

The heeling response which functions so readily on land consists of the calf's "follow up" reaction to its dam. The calf heels behind and close to the mother in a manner which has been likened to the goslings'

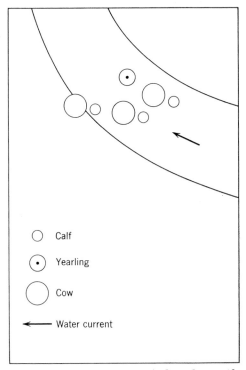

FIG. 4. *Elk cows and calves crossing river. (Adapted from Altmann 1956a.)*

and ducklings' "imprinting" response to its parent figure. One charac-teristic of this response is that the faster the mother elk moves the closer is the calf.

Gestures or posture signals from the elk mother and from other elk, like the warning gait or the freezing stance, are increasingly responded to by the calf. On the other hand, the signal gestures executed by the calf in play are not responded to by the herd or band. A system of vocalization between mother elk and calf is also in operation during migration or travel in a group. The forest rangers often speak about meeting an elk nursery herd which made a "racket" with its calling. This security calling is particularly used in dense vegetation where cohesion by visual stimuli is difficult. The continuation of calls means safety, an interruption means danger or warning.

A combination of maternal care and group protection for the calves can be seen when a disturbance causes the elk nursery group to exhibit shielding maneuvers (Fig. 5). The lead elk cow noisily breaks into flight, but turns toward the intruder while some other females, often

Naturalistic Studies of Maternal Care in Moose and Elk   239

yearlings, swiftly and quietly lead the calves into cover and safety. Such cases indicate that the following reaction, which the calves normally execute only when the mother gives warning signals, can in an emergency be transferred to other elk.

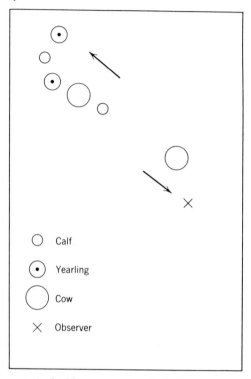

FIG. 5. Shielding pattern in elk. (Altmann, 1956a.)

In the social rank order of the elk herd, the calf order is clearly set by the rank of its mother. For example, in a hailstorm the calf of a high-ranking elk cow will enter the shelter-tree group with its mother, whereas yearlings and other lesser elk remain outside. The elk mother sees to it that its calf it not threatened by other elk.

In time, the close bond between mother and elk calf weakens and the calf becomes integrated with the elk herd. The period of weaning therefore creates less of a shock to the elk calf since participation in herd activities establishes a strong attachment to the group as such, and at times to specific individuals in the herd, independent of sex or age status, as far as is known. Many bonds between mother elk and calf remain important beyond the weaning period, such as the selection of living and feeding space, the daily timing of activities, social interaction, and safety guidance in critical situations.

Preceding the mating or rutting time of the elk in fall is a transitional period, called the "prerut." During the prerut, which occurs in August, the unrest and herd breakup contribute to a reestablishment of a closer bond between mother elk and calf. During harem formation and regrouping in the fall, a close mother-young relationship is maintained and carried over to some extent into the winter herd.

As winter fades into spring and into open weather, the approach of the new calving season brings a critical change in maternal behavior toward the elk yearling (Fig. 2). The elk cow becomes hostile and chases the yearling away to fend for itself while she becomes absorbed in the birth and raising of her new calf. As summer progresses, the enforced exile is relaxed, and the mother elk displays some peripheral awareness of the yearling.

In some cases, where the calf dies, the yearling is taken in again by the mother elk and allowed to nurse. A picture of such a situation (this one in a zoological park enclosure), repeatedly seen in free elk, shows the big yearling kneeling while nursing the elk cow (Fig. 6).

The male elk yearling is separated from its dam for a second time

FIG. 6. Big yearling elk nursing. (Reproduced with permission from Kodachrome slide by D. Van Horn.)

Naturalistic Studies of Maternal Care in Moose and Elk   241

by the harem bull when he joins the elk cow group in forming a harem. Previously, during the prerut, the elk group had tolerated the noisy and uninhibited expression of juvenile sex urge by the "spike" bulls (the yearling elk bulls). The cow elk, not yet in heat and unready for the rutting season, had endured the playful commotion of the yearling spikes. High pitched bugling, squealing, driving, chasing, mounting, and kicking are expressions of this early sex drive. But all this comes to a sudden end when the big mature bull appears and joins the group. The spikes' sex behavior ceases. In most cases there is no actual fight or hostile bodily contact. Threat and intimidation display are sufficient to cause the spike bulls to leave the harem group. Most of the spikes seek attachment to other spikes or older males and wander in fear of the big bull's voice until the rut is over.

No hostile expression is shown at rutting season to the female yearling by the mother elk in the harem band. This is quite in contrast to the situation in other species, for example, in moose at rutting time when mature females are hostile to any other female, including their own yearlings.

Maternal care in the moose

In the Shiras-moose *(Alces alces shirasi)*, a species with strong solitary phases, maternal care is built around extremely close contact with the calf. The moose mother selects for the impending birth a solitary place combining features of a secluded shelter with some feeding space (willowhedge) and a nearby small stream. At no time during the early weeks does the moose cow leave her young calf.

The birth act is swift and usually without complications since moose calves are relatively very small (18 to 35 pounds compared to the 80 to 100 pounds birthweight of domestic calves). Licking and nudging the newborn calf seem to stimulate the calf to get up and nurse. The nursing routine, at first irregular, is gradually established by the calf's demands. Since the wobbly new calf in some cases cannot reach the tall cow moose's udder, the mother moose may squat or even lie down for nursing during the first few attempts. Licking and nudging seem to play an important role in encouraging the nursing and eliminative activities of the moose calf. The nursing calf also exhibits a clearly expressed drive for care and attention. Changes in the moose mother's activity are frequently utilized by the calf for its own purposes. If, for example, the mother moose changes position, the calf may respond with an attempt to nurse and also later on to lick and rub the mother's face and neck region. Stopping after a change in location also induces nursing (this is true for all ungulate species). Most nursing is done in the sidewise angle position with the calves' tail end toward the moose cow's shoulder. Nursing through the hindlegs from the cow's tail end, as Schloeth (1958) reported for 5 to 10% of nursing in half-wild Camargue cattle herds, has never been observed in moose. The moose cow's small and drawn-up udder would not be easily accessible from that approach.

The cow moose and the newborn calf spend the first few days after parturition within a dozen square feet of living space. (Table 1 gives a summary of the moose calf's progress.) In the next period of care, from 4 to 20 days of age, both mother and moose calf move around more, with the calf beginning to show the "following reaction." It heels or tries to heel whenever the mother moose moves or turns. The moose calf is almost never left alone. The moose cow obviously adapts to the calf's pace when high vegetation or fallen logs slow it down. Swollen streams or other major obstacles like ditches with steep inclinations and rockslides are avoided by the cow moose when with a very young calf. Only when the mother moose is feeding in the water is the calf hidden on the shore.

When an intruder (for example, man or horse) comes close to the resting moose calf, it will get up and approach or even follow the stranger. The calf at this age does not yet show fear. The cow returns quickly and vigorously attacks the intruder and retrieves the calf by a well-coordinated cutting maneuver. If possible, the enraged moose cow will signal the calf to drop back, then continue to run after the fleeing intruder, even a big moose bull, for quite a distance. I observed and described (Altmann, 1955) a case on an island where a cow moose swam after a bypassing horse, beat it seriously in a water battle, and did not relent and return to the calf until the horse was driven to another island, completely exhausted by the attack. Conley (see "Moose versus bear," 1956) reported that a moose cow, upon seeing a bear carrying off her calf, pounced swiftly on the bear with her front hooves and wounded it so badly that she was able to retrieve her calf without either suffering serious injury. The maternal state obviously endows the moose cow with an aggressive spirit comparable to that of the broody hen defending her chicks.

Observations have shown instances where the moose calf, momentarily distracted, fell back and lost sight of its mother. Such cases revealed the mechanism by which the mother moose manages or disciplines the calf. The moose cow initiates and gradually utilizes the

TABLE 1
Periods in Social Development of Moose Calf

Age of Calf	1–3 Days	4–20 Days	20–90 Days	90 Days until Weaning	Weaning– 1½ yr Old
	I	II	III	IV	V
Period Name	Neonate	"Heeling"	Solitary Training	Beginning of Socialization	Juvenile Group Training
Characteristics and potential activity.	Poor locomotion. Contactual and ingestive behaviors are established.	Locomotion improves. Imitative behavior and heeling pattern begin.	Radius of activity widens. Investigative behavior increases. Dam enforces territorial defense; keeps calf from all social contacts.	Dam's rutting season brings bull into group. Calf meets bull and other moose. Social integration under way, but on selective basis.	Socialization progresses. Calf still with dam until next calf born, then in fringe area.

Adapted from Altmann, 1958.

"heeling pattern" by a delicate sequence of moving away and waiting for the young calf. The moose calf, when suddenly alone, musters all its energy to find its dam and to stay close to her for quite a while thereafter. The moose mother's manner of waiting nearby in concealment from the calf, instead of returning to it, works as a strong and efficient reinforcement for the heeling response.

This heeling response of the moose calf, often likened to the imprinting phenomenon of newly hatched geese and ducks, is in our opinion similar but not identical behavior. The classical definition of imprinting (Lorenz, 1935) postulates that the event is irreversible and takes place in very narrow time limits. The corresponding behavior pattern in the ungulates is reversible, more flexible, and less limited in respect to its sensitive period. An interesting variation of the heeling indoctrination is reported by Pruitt (1960) for the Barren Ground Caribou. He described the head-bobbing signal of the caribou mother which causes the small calf to approach and to follow her.

All during this time the mother moose keeps other potential intruders, even her own species, at a safe distance from the calf. When moving with the calf, the "ring of sliding territoriality" (Altmann, 1958) moves with the calf-mother team. Such isolation of the calf moose appears necessary for the calf's safety, since the heeling response is not as irreversible as imprinting in ducks and geese. Gradually, during the next developmental period [3 weeks to 3 months (Table 1)], the moose cow widens the radius of activity (Fig. 7). The calf begins to nibble grasses and browse and shows more investigative behavior. At intervals the calf is seen at play, mostly in rush and flight games in which the mother moose does not actively participate. The play of the calf sometimes incorporates the moose cow and usually centers around her.

Communications from mother to young are no longer limited to close and direct physical contact (nudging, licking), but begin to include general species-specific gestures and postures used as signals, in addition to low calls and answers. The main warning posture and gesture of the mother moose are freezing, a motionless posture, and bristling with head lifting, signifying defense and potential aggression. The first reaction of the moose calf to these signals is to stand close behind its dam, ready to follow when the moose gives intention movements. In the following months the calf intermittently begins to practice the other postures and gestures of the mother moose which occur in case of a disturbance. When the calf is alone, the submissive friendly grazing pattern prevails.

Naturalistic Studies of Maternal Care in Moose and Elk   245

FIG. 7. Moose cow and calf widen activity.

During the summer period, infantile sex behavior is frequently observed (Fig. 8). Calves of both sexes will mount the cow moose. Some male calves wrinkle and draw up the upper lip after sniffing the cow's genitalia. Mounting behavior is apparently used to get attention from the mother moose and to get her to move. The cow moose usually shows little or no response to such activities, except that she may move slightly out of the way.

As the summer proceeds the cow moose gives considerably more leeway to the movements of the calf and the strictly enforced isolation from other species members becomes less exacting. The calf shows a distinct curiosity and an active interest in the occasional strange moose, which is indicated by its approaches, stilted gait, and ruffled mane. The time of the prerut has started, and the reshuffling of the moose populations brings much unrest and change of location to the mother-calf group.

A few weeks later, when the rutting time begins in earnest, the cow moose and her calf will be joined by a mature bull moose. The courtship of the bull, however, will not be tolerated by the cow unless he is nonaggressive and friendly toward her calf. In this turbulent rutting season, the moose calf, which had rarely contacted another moose, except its own dam, is suddenly in close proximity to the bull moose. The calf also may encounter other strange moose of both

FIG. 8. Infantile mounting behavior in moose. (Reproduced with permission from Kodachrome slide by E. McMurray.)

sexes which appear as rivals to the mating group or which incidentally pass by the area. The moose mother will stand carefully aside with her calf when another bull challenges her bull moose, but will swing into violent rage and aggression toward any female moose that approaches. Ears folded back, head high, eyes showing white in the corners, neck and back hair bristling, mouth chewing, teeth grinding, the moose cow advances toward the intruding female. The calf, in close imitation of its mother, follows her into the attack. Such a battle of female moose (Altmann, 1959) usually centers around a fresh moose wallow which had been prepared by the bull and bears his strong scent. Dug into loose, swampy soil the moose wallow, about 3 feet by 8 feet, is usually the territorial base of the moose mating group. Its construction is an integral part of the moose bull's rutting ritual; his body and urine scent presents olfactory stimulation for the moose cow. In a battle of females the moose cow and calf try to occupy the wallow by crowding and pushing the intruding cow out. Each party tries to lie down in the muddy oval-shaped pool, apparently a token of defense and the home goal of significance to both parties.

The care and attention the mother moose gives the calf do not lag or cease during her receptive rutting stage. At no time does she neglect or desert the calf during her association with the bull. This point is best borne out by the swift action of the cow moose in defending and guiding the calf in case of a disturbance at the height of the rutting situation, that is, during the bull's "tending" and mating stages. The caretaking behavior with which the moose cow tends her calf during the rutting period is very different from the elk cow's behavior in the harem situation where elk calves are attached to the same harem group or band but stay at a distance from the mother elk during her rutting activities. Table 2 shows the main differences in the maternal care of the two species mentioned.

TABLE 2

Comparison of Mother-Young Relationship in Elk and Moose

Behavior	Cow Elk and Calf (*Cervus canadensis nelsoni*)	Cow Moose and Calf (*Alces alces shirasi*)
Ingestive care	Is hidden alone or in "pools." Waits for dam to return to nurse and lick during first 20 days.	Calf takes initiative in nursing at intervals. Huddles up to dam to be licked and nosed. Close contact.
Communicative warning, flight.	Bark warning causes calf to drop and hide. Cow elk takes off, leaves calf. Back and forth call as a bond on migration route. Later shielding pattern.	Sparse vocal expression. Warning by gait and posture. Flight in unison with dam after delayed reaction.
Play	Social play with other calves. Tag and rush game. Water game, squealing, and rushing. Yearlings and cows participate at times.	Solo play around dam. Rushing and kicking game. Dam does not participate.
Imitative and antagonistic	At time of herd integration, exhibits all gait and posture signals; vocal communication still limited. No antagonistic behavior observed in first year.	Executes warning gait and angry bristling and chewing like dam from 2 months on. At times disregards dam's efforts to keep it from other moose.

Table 2 (Continued)

Behavior	Cow Elk and Calf (*Cervus canadensis nelsoni*)	Cow Moose and Calf (*Alces alces shirasi*)
Integration into social group life	At 3 weeks, during spring migration with nursery herd.	Limited, at 3 to 4 months, at rutting period of dam. Loose integration; stays with dam.
After weaning	Stays with herd but at a distance from dam.	Stays in close contact with dam.
Yearling (At birth of new calf)	Stays in fringe of herd or joins roaming bands.	On outer fringe of area. Many attempts to return are frustrated.

Adapted from Altmann, 1958.

By now the moose calf is in the process of weaning. Nursing contacts are infrequent or may stop entirely, but other mother-calf responses continue to function smoothly. Posture and gait are the responses predominantly used for communication, vocal signals to a much lesser extent.

The persistence of maternal care in a mammal beyond weaning shows the importance of other factors besides nursing in mother-calf relationship (Altmann, 1960). These factors include the choice of feeding and shelter places, safety and flight decisions, and later the selection and timing of winter grouping in the river drainages. Other observers (Denniston, 1956 and Daniels, 1953) also agree that the maternal guidance bond with the growing calf continues through the winter and early spring to the time of the approaching birth of the next calf. Then signs of hostility toward the young yearling appear and quickly lead to expulsion or displacement. If the moose mother is not bearing a new calf, however, the yearling enters the next pasture season in association with its dam and still socially dependent on her.

Maternal care in three other species

Observations on three other wild ungulate species, bison, chamois, and wild boar, offer insight into differences in maternal-care patterns with respect to social organization and species patterns. The species presented in Table 3 differ in various respects, but most importantly in herd structure.

The movements and communications of bison and wild boar are of the contact type. The young are managed and disciplined by crude

TABLE 3
Mother-Young Relationship in Other Wild Ungulates

	Bison (Bison bison)	Chamois (Rupicapra, rupicapra)	Wild Boar (Sus scrofa europ.)
Birth	Near herd margin	Within band	Within kinship group
Activity	Stays close to mother	Follows mother at once	Trails sow with littermates
Sleep	Contact with mother	Spaced but in visual contact	Close contact in a pile
Herd integration	At once, calf ranks with mother	Is always in group	Stays in 2 litter band
Enforcement of signals	Crude butting by mother	No threat observed; heeling pattern strongly developed	Mother rushes and bites young; littermates fight for dominance
Reaction to intruders	Mother and herd adults shield calf	Warning whistle; takes off with group	Abrupt grunt by sow; young dodge, lie motionless
Play	Rush games; mother and herd often participate	Jumping and butting games of kids; mother participates at times	Mock fights and rushing games; mother does not take part

Adapted from Altmann, 1956b.

contact handling, butting in bison, biting and pushing in wild boar.

In bison the calves play rushing and flight games which often involve the whole herd of adults, including their dams, in a wild, thunderous stampede. The wild boar young play individual fighting games with their littermates. In their rushing play they may involve the juvenile half-brothers and -sisters from the previous litter. The adult wild sows do not participate in play.

In the chamois the signals and communications between mother and young are based on visual and auditory cues. Threat as a means of maternal care has never been observed. The chamois kids are able-bodied runners and jumpers from birth and display a strong heeling response in critical siuations. Contact and antagonistic behavior, however, are included in the play, which has many elements of the adult sexual pattern. Their jumping games culminate invariably in butting games very similar to the "King of the Castle" game of red deer *(Cervus elaphus)* described by Darling (1937).

The reaction to intruders in these species shows three interesting, basic patterns: the herd-shielding of bison calves in which nonrelated herd members participate, the flight in unison of the chamois band, and the "dodging" display of the wild boar litter. This latter reaction poses another riddle of species evolution. Although wild piglets disperse and lie motionless among the ground vegetation, their domesticated cousins have exactly the opposite reaction to the mother's warning grunt, rushing toward her and assembling in close body contact.

Discussion

As the highly variegated patterns of maternal care in the wild free-ranging ungulates are surveyed, many remaining problems are seen whose solution will require the full array of modern instrumentation and, most of all, a good deal of human ingenuity. The probability must be faced that our senses may not easily perceive the modes of communication used by these animals. Further comparative research is needed on the nature of the "heeling" or following response in wild mammals, particularly its plasticity and limitations in a variety of environments. It may even be possible to design experimental studies to identify the nature and quantitative characteristics of the heeling stimulus and its response in wild ungulates.

At present the substitution and adoption of young are being analyzed, as well as the transfer of maternal expressions to other age groups and even to other species. Adoption experiments in free-ranging animals, if successful, will also provide quantitative data on the comparative strength of maternal defense and other reactions to distress. A scale of various disturbances, graded in strength, may be used to test the mother's drive to stay with or reach the young, or to flee.

Studies of social changes in the role of aging and aged ungulates also lead us to focus attention on how the aging female adapts to the transition from the maternal role. The aging bison cow (Altmann, 1961), for example, substitutes as "auntie" or guardian for the calves of other herd members, and in general also participates in herd leadership and safety activities. These activities appear to be a transfer from firsthand to substitute maternal behavior, and serve to keep old females actively involved in the herd organization; the aging bison bulls in contrast leave the group and become more or less solitary.

Summary

Maternal care in unrestricted wild ungulates was studied by means of long-range naturalistic observations. The two species studied in detail were the Wyoming elk, a highly social animal, and the Wyoming moose, a representative of a highly solitary species.

With the approach of parturition, the cows of both species display increasingly hostile behavior toward the yearling and retreat from the group to select a birth site. Licking and nudging stimulate the newborn to rise and nurse. The intervals between nursings lengthen over the first few days as both calf and mother increase their locomotion.

The elk calf is left in hiding until the mother returns from grazing with the group, although sometimes several calves are deposited together. At 18 to 20 days of age the elk calf begins to follow the cow into the grazing elk group. The moose calf, in contrast, is almost never left alone, the heeling response appears earlier, and both mother and calf stay apart from other moose during the early weeks.

Defense and flight behavior in the elk lead to the integration of the calf into the social group; in the moose, such behavior results only in establishing a still closer cow-calf bond.

In both moose and elk, communications between cow and calf are effected by changes in gait and posture. The elk, in addition, employs a wide variety of vocalizations, especially during migration and group travel; the moose, except for low calls and answers, uses few vocal signals.

Play behavior of elk calves increasingly involves other calves and herd members, but that of the moose calf is solitary or incorporates only the mother.

During the rutting season, the elk calves are attached to the same harem group as the mother's but stay at a distance; the moose calf, even at the height of the season, continues to receive close attention from its mother.

In both elk and moose, maternal care continues beyond the rutting season, the weaning period, and into the winter. Hostility toward the yearling appears in the spring at the time of the approaching birth of the next calf, and quickly leads to expulsion or displacement of the yearling. Disruption of the mother-yearling bond, however, is not inflexible; an elk cow may nurse her yearling when the new calf has died, and a moose cow not bearing that season may continue close association with her former calf.

Observations on three other species of wild ungulates, bison, chamois, and wild boar reveal other differences in maternal care and herd structure. The movements and communications of bison and wild boar are of the contact type, whereas those of the chamois are visual and auditory.

Further research into the nature of the heeling response in a variety of environments and into the role of the aging female in the herd is needed.

References

Altmann, Margaret (1952), Social behaviour of elk, *Cervus canadensis nelsoni*, in the Jackson Hole area of Wyoming. *Behaviour*, **4** (2), 116–143.

Altmann, Margaret (1955), Moose, *Alces alces* battles horse in water. *J. Mammal.*, **36**, 145–146.

Altmann, Margaret (1956a), Patterns of herd behavior in free-ranging elk of Wyoming. *Zoologica*, **41**, 65–71.

Altmann, Margaret (1956b), Patterns of social behavior in big game. *Trans. 21st N. Amer. Widl. Conf.*, 538–545.

Altmann, Margaret (1958), Social integration of the moose calf. *Anim. Behav.*, **6**, 155–159.

Altmann, Margaret (1959), Group dynamics in Wyoming moose during the rutting season. *J. Mammal.*, **40**, 420–424.

Altmann, Margaret (1960), The role of juvenile elk and moose in the social dynamics of their species. *Zoologica*, **45** (4), 35–39.

Altmann, Margaret (1961), Sex dynamics within kinships of free-ranging wild ungulates. Paper read at the AAAS, Symposium on Incest, Denver, December 30, 1961.

Daniels, T. W. (1953), Winter at Blackrock. *Wyoming Wildlife*, **17** (2), 20–27.

Darling, F. F. (1937), *A Herd of Red Deer*, London: Oxford University Press.

Denniston, R. H., II. (1956), Ecology, behavior and population dynamics of the Wyoming or Rocky Mountain Moose, *Alces alces shirasi*. *Zoologica*, **41**, Part 3, No. 14, 105–118.

de Vos, A. (1960), Behavior of barren ground caribou on their calving grounds. *J. Wildlife Mgmt.*, **24**, 250–258.

Lorenz, K. (1935), Der Kumpan in der Umwelt des Vogels. *J. Ornithol.*, **83**, 137–213.

Meyer-Holzapfel, Monika (1949), Die Beziehungen zwischen den Trieben junger und erwachsener Tiere. *Schweiz. Z. Psychol.*, **8**, 32–60.

Meyer-Holzapfel, Monika (1956), Das Spiel bei Säugetieren. *Handb. Zool.*, Berlin, Bd. 8, Lfg. 2. Teil 10 (5), 1–36.

Moose versus bear, (1956), *Wyoming Wildlife*, **20** (9), 37.

Murie, O. J. (1932), Elk calls, *J. Mammal.*, **13**, 331–336.

Pruitt, W. O., Jr. (1960), Behavior of the barren-ground caribou. *Biol. Pap. Univ. Alaska*, No. 3, 1–44.

Schloeth, R. (1958), Über die Mutter-Kind Beziehungen beim halbwilden Camargue-Rind. *Säugetierkundliche Mitteilungen*, Bd. 6, Heft. 4, 145-150.

Scott, J. P. (1950), The social behavior of dogs and wolves. *Ann. N. Y. Acad. Sci.*, **51**, Art. 6, 1009–1021.

8

the maternal affectional system of
RHESUS MONKEYS

Harry F. Harlow, Margaret K. Harlow, and Ernst W. Hansen

As adequate data accumulate from field studies and laboratory investigations, it becomes increasingly apparent that the affectional ties which exist among members of subhuman primate social groups play extremely important roles as social organizational forces. Indeed, these are doubtless the primary forces that hold monkeys or apes together as a social group and give the various subgroups their proper place and status.

In a monkey society individuals and the group make mutual contributions, real or potential. Separated from associates, the individual's chance of survival is precarious and its opportunity for genetic contribution is nonexistent. The orderly functioning of social organizations enables individual monkeys to meet basic needs for food, water, sleep, and sex with maximal efficiency. These physical needs, however, are only one set of forces determining monkey social organization. In fact, it is more than likely that the resolution of biological needs is largely a result, not a cause, of social organization. The basic mechanisms for primate social structuring are the complex affectional relationships among the members of the societies, and the continuance of these socie-

The researches reported in this paper were supported by funds supplied by Grants M-722 and HE-6287, National Institutes of Health, and by a grant from the Ford Foundation.

ties is dependent more upon love than lust, more upon happiness than hunger.

Because of the importance of the affectional systems to social structure and to individual animals, each affectional system must be studied in detail. Each system is expressed through multiple behavior patterns, each system develops in a series of orderly stages, and each possesses underlying variables and mechanisms that differ considerably in nature, number, and importance.

There are at least five affectional systems: (1) the affection of the infant for the mother—the infant-mother affectional system; (2) the affectional relationships between infants or between juveniles—the infant-infant or peer affectional system; (3) the affectional relationship between adolescent and adult males and females—the heterosexual affectional system; (4) the affection of the mother for her infant—the mother-infant affectional system; and (5) the affection of adult males for infants and juveniles—the father-infant affectional system.

In this chapter we are concerned with the analysis of a single affectional system in rhesus monkeys, the maternal affectional system, but because the physical and psychological bonds between mother and infant are so intimate, it is not possible to explore or describe mother-infant affection independently of the responses of the infant to the mother. Thus we cannot limit ourselves to a description of how maternal behaviors affect infants; we must also discuss how infant behaviors affect the expression of maternal behavior.

The analysis here of the monkey mother's affectional system has been made by a series of observations and experiments, some complete and some in progress, conducted within the laboratory. A large part of our basic information concerning the development of the maternal affectional system has been obtained in a situation which we call the playpen, illustrated in Fig. 1. Essentially the playpen apparatus consists of a series of four living cages and a play area subdivided into four individual play cells, each of which abuts a large living cage. A 3.5-inch × 5.5-inch opening cut into the wall of each living cage and the adjoining play cell allows free passage of the infant while effectively restricting the mother to the living cage. The apparatus is constructed of stainless-steel wire mesh, which permits full view of the animals and thereby facilitates continuous, detailed observations. Each playpen unit is housed in an individual room approximately 14 feet square with a one-way vision screen in the corridor wall. Thus supplementary observations can be made from the corridor without alerting the animals, although the primary observations have been made inside the test room.

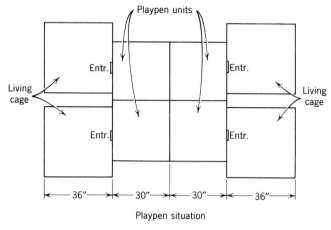

Playpen situation

FIG. 1. Playpen test situation.

Three different groups of four babies and their mothers were intensively studied in the playpen situation. Two groups were composed
of four multiparous monkey mothers and their infants, taken from our
breeding colony, and the third, of four infants living with inanimate
cloth surrogate mothers (Harlow, 1958). All mothers and infants were
placed in the living cages within 24 hours of the infant's birth. The
surrogate mothers had round or square faces and cloth bodies of different colors so that the human observer, and presumably the monkey
infants, could differentiate the individual cloth surrogates as easily as
they could the real monkey mothers. The four infants in mother-group
1 were males with an age spread of 27 days; it was necessary to take
the animals as they came, and the monkey mothers gave birth to infants
without regard to experimental design. The sex split for the infants in
both mother-group 2 and surrogate-group 1, however, was two males
and two females each. The role of mother-group 2 was primarily to
provide supplementary information about the sex variable after 9½
months of age, when the animals became available following participation in an infant-separation study reported by Seay, Hansen, and
Harlow (1962). Although they had lived in a playpen situation
from birth, their early treatment differed somewhat from that of the
other two groups (for details, see Seay, et al., 1962, or Hansen, 1962).

During days 16 to 180 the partitions between pairs of play cells
were removed for two 1-hour sessions a day, 5 days a week, permitting
the babies to interact with one another and with either or both mothers.
Cage positions were shifted weekly on a predetermined schedule so that

each infant interacted with every other infant an equal number of weeks. Observations were made of both mother and infant behaviors. Two observers scored the behaviors exhibited during separate 30-minute test sessions, and time of day and order of testing were balanced for all subjects. Subsequently, throughout the second half-year of the infants' lives, the monkeys were allowed to interact 1 hour a day in pairs and 40 minutes a day as a group of four.

The mother and the infant behaviors in the two-animal interaction sessions were measured in terms of the occurrence, within 15-second intervals, of behaviors included in an inventory of 96 items. This was accomplished by using a system of symbols to record sequential behaviors. There were discrete master symbols for each of 13 major behavioral categories: play, sex, mother contact, cradling, maternal protection, maternal punishing, grooming, breast contact, clasping, threatening, exploration-manipulation, disturbance, and vocalization. Specific behaviors within these categories were indicated by variations either within the master symbol or appended to it. There were also special symbols for 12 discrete items of behavior: approach, withdrawal, food-stealing, lip-smacking, signals to return, fear, grimacing, nonspecific contact, facilitation, self-mouthing, scratching, yawning, and convulsive jerking. A description of the major behavioral categories which provided the data utilized herein is reported elsewhere (Hansen, 1962, Appendix I). The reliability for most of the major behaviors was above .90 as determined by the product-moment correlations of the daily scores of two individual observers scoring the same animal during 20 half-hour sessions.

Because of the complexity of behaviors exhibited in the four-animal interactions, observation was restricted to 24 behaviors (Hansen, 1962). The reliability for these measures was slightly depressed but, with few exceptions, above .85.

No attempt is made to present data here on all the recorded items. In fact, the data recorded for many of these behaviors were so scanty as to be of only limited or specialized usefulness (for further details see Hansen, 1962).

The stages of maternal behavior

The maternal affectional system, like the other affectional systems, can be described more adequately in terms of sequential stages. The three principal maternal stages are those of attachment and protection, ambivalence, and separation or rejection. The stage of attachment and protection is characterized by maternal responses which are almost totally positive, including cradling, nursing, grooming, restraining when the infant attempts to leave, and retrieving when the infant does escape. The stage of ambivalence includes both positive and negative responses, which eventually become almost equal in frequency. Negative responses include mouthing or biting, cuffing or slapping, clasp-pulling the fur, and rejecting the infant's attempts to attain or maintain physical contact. The stage of separation, as the name implies, results in the termination of physical contact between mother and infant.

The various stages in the development of the maternal affectional system, and this is true for all the affectional systems, do not appear suddenly in terms of hours or days and are not sharply and discretely defined. On the contrary, they are characterized by extensive temporal overlapping. Thus the stage of ambivalence contains many components of the previous stage, and special events, such as any threat or danger, may cause the infant to seek its mother's protection, and may reestablish the mother as a totally affectionate and protective monkey for long periods of time.

On the other hand, separative mechanisms are also clearly developing throughout this stage both on the part of the mother and the infant until separation is complete. In the wild the mother may actively protect the infant in emergencies even after physical separation, suggesting a temporal lag between nearly complete physical separation and nearly complete psychological separation, although it is likely that the specificity of protective behaviors decreases during this interval.

The temporal delineation of all the stages depends on the operation of such multiple variables as the nature of the physical and social environment; the life history of the animal; previous pregnancies and experience with infants; endocrinological factors; and even the behavioral criteria chosen or the time of day that the data are collected.

It should be noted that the maternal affectional system differs from most of the other affectional systems in that it is cyclical, recurring with full intensity with the advent and maturing of each new baby. It is probable that maternal affectional responding is never completely absent in the rhesus female, particularly after the birth of her first baby. However, the variables underlying the maternal affectional system differentially affect the attitude and behavior of females and provide for considerable individuality in maternal responsiveness.

THE STAGE OF MATERNAL ATTACHMENT AND PROTECTION

During the stage of maternal attachment and protection, the mother monkey spends a great deal of time holding the baby close to the ventral

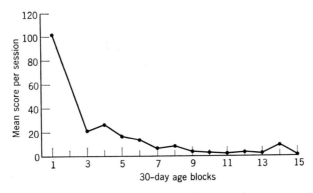

FIG. 2. *Development of infant-mother ventral contacts.*

surface of her body or cradling it loosely in her arms and legs, but still providing it with active contactual support. The developmental course of intimate infant-mother bodily contact is illustrated in Fig. 2 in terms of ventral contacts. It will be noted that the frequency of these responses, although initially high, progressively decreased after the first month and became relatively infrequent by the third month. Undoubtedly this resulted in part from the greater mobility of the infant, but it also reflects a gradual waning in the strength of the first developmental stage of maternal affectional responding. An almost identical developmental course is followed by the cradling response, shown in Fig. 3. Thus, the powerful infantile reflexes, which early in life lock the infant to the mother's body (Harlow, 1960), are supported and complemented by reciprocal maternal behaviors.

Nonnutritional and nutritional contacts with the nipple followed a

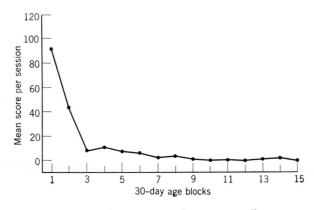

FIG. 3. *Development of mother-infant cradling.*

The Maternal Affectional System of Rhesus Monkeys   259

comparable developmental course (Fig. 4), and nipple contacts during the infant-interaction sessions were relatively infrequent after the third month. These data, as well as most of our other measures of mother-infant interactions, are in part a reflection of the measurement situation, and limited diurnal observations of mother-infant interactions during periods when the infants were not permitted to interact with each other support this view. In effect, the infants used the time offered by the interaction sessions to romp and play with other infants and only occasionally returned to the mothers. Indeed, after the first few months the only time that they consistently returned to the mother and attached to the nipple was when they were frightened. The frightened infant clasps the mother's body with its arms and mouths her nipple, but in this situation mouthing the nipple may be only one component of the total infant-mother contact-clinging pattern and is not necessarily nutritionally directed. Thus mother-infant contact measurements are in part a reflection of infant-mother dependency on the one hand and the development of infant-infant interactions on the other.

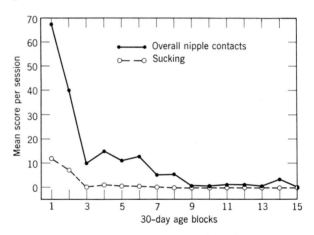

FIG. 4. Nutritional and nonnutritional nipple contacts.

In late evening and early morning hours overall breast contacts and nutritive sucking were more frequent than during the infant play sessions. Lactation continued for a considerable period of time, and seven of the eight monkey mothers continued to lactate for 18 months postpartum as determined by manual palpation of their nipples.

An extremely powerful social response observed throughout the monkey kingdom is that of grooming, and this response actually increased throughout the first 30 days as the mothers probably became more socially aware of, and responsive to, their infants (Fig. 5). Perhaps these data represent an intensification of the specific psychological bond between the mother and the infant. After this initial increase, there was a sharp reduction paralleling that reported for bodily contacts and cradling.

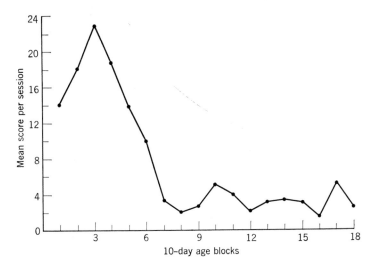

FIG. 5. *Development of mother-infant grooming.*

Maternal affection and protection were also measured by restraining-retrieving responses, a pattern which increased during the first 40 days and then decreased sharply, as seen in Fig. 6. Restraining and retrieving are dependent upon and consequent to the infant's voluntary attempts to break contact with the mother, and the developing locomotor ability of the infant is an important factor in the increasing frequency of restraints and retrievals during the first 30 days or more.

The sharp decrease at 45 to 50 days is not, however, directly ascribable to the behavior of the infant. During this period, the infants actually increased their attempts—and successes—in breaking away from the mother and engaging in infant-infant interactions. The change in restrain-retrieve responses was a function of the mother's making progressively fewer attempts to restrict her infant's activities. In place of restraining and retrieving responses, escapes now elicited little more from the mother than a pattern of watchful waiting.

During the first 3 months, monkey mothers sometimes retrieved infants, when beyond reach, by two intriguing communication mechan-

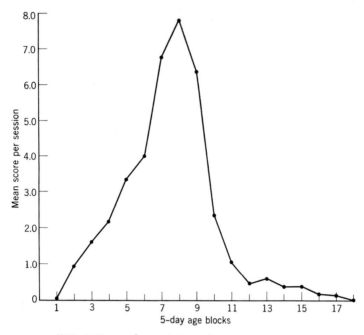

FIG. 6. *Maternal restraining and retrieving responses.*

isms, categorized as the "silly grin response" and the "affectional behavior pattern exhibited at least once by all four mothers in mother-present." The silly grin was seen as a rare but particularly striking group 1 during the first 3 months. In 12 of the 22 observed occurrences the silly grin was successful in bringing about an *immediate* return of the infant to its mother regardless of the infant's position or orientation. Since many kinds of responses were available to the infants at this time, the probability is extremely remote that return to the mother was a product of chance. In experiments outside the playpen situation, these behaviors occurred only when an infant had been separated from its mother, and both mother and infant appeared extremely disturbed. On one occasion this response was seen twenty-two times within a given 10-minute period after the insertion of a Plexiglas screen between the mother and the infant.

The second communication mechanism used for retrieving at a distance occurred more frequently than the silly grin during the corresponding period of time and consisted of a posturing which was, at times, indistinguishable from the female sexual present pattern. Because of its apparent differential function, however, the term affectional present was applied to this category. Of 96 occurrences of this pattern, 56 were successful in bringing about an *immediate* return to the mother regardless of the position or orientation of the infant. Both mechanisms for retrieving at a distance, like the contact-retrieving responses, practically disappeared after 90 days.

As already implied, the initial stage of the maternal affectional system is one in which the mother is constantly vigilant for any impending danger. The mothers at first frequently threatened the observers (Fig. 7) in the stable and safe playpen situation, but these responses rapidly dropped to a low level. We believe that this decrease reflects, in part, adaptation and, in part, an actual decrease in maternal vigilance.

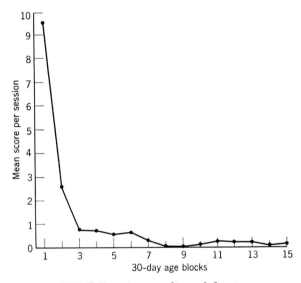

FIG. 7. *Experimenter-directed threats.*

Most normal monkey mothers show affection and protection toward infants not their own ("other-infants") during the first few weeks or months after parturition, and this was objectively measured as a ratio of positive to negative responses exhibited toward other-infants (Fig. 8). The initial contacts between the playpen mothers and the first other infant to enter their cages occurred from 19 to 27 days postpartum. These initial interactions were nearly totally positive and consisted of cradling, grooming, and exploring. However, the stage of maternal

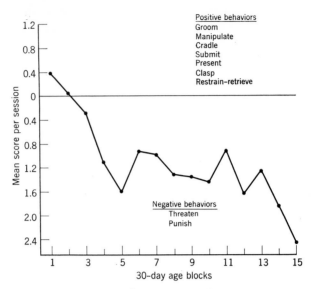

FIG. 8. *Maternal responses to other-infants.*

acceptance of other infants was brief, and the infants rapidly learned that physical associations with most other-mothers quickly changed from positive to punitive.

THE STAGE OF MATERNAL AMBIVALENCE

As the initial stage of attachment and protection wanes, the stage of maternal ambivalence gradually develops. There are many criteria that could be used to assess this transition, and one of these, maternal punishment, is plotted in Fig. 9. Maternal punishment was almost non-

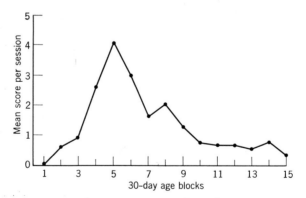

FIG. 9. *Course of maternal punishment.*

existent during the first 2 months of life and seldom occurred during the third month. During the 4th and 5th months, punishment increased to a maximum frequency. It is evident that punishment decreased after 5 months, but not because of a decrease in the mother's readiness to punish. It was more likely a function of the infant's improved ability to avoid punishment. The infants learned to approach their own mothers warily, and they progressively decreased the frequency of behavior which elicited punishment.

Although we have little objective evidence that babies learned how to avoid being punished by their own mothers, we do have data indicating their mastery of skills in avoiding the punishment meted out by other-mothers. Thus, in the four-animal interaction sessions, mothers made 784 attempts to punish other-infants and succeeded in only 62, or 7.7%. During the first half of these sessions, punishment was effective on 12.1% of the attempts, and in the second half on only 4.1%, a statistically significant difference.

The delineation of the stage of maternal ambivalence can also be made in terms of an overall index of maternal responsiveness to both own and other-infants. This has been done for the data presented in Fig. 10. Positive responses to other-infants predominated during the 1st month, positive and negative responses were essentially equal during the 2nd month, and negative responses predominated thereafter. Thus, if one arbitrarily takes the .50 value as a measure of maternal ambivalence and some arbitrary ratio (for example, .10) for separation, ambivalence appeared within the second month toward other-infants

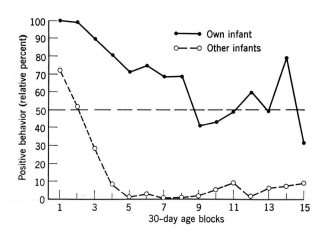

FIG. 10. *Maternal responsiveness to own and other-infants.*

The Maternal Affectional System of Rhesus Monkeys   265

and not until the 94th month toward the mothers' own infants. Separation appeared at 4 months toward other-infants and did not appear with respect to the mothers' own infants during the 15 months of development included in this study.

The stage of maternal ambivalence is characterized by both positive and negative responses. The negative responses consisted largely of threatening and punishing behaviors. Punishment during the early months of the infant's life was typically mild and highly relevant to its behavior. The stimulation which most frequently elicited maternal punishment during this stage involved vigorous tugging at the mother's hair. Excessive biting or mouthing of the nipples may also have been important, but definitive data were not obtained. Contrariwise, punishment during the stage of maternal ambivalence often occurred when the experimenters observed no infantile behavior that might have provoked maternal wrath. Moreover, punishment responses became increasingly harsh as a function of time, and this was especially evident in the category labeled rejecting. The rejecting responses in this stage consisted of vigorously terminating or prohibiting contact and took the form of shaking the infant loose from the body or even stiff-arming the infant when it attempted to initiate contact. One mother developed the stiff-arm pattern with maximal finesse, at times sending her infant sprawling head over heels as though abiding by the advice of Lewis Carroll.

> Speak roughly to your little boy,
> And beat him when he sneezes;
> He only does it to annoy,
> Because he knows it teases.

There was, it should be noted, marked variation in the extent and severity of the punishment exhibited by individual mothers. In this, as well as in every measure of maternal behavior used, marked individual differences were obtained.

THE STAGE OF MATERNAL SEPARATION OR REJECTION

We know from observations of macaques, baboons, and langurs in the wild that there is a stage when the mother physically, and later psychologically, separates from her infant. As the responses of the mother become increasingly punitive during the stage of maternal ambivalence, the mother-infant bonds become more tenuous. Nevertheless, we did not see true physical or psychological separation of the mother from her own infant in the laboratory during the 21 and 18 months we studied monkey-mother groups 1 and 2, respectively. It is even possible that if we had continued this study for a longer period, sexual relationships might have developed between the mothers and their male infants.

In the feral state, physical separation between the rhesus mother and her own infant takes place with the appearance of the next baby, generally a year later. Even so, the displaced infant is frequently seen in physical proximity to the mother for an additional period of time before psychological emancipation becomes complete. In the case of the Japanese macaque (Macaca fuscata), it has been reported that female offspring may remain close to the mother even after they become mothers themselves, but most males leave by the end of the second year. The exceptional males are those with dominant mothers (Imanishi, 1957). Although we did not see the stage of separation between the mothers and their own infants in our laboratory study, we were able to observe complete alienation between the adult females and infants not their own, and there is every reason to believe that there is much overlap in the separation mechanisms of mother and own-infant and mother and other-infant.

Variables influencing maternal behavior

Maternal affection is a function of multiple variables involving external incentive stimulation, various experiential factors, and multiple endocrinological forces. External incentives are those relating to the infant and involve contact-clinging, warmth, sucking, and visual and auditory cues. Experiential variables influencing maternal behavior probably embrace the mother's entire experience, but it is likely that her early experience is of special importance as are her relationships with each individual infant she bears and the cumulative experiences gained from raising successive infants. In free-ranging colonies, observations of other mothers with infants probably play a role. Endocrinological factors are both those relating to pregnancy and parturition and those associated with the resumption of the normal ovulatory cycle.

The analysis of monkey maternal affection must be made primarily in terms of the mother's day-to-day actions and interactions with real monkey babies. Unfortunately, the mother-infant relationships are so intimate and complex that analysis is difficult. A final determination of the operating variables and their relative importance must await the accumulation of a large body of experimental data in which all major variables are subjected to rigid controls.

On the basis of direct observations we would postulate that contact-clinging is the primary variable that binds mother to infant and infant to mother. Maternal affection is at a maximum during close ventral-ventral contacts between mother and infant, and maternal affection appears to wane progressively as the frequency of this type of bodily interchange decreases.

Intimate ventral-ventral clinging responses between mother and child gradually decreased and were partially replaced by less intimate patterns involving contact but not clinging. It is not possible to assess the degree to which this resulted from a decreased incentive value of contact to the infant or to the mother, nor can we at the present time isolate the role of sucking or thermal variables. As long as the baby maintained intimate contact with the mother, maternal affection was at a maximum, and there was high correlation between the decrease of intimate contact and the development of maternal ambivalence.

The enormous importance of intimate contact-clinging of an infant to mother is illustrated by the feral rhesus monkey mother physically separating herself from the previous infant when the stimulation of neonatal contact-clinging is reinstated by a new infant. The contact-clinging incentive must be so strong that it overrides both the relatively weak physical ties and all acquired experiential variables associated with the older infant.

Although direct observation of monkey mother and neonate gives no information concerning the relative importance of contact and nursing, some suggestive information has been obtained. The baby of a rhesus mother was removed from her a few hours after birth and the mother was given the opportunity to adopt a kitten. The adoption was complete as long as the mother clung to the kitten and successful nursing was initiated. Unfortunately, the kitten could not cling and, as the mother gradually intermittently relaxed her clasping responses and moved about the cage, the infant fell from her body. For several days the mother repeatedly retrieved the kitten and reattached it to the breast. However, as this act of involuntary separation was repeated over and over again, the mother indicated increased frustration, increased latency in retrieving, and eventually abandoned the kitten. Thus nursing, although probably an important variable, does not appear to be a variable sufficient in and of itself to maintain monkey maternal affection.

Bodily contact is such an important variable that it may elicit the full pattern of maternal behavior in a nonnursing monkey mother. We have observed the behavior of two multiparous rhesus monkeys (299 and 385) whose own infants were removed on the day of birth. After a separation interval of 9 and 4 months, respectively, these females were given the opportunity to adopt infant monkeys.

The procedure in the case of female 385 was to separate a 78-day-old infant from its real mother by inserting a Plexiglas screen between them and to give the infant access to the cage of the prospective adopting mother. After the infant's real mother was removed from the room, the infant immediately ran to and contacted female 385. Overtly normal patterns of motherhood appeared and were maintained until the infant was forcibly removed 3 months later.

A different procedure was used with female 299. A 38-day-old infant was placed in an open-field test situation and the female subsequently introduced. During the first few minutes after the female entered, the infant oriented and moved toward her several times but could make no contact because she was seated on a shelf 3 feet above the floor. The infant, noticeably disturbed, alternately cried and screeched, while the female frequently looked at the infant. After this brief delay, the female suddenly dropped to the floor, picked up the infant, and held it for the remainder of the session and during transport back to her cage. She was not observed to release it for 3 days. Again, entirely normal mother-infant relationships were established and maintained until the pair was separated by the experimenter some months later.

In both cases, the behavior of the infants was similar in that they actively sought out the female. We do not know the relative importance of the variables which underlie the original acceptance of the infant by the females, but many variables, including visual and auditory factors and previous maternal experience, probably play important roles.

We believe that the maintenance of the normal mother-infant relationships that ensued was primarily attributable to the incentive value of contact both to the mother and to the infant. The fact that normal mother-infant relationships were established while neither mother was lactating (insofar as observed—we made no test because we had not anticipated the eventual results) indicates that lactation is not an essential variable for eliciting normal mother-infant relationships. Both infants sucked at the breast and, although we cannot precisely delineate the temporal factors involved, the females subsequently produced milk in quantity. A detailed chemical analysis indicated that the nitrogen and calcium content was appropriate and the milk biochemically normal.

The one case in which attempted adoption failed was equally informative. The baby of mother 294 was removed after 34 days, and 3 days later she was given a 38-day-old infant for adoption. This infant

(B20) had been separated from its mother a few hours after birth and housed in a wire-mesh cage adjacent to that of 294. During the first month of life, while living alone, B20 developed a bizarre, autistic pattern of self-clutching, rocking, and penis-mouthing. When placed in mother 294's cage, the infant folded itself into a tight ball and screamed when contacted by the female. During the daily 30-minute exposures, the mother vacillated between approach and avoidance, made some body and hand contacts, and, from the fourth day on, occasionally groomed the infant. However, the infant never responded contactually to the mother, and the potential foster mother never responded adequately to the infant. These observations suggest that the appearance and vocalizations of an infant monkey, by themselves, are inadequate for eliciting and maintaining maternal affectional responses. We are convinced that the mother did not adopt simply because the baby made no effort whatsoever to cling to, clasp, or contact her. Indeed, the baby resisted all maternal approaches. An infant that does not feed back will not be fed. Further evidence that the fault was the infant's lies in the fact that this mother subsequently adopted a congenitally blind infant that had been mercilessly abused for 2 weeks by its own mother, one of the so-called motherless mothers that had never known a monkey mother of her own.

The contact variable's importance to the mother is illustrated by the form of infant-retrieving responses during the first few months. In this period of time the infant is not merely brought into the cage, but is placed by the mother on her ventral surface. Within the first few weeks this behavior is primarily maternal, but as a function of time the infant plays an increasingly larger cooperative role until it is frequently impossible to isolate maternal and infantile components. We frankly cannot assess the differential contribution to this pattern of the various stimulus-incentive components of contact-clinging, warmth, nursing, and visual-auditory cues. Although the retrieving responses rapidly diminished in frequency after 40 days, they could still be elicited consistently by any sudden stimulus change, sudden movements by the observers, or the presence of intruders. However, these acts of retrieval appeared qualitatively different in that placement of the infant on the mother's ventral surface was seldom a result of maternal positioning but was initiated by the infant.

Temporary reestablishment of the intimate contact-clinging responses more than 200 days after parturition was observed in an experimental study by Seay, Hansen, and Harlow (1962). Four rhesus infants were separated from their mothers at approximately 210 days by inserting transparent Plexiglas panels between the living cages and the play cells of the playpen apparatus. After 3 weeks the panels were removed and all the infants went to their appropriate mothers. In three of the four cases, intimate ventral-ventral clinging was immediately reestablished. In the remaining case, the mother appeared totally indifferent and the infant was unable to "retrieve" the mother for more than 24 hours. After this delay, however, the infant made ventral-ventral contact and there followed a resurgence of the mother-infant tie.

Although we have emphasized contact variables, we recognize the important role of other exteroceptive stimuli in regulating maternal behavior. It is more than likely that motherhood specifically attunes and sensitizes the female to specific infantile vocalizations and visual cues.

An experiment by Cross and Harlow (1963) gives presumptive evidence that the sight and sound of a neonatal monkey are significant incentives to monkey mothers. Three groups of five monkeys each were placed in a Butler-type exploration box (Butler, 1953) with the option of viewing either an infant or a juvenile monkey. As shown in Fig. 11, a multiparous group, which had given birth to their last infants 2 to 4 months prior to this experiment and had had their babies removed during the first day, showed a clear-cut preference for baby-viewing throughout the experiment. The group of nulliparous adult females showed no preference whatsoever. The most interesting group consisted of females that gave birth to babies during the course of this experiment. These babies were removed from their mothers after 3 days, and the mothers were returned to the apparatus for additional

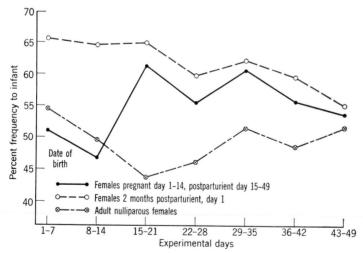

FIG. 11. Preferential infant-viewing by female monkeys.

The Maternal Affectional System of Rhesus Monkeys   271

testing. Before the birth of their babies, these females showed no preference for infant-viewing; following birth, a sudden rise in preference for baby-viewing developed. Although the basis for this is not clear, the most likely explanation is that the transient contact experience enhanced monkey-baby incentive values.

The foregoing data indicate that exteroceptive incentives provided by the sight of the baby and the sounds that monkey babies utter are measurable variables in eliciting maternal affection. We doubt they have the power apparently intrinsic to contact-clinging, but vision and audition are probably additional primary modalities through which learned affectional responses develop. In other words, these modalities serve as both unconditioned and conditioned channels in the formation and expression of maternal bonds.

Although there is reason to believe that baby-viewing stimulates maternal behavior, there is also contradictory evidence. Viewing divorced from contactual responding soon wanes. In the separation study of Seay et al., mothers deprived of contact with their babies increased their visual responses to the infant, measured before, during, and after separation, from a mean of slightly over one visual response per 30-minute period during the week before separation to a mean of over three responses during the first week of separation. This increment was largely a function of the behavior of two of the four mothers. The variability is evident in Fig. 12. It is also apparent that in the subsequent 2 weeks of separation, visual responses decreased. The viewing data, taken together, suggest that the sight of the baby is secondarily reinforcing, deriving from learning that is reinforced by other rewarding properties of the baby and its behavior.

In a current study of two mothers and their infants there is also a suggestion that auditory cues provided by the baby may arouse a mother even though she cannot herself act to relieve the distressed baby. A multiparous mother with strong maternal behavior and a primiparous "motherless" mother and their babies share a half-playpen unit. It has been noted that when the primiparous mother fails to contact her screeching baby, the multiparous mother threatens the neglectful mother. Since there are no threats when the screeching baby is held by its mother, we believe the behavior reflects a frustrated maternal response, not a response to an aversive sound.

EXPERIENTIAL VARIABLES

The maternal affectional system, waxing and waning with the birth and growth of each particular baby, is unlike most other affectional

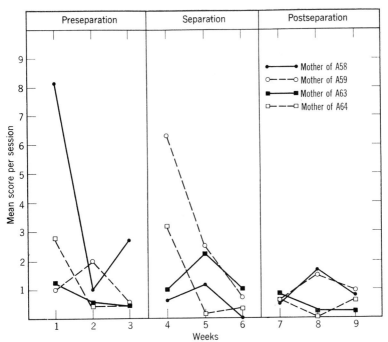

FIG. 12. *Maternal baby-viewing before, during, and after separation. (From Seay et al., 1962, p. 129.)*

systems. Doubtless, maternal affection is influenced by several families of experiential variables: (1) the experience associated with each baby that it observes or produces, (2) the accumulative effects of multiple motherhood, and (3) the mother's personal life history.

The variables of individual infant-raising. Traumatic experiences happening to a particular mother-infant combination can alter the expression of maternal behaviors, but this is probably specific to the particular infant involved. On one occasion we were forced to separate a mother and her 36-day-old infant for 3 days to treat the baby's infected hand. After the infant was returned to its mother, we observed a resurgence of the intimate contact responses which characterized the mother-infant pairs during the first month of life, and this augmentation of contact endured more than a month. The results of our separation study (Seay et al., 1962) also indicated that, in general, mother-infant separation was followed by a resurgence of intimate physical contact characteristic of an earlier developmental stage.

Maternal overprotection and infantile overdependence were produced by allowing individual infants to live with their mothers a period of

The Maternal Affectional System of Rhesus Monkeys 273

7 months in standard 30-inch × 30-inch × 30-inch living cages. During this time the infants were raised by affectionate, normal, multiparous mothers. The mother-infant pairs were then placed in the home cages of a two-unit playpen situation in order to study infant-infant interactions. Observation was simple and totally reliable—there were no infant-infant interactions. One infant never left the home cage during 12 weeks of observations, and, although the second infant did enter its play cell, it made no social overtures to the other mother-infant combination. It is probable that the early restricted living conditions imposed upon these animals resulted in maternal overprotection and infant overattachment which inhibited the development of infant-infant interrelationships at this point in time.

There are, however, several uncontrolled variables in this pilot investigation. Not only had the infants had no opportunity to interact with other infants, but they also had been denied opportunity to explore a larger, more challenging world than that of the living cages prior to the playpen placement. Furthermore, the new situation was strange to the animals and may have enhanced infantile dependence and maternal overprotection. It is also possible that there is a critical time—some lapse of weeks or months—during which conditions favoring the development of maternal ambivalence must occur if this stage of maternal behavior is to appear. Unless the baby has frequent opportunities to leave and return to the mother during the first year of life, it may reach the point of no voluntary separation.

The variables of multiple motherhood. It is the general impression of primatologists that multiparous females are more effective mothers than primiparous, although the absence of supporting or negative data indicates our lack of knowledge concerning this variable. There is neither scientific support for this general statement nor information about the degree to which it might apply to particular stages of maternal responding or to individual mothers.

At present we are making an experimental attack on the problem by comparing in the playpen situation the behaviors of two groups of four primiparous and four multiparous females and their babies. Although most of the data remain to be analyzed, we have been pleasantly surprised by the very efficient maternal behaviors of the primiparous mothers and the normal social behaviors exhibited by their infants. Typical of the comparisons of maternal responses are those for cradling and retrieving (Figs. 13 and 14). In both instances, the response showed a similar course of development in the primiparous and multiparous groups, and differences were in no instance significant.

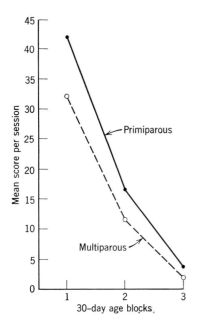

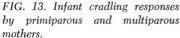

FIG. 13. Infant cradling responses by primiparous and multiparous mothers.

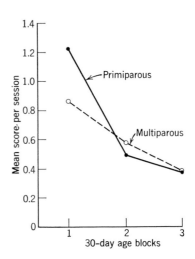

FIG. 14. Infant retrieving responses by primiparous and multiparous mothers.

The variables of early experience. Another kind of experiential variable that can have an enormous influence on maternal affectional responding is the mother's personal life history. This was dramatically illustrated when we traced the maternal behaviors of a group of five so-called motherless mother macaques which had never known a real monkey mother of their own, had been denied the opportunity to develop normal infant-infant affectional patterns, and subsequently had had only limited physical association with other monkeys.

All five females were totally hopeless mothers, and none of the infants would have survived without artificial feeding in the first days or weeks of life. Two mothers were essentially indifferent to their infants; three were violently abusive. Indeed, the last infant was separated when it became apparent that otherwise it would not live. The maternal inadequacies of these animals cannot be attributed to faulty responding by the babies. Early in life the babies repeatedly offered visual and auditory cues normally appropriate for eliciting maternal responses (Fig. 15), and as soon as the first four infants were physically able to initiate approach and body-contact responses, they made repeated

The Maternal Affectional System of Rhesus Monkeys 275

FIG. 15. Infant cues to elicit maternal responding.

attempts to attach to the mothers, only to be repulsed and rejected (Fig. 16). So strong were these contact-seeking responses in two infants that they withstood brutal and continuous abuse by the mothers until they attained the breasts for reasonable periods of time.

These data not only show that monkey mothering can be drastically altered by experiential factors, but they also indicate the importance of social learning for the normal expression of maternal behavior. Unfortunately for the interpretation of the results, these motherless mothers had been denied both monkey mothering and any adequate opportunity to develop normal social relationships with other monkeys. Although we strongly suspect that inadequate infant-infant experience played an overwhelmingly important role in contributing to their maternal inadequacies, we cannot, as yet, make any definitive statement.

It is conceivable that specific factors of inadequate early experience produce specific types of inadequate mothering. For example, failure of normal gratification of contact-clinging in infancy may make it impossible for the adult female to show normal contact relationships with her own infant. Likewise, maternal brutality may stem from inadequate social experience with other infants within the first year of life. Our data do not suggest any such correlations. Rather, they suggest that maternal affection in the monkey is a highly integrated, global system, not a series of isolated components that vary independently.

FIG. 16. Infant rejection response by motherless-mother.

On this basis it seems plausible that the expression of adequate, normal, maternal affection depends more upon general social experience than upon specific experiences.

Our data to date indicate a relationship between normal and abnormal maternal behavior and the adequacy of previous heterosexual behavior. Thus none of the motherless-mother animals ever showed normal female sex posturing and responding. They were impregnated, not through their own effort, but because of the patience, persistence, and perspicacity of our breeding males. Although we do not regard heterosexual inadequacy as a cause of maternal inadequacy, we believe both are products of a common factor or factors. By and large, feral-raised female monkeys are adequate sexually and maternally. Occasionally, a feral-raised mother shows no interest in her offspring and even destroys them. The one such inadequate feral female we have closely observed engaged in the procreative act with enthusiasm but was uninterested in the end product, killing one infant and maltreating a subsequent baby, forcing separation to preserve life. We, of course, have no knowledge of this female's prelaboratory life history and are in no position to make any assessment of possible hormonal disturbances.

We have stressed the primacy of infant-infant affectional development for normal maternal behavior on the basis of indirect evidence. Almost all of our infant monkeys given the opportunity to interact intimately with other infants during the first half-year of life have developed normal adult-type sexual responsiveness, whether raised without mothers, with cloth-surrogate mothers, with motherless mothers, or with normal mothers. Only one female among the scores denied infant-infant interactions during the first half-year of life has shown normal adult-type sex behavior, and this population includes males and females, monkeys raised alone in bare cages and monkeys raised with wire- or cloth-surrogate mothers. We predict that rearing conditions that produce normal sexual behavior patterns will also produce normal maternal behavior patterns. Unfortunately, we must wait at least two more years to validate this hypothesis since there is a time lag between preadolescent sexual play and motherhood.

So far in our description and analysis of the variables influencing maternal behavior we have largely limited ourselves to the first stage of maternal affectional development, the stage of attachment and protection. The variables that bind the mother to the infant are most accessible to analysis when the maternal bond is at its peak.

Obviously, as the mother passes through the succeeding stages of ambivalence and separation, previously operating variables must fade and disappear, and fade and disappear at different rates. Entirely new variables may appear and have pervasive effects as one passes from one stage to another. Thus the resumption of the estrous cycle involves a change in endocrinological variables which may play important roles in guiding the expression of maternal behaviors.

We can make reasonable hypotheses concerning the variables which operate in the stage of attachment and protection and reasonable estimates concerning their relative importance. Thus contact-clinging, which may also involve warmth, is a primary variable for the initiation and maintenance of this stage just as it is in the infant-mother affectional system (Harlow, 1958). Nursing is apparently a variable of measurable importance in both affectional systems but not an essential variable. Relatively specific visual and auditory variables play a supplementary role—they are additional sensory modalities through which learned affectional responses are mediated.

Unfortunately, we have less information and can only speculate about the variables and changes in variables which give rise to the stage of maternal ambivalence and mother-infant separation. Changes in the relative importance of different variables as one passes from the stage of maternal attachment and protection to the stage of maternal ambivalence are illustrated in Fig. 17, which shows the hypothetical course of development of contact needs for the infant and for the mother based on behavioral trends observed in the playpen situation. During the first few months, the mother's need for intimate contact exceeds the infant's, producing maternal protection. This early protectiveness becomes apparent when the infant attains sufficient strength and agility to make repetitive attempts to leave the mother. Maternal protection is manifested by the high frequency of restrain-retrieve responses and the communicative responses for retrieval at a distance.

Subsequently, the intensity of maternal and infantile contact needs is reversed until the infant's needs exceed the mother's. This is illustrated by the point of intersection of the two curves (Fig. 17). Beyond this point, the stage of ambivalence exists, and the infant's attempts to make physical contact are rebuffed with increasing frequency and severity. As attachment abates, ambivalence arises and anticipates alienation.

> From here on mother does not care
> For baby fingers in her hair;
> A touch that once went to her heart
> Now merely makes the hair depart.

Changes in both mother and child normally tend to produce gradual separation. We make the assumption that not only are there endocri-

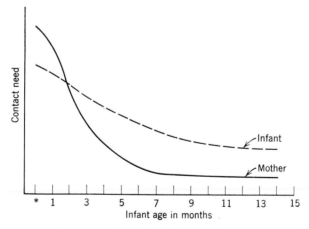

FIG. 17. Hypothetical course of mother and infant contact needs.

The Maternal Affectional System of Rhesus Monkeys 279

nological factors influencing the mother and causing the waning of affectional responding, but there are behavioral changes in the infant which contribute to the same end. Thus we believe that maturational factors intrinsic to every infant tend to dilute the infant-mother affectional tie. The infant gradually changes from a reflex, clinging, cuddling individual to one that moves about freely, squirms when held, inflicts physical discomfort, and reaches out physically and intellectually to the world around it. As the world expands from one consisting only of the mother's face and body, the infant progressively becomes an organism which fails to feed back basic incentives which tie the mother to the infant. With each step of development, the infant is less reinforced by the mother and the mother by the infant; in both cases the net result is the same. The mother is more capable of accepting ensuing progeny and the infant of breaking the maternal bonds that would otherwise inhibit social development.

The inevitable stages of maturation shape and reshape the mother-infant bonds in monkeys. The process of growth, augmented by continuously accompanying learned processes, creates and destroys the ties between individual mothers and infants. However, the capacity for maternal affection is not destroyed, and with the next baby comes a reinstatement of the cycle. For the separated infant, other affectional systems become preeminent and ensure successful social adaptation within the culture of its particular primate group.

Summary

The maternal affectional system is one of a number of affectional systems exhibited by rhesus monkeys. Its course has been studied in the laboratory by observing rhesus mothers with their infants from birth until 18 or 21 months of age in a special apparatus designed to provide both living quarters and infant play facilities. Supplementary studies have been directed toward isolating variables determining the mother-infant relationship.

Maternal behavior in the rhesus monkey is characterized by sequential stages designated as attachment and protection, ambivalence, and separation or rejection. During attachment and protection, the earliest phase, the mother has close physical contact with the infant and responds to it positively, holding it close to her much of the time and restricting its free locomotion in large degree. Negative responses such as rejecting some of the infant's approaches and punishing it for encroachments gradually appear. These, nevertheless, mark the start of the ambivalence stage, characterized by positive and negative responses to the infant. Finally, physical separation takes place, although this stage did not appear by 21 months in the laboratory situation. Generally, physical separation in the natural envionment appears with the birth of a new baby, which reinstates the maternal cycle with the newborn now the center of the mother's attention and the older offspring occupying the periphery.

The variables operating to determine maternal roles in rhesus monkeys can be grouped into external incentives, experiential factors, and endocrinological forces. External incentives are those relating to the infant, such as contact-clinging, warmth, sucking, baby vocalizations, and the baby's visual properties. Experiential variables influencing the mother's responses to the baby include her early experiences, especially with age-mates, and probably cumulative experiences from raising earlier offspring or observing other females caring for babies. The exact contribution of the hormonal system prevalent in the postparturient period awaits experimental attack.

References

Butler, R. A. (1953), Discrimination learning by rhesus monkeys to visual-exploration motivation. *J. comp. physiol. Psychol.,* **46,** 95–98.

Cross, H. A., and H. F. Harlow (1963), Observation of infant monkeys by female monkeys. *Percept. mot. Skills,* **16,** 11–15.

Hansen, E. W. (1962), The development of infant and maternal behavior in the rhesus monkey. Unpublished doctoral dissertation, University of Wisconsin.

Harlow, H. F. (1958), The nature of love. *Amer. Psychologist,* **13,** 673–685.

Harlow, H. F. (1960), Primary affectional patterns in primates. *Amer. J. Orthopsychiat.,* **30,** 676–684.

Imanishi, K. (1957), Social behavior in Japanese monkeys, *Macaca fuscata. Psychologia,* **1,** 47–54.

Seay, B., E. W. Hansen, and H. F. Harlow (1962), Mother-infant separation in monkeys. *J. Child Psychol. Psychiat.,* **3,** 123–132.

9

mother-infant relations in
LANGURS

Phyllis Jay

The infant monkey is born into an organized social group of all ages and both sexes, a group whose membership is constant and whose social organization does not change during the yearly cycle of activity. Life in a social group is constant reaction and interaction with other monkeys, a complex process of adjustment and adaptation, of which the relation between mother and infant is only one of many. Laboratory experimentation demonstrates the importance of specific patterns of mother-infant relations (Harlow and Zimmerman, 1959; Harlow, 1959), and field observation reveals the importance of these patterns in normal individual development and emphasizes the need for maturing in a social group.

All Old and New World monkeys on which naturalistic observations have been made have many common features of social life, but vary considerably in group size. Monkeys and the African apes live in relatively large heterosexual groups which include all ages. The average size of gorilla troops is seventeen (Schaller and Emlen, in press) and

The organization and presentation of the field data were supported by the National Science Foundation and by Fellowship MF-12120 CL, National Institute of Mental Health, United States Public Health Service.

chimpanzee groups are even larger. Only among gibbons and possibly orangutans is the typical group one adult male, one female, and their offspring.

The common Indian langur monkey is one variety of the many closely related leaf-eating monkeys distributed throughout south and southeast Asia, which, with the African colobus monkeys, comprise the subfamily Colobinae. Asian langurs are quadrupedal, primarily arboreal monkeys with stomachs specialized to digest large quantities of relatively unnutritious mature leaves. The common Indian langur *(Presbytis entellus)*, frequently called the Hanuman monkey, spends more time on the ground than other kinds of leaf-eating monkeys, some of which seldom if ever descend to the ground. *Pithecus* and *Semnopithecus* may appear in the literature as synonyms for *Presbytis*.

Although laboratory research has concentrated on the rhesus macaque and recent field studies have included the closely related baboons, the behavior of these aggressive, ground-living forms is not representative of all monkeys. Baboon-macaque monkeys are adapted behaviorally and morphologically to life on the ground where great predator pressure has placed strong selective advantage on powerful adult males with large canines, on forms of social behavior which produce constant alertness, and on ability to react quickly to danger. Sexual dimorphism is much less pronounced among langurs than among baboons or macaques, but adult male langurs can be distinguished from adult females at a distance because of the male's slightly larger size and more robust body. In contrast to the tense and aggressive relations among adult male baboons, adult male langurs are relaxed. One characteristic of social life among arboreal monkeys, in contrast to the ground-living monkeys, is the relative unimportance of dominance in daily life. Aggressive threats and fighting are exceedingly uncommon. Adult males and females are related within a dominance system, but dominance is seldom asserted. When dominance interactions occur, they usually concern access to food, right of way on paths and in trees, a reaction to being disturbed by a subordinate monkey, or, in the instance of males, access to estrous females. The animal which succeeds in taking the food, walking first on a path, chasing or asserting himself or herself over another animal is dominant in that particular interaction.

Each adult male acts independently in a stable, clearly defined, linear dominance hierarchy which is established and maintained with a minimum of aggressive behavior. Adult males, as the most dominant members of the group, determine patterns of activity by controlling the direction of troop movement, maintaining peaceful relations, and repelling strange adult males.

Dominance patterns among adult females are variable and relatively unstable, fluctuating with changes in the reproductive cycle. Females are normally much less dominant than adult males, but under special circumstances an adult female may dominate adult males. Dominance increases when an estrous female is in consort with an adult male and during the last weeks of pregnancy. A female with a newborn infant avoids all dominance interactions. Whereas part of langur social behavior is derived from the dominance status of troop members, most daily activity—feeding, resting, and grooming—is nonaggressive and only indirectly related to an individual's dominance status.

The daily pattern of activity of a langur troop is similar to that of other primates. The troop begins to move about in the trees at sunrise and is active during the early morning hours. The middle of the day is spent in quiet grooming, eating, and resting. Adult females with infants stay together in the center of the troop, whereas juveniles and large infants play together or rest near the adults. When the troop moves, several adult males precede the troop, but there is no regular pattern to the progress of the rest of the troop. In dense forest where it may be difficult for the monkeys to see each other, the troop stays close together. Langur troops do not follow a regular circuit each day and do not ordinarily return to the sleeping trees of the night before. A troop usually moves approximately one mile a day within a home range that seldom exceeds 3 square miles (Jay, 1963).

Between October 1958 and November 1960, I observed Indian langurs for approximately 750 hours. After a survey of the location and sizes of langur troops, several groups were selected for concentrated observations. One troop of fifty-four monkeys living near Kaukori Village, 14 miles from Lucknow, Uttar Pradesh, was observed for 4 consecutive months. Three troops near Orcha Village in Bastar District, Madhya Pradesh, were observed over 12 months. The standard procedure of observation was to locate the group each day and remain with it for from 6 to 9 hours. After a group had been observed during the daytime for several weeks, I alternated evening and night observations to obtain data for all 24 hours of the day.

The langur's initial reaction to my presence was varied and depended to a great extent on previous experience with people. Groups which lived in or near villages were usually accustomed to people, although the monkeys tended to avoid close contact with people in areas where the animals are chased. Groups of langurs living in forests where there is little or no contact with people were often easily alarmed and fled as soon as they noticed me. However, if I made no sudden movements and followed them whenever they moved, all troops eventually became used to me and no longer walked or ran away. The time it took for a group to allow me to stay within 100 feet varied from only several days in the Kaukori troop to over 3 months in the forest Orcha troops. After a group did not move away at my approach, there was a period during which they became used to my sitting among them and moving with them rather than staying 100 or more feet behind the group. At first the monkeys were very cautious and did not approach closer than 30 to 50 feet. If I attempted to move closer, they threatened me and moved away. After a few days they stopped threatening and I was able to sit among them. Several of the adults in the Kaukori troop groomed me, and young langurs played around and on me whenever I sat quietly. Young animals often tried to solicit me to play by dashing up and slapping my ankles or pulling my clothing. I did not take an active role in group activity and was usually ignored by most of the members of the group—they were no longer cautious in their treatment of me. I avoided looking directly at them whenever they were within 10 feet, since a direct stare is a mild form of threat. As soon as the members of the group were used to my presence, their social behavior was apparently normal.

Thirty-five millimeter black and white and color photographs were taken of all major types of behavior. Field equipment also included binoculars which were seldom necessary because observation was from very close range. Notes were recorded as events occurred and included the participants, activity, and time of the event. It was possible to identify all the members of the four major groups studied after a few weeks of observation because there was considerable variation among the animals in coat color, locomotor patterns, temperament (speed of reactions, amount of vocalization, and peculiarities of gestures), and size.

Birth periodicity

There is a concentration of births in the hot, dry months of April and May in the flat plains area of central India. Infants born at this time begin to supplement their milk diet with solid vegetable food in the next monsoon season, 2 to 3 months after birth. Many births occur in January and February in troops living in the forest near Orcha where there is some rainfall and fresh vegetation all year, but infants are born in all months. The influence of local ecological conditions on the reproductive cycle of the langur is not known.

The birth interval for a langur is probably from 20 to 24 months, but it was not possible to examine the females. A female is not sexually active, she does not solicit mounting by adult or subadult males, until her infant is from 12 to 15 months old. If gestation is approximately 6 months, the minimum interval between consecutive births is 18 months. Seasonal variations where birth peaks are pronounced may extend this minimum period.

Stages of development

The development of the young langur may be divided into six stages: (1) from birth to one month; (2) the infant-one, from 1 month to 3 months; (3) the period of color change from 3 to 5 months; (4) color change to approximately 1 year (infant-two); (5) the weaning period, from the 11th to the 15th month; and (6) the second year of life (the young juvenile). The period of color change from dark brown to light gray is the only stage of development marked by an obvious physical change.

THE NEWBORN LANGUR: BIRTH TO ONE MONTH

The mother-newborn association is the strongest and most intense social relationship in the life of a langur monkey. Mother and newborn are in closer contact for at least 5 months than either is with another langur at any time in life. During these 5 months the infant depends completely on her for protection from other monkeys and from predators. The clinging infant is also dependent on its mother for nourishment and transport, and she directs all her attention to its care during the first few weeks of its life. No births were observed, but one infant was noted immediately after birth. The mother was cleaning herself and the wet infant. From the hour of its birth she inspects, licks, grooms, and manipulates the infant (Fig. 1). When the newborn is nursing quietly or sleeping, she grooms and strokes it softly without disturbing or waking it. For the first week of life the newborn is never away from its mother or another adult female.

The infant can cling to its mother at birth, but for several days it needs assistance when she walks or runs. During the first week the mother must help it into a riding position by a touch of her hand or a sweeping gesture of her arm. The infant slips down from her body unless she supports it a moment and presses it against her. Soon the infant clings in response to a light pressure of her hand when she is

FIG. 1. Mother holding newborn infant, several hours after birth.

going to move. Since the troop seldom travels more than a mile a day, it is not difficult for a mother and her newborn infant to keep up with the troop (Fig. 2).

The first week of a newborn's life is spent nursing and sleeping. It clings with a nipple in its mouth and presses its head against the mother's chest or looks around at other monkeys. The infant struggles if the mother holds it away from her body for inspection or grooming, but she never releases her hold or loses control of it. The newborn infant struggles and appears to be very uncomfortable when not in contact with its mother's body. Signs of discomfort increase until it

FIG. 2. One-day-old newborn clinging to mother.

is allowed to nurse or to cling. The contented infant is usually silent, in contrast to the uncomfortable newborn which produces a range of soft to loud squeals. A female holding a squealing infant "chirps" and, if not handling it, strokes or touches the infant. The louder the cries, the more a female strokes and grooms it.

From birth the newborn is a focal point of interest for all adult and subadult females in the troop. Females gather around the mother as soon as they notice the newborn. Regardless of dominance status, they move directly to the mother without threat or submissive gestures. A group of from four to ten females quickly surrounds and grooms the mother, but not until the infant is almost dry does she stop turning her back and moving a few feet to avoid the pressing females. Each time she sits, three or four females crowd in front of her to touch, smell, and lick the newborn. Mild threats such as patting the ground with one hand are exchanged among females waiting to hold the newborn, but at any stronger threat or a vocalization the mother quickly moves away with her infant.

Several hours after parturition the mother will allow an adult female to hold the infant for several minutes. After two or three females have held it, one carries it 5 or 10 feet. An infant may be held by as many as eight or ten females and carried as far as 75 feet from its mother in the first 2 days of life (Fig. 3). If the newborn struggles, another

FIG. 3. *Newborn being held and nursed by multiparous female, not its mother. Other female waits to hold the infant.*

female immediately tries to take it unless the mother is nearby and retrieves it. The squealing infant quiets for a moment regardless of which female takes it, but begins to squeal in a few minutes if not allowed to cling. If a female, whether lactating or not, allows a newborn to suck, it remains quiet and content. Subadult females have few opportunities to hold the newborn during the first few days of its presence in the troop. The mother is always aware of her infant and at the slightest indication of danger, such as fighting among adults or the presence of predators, she immediately runs to hold her infant.

No adult was observed to attack an infant, but it is possible that during a dominance fight an infant could accidentally be injured.

A mother can take her infant from any female in the troop regardless of dominance status, and she avoids all dominance interactions. Her day is spent quietly with other females and infants in a protected part of the troop. The primary concern of a mother is her infant and its safety, regardless of where she is or which other female is holding her infant.

There is great variation among females in infant care, and a corresponding range in infant behavior—some infants are always quiet but others frequently whine and struggle. Some females are extremely competent; they are casual but firm, and appear unaware of the movement of the often very active newborn infant. In adeptness in holding an infant, females range from the very capable, through those which constantly readjust the infant's position, to a few extremely inept ones, which hold the newborn infant too tightly, in awkward upside-down positions, or constantly away from their body to inspect and to handle it.

In general, multiparous females handle newborn infants more efficiently and in a more relaxed manner than do primiparous females. Nulliparous subadult and young adult females show some difficulty and awkwardness in handling a newborn. In addition to experience, female temperament and personality are other sources of variation in interest in and aptitude for holding infants. A tense, nervous, and easily irritated female frequently startles the infant with quick or unpredictable motions; a calm, relaxed female makes few sudden movements.

The 2-week-old infant actively orients toward its mother and readily distinguishes her from other adult females from a distance of 15 or 20 feet. The infant often tries to move away from the female holding it when it sees its mother approaching. If the female releases her grasp, the infant takes a few hesitating steps to meet its mother.

Muscular coordination of the newborn improves rapidly. By 2 weeks the infant plays between its mother's legs and climbs on her shoulders and head. If it falls, she immediately turns to face it or places it in front of her. During these brief periods of activity, the infant's poorly coordinated movements may carry it 2 or 3 feet from her. She usually restrains it by pulling back on its tail or leg. In a tree, the mother keeps the infant between her legs. By 1 month of age the infant moves freely within a radius of 3 to 5 feet of the mother, who frequently touches or looks at it but allows it to remain away as long as 4 minutes at a time. This is a period of exploration for the infant during which coordination is improved, but the infant still trips over its tail and legs. A few steps in one direction are followed by pauses to crouch or roll on the ground. The infant investigates a rapidly expanding environment and discovers a new world to observe, touch, smell, and lick.

Field observation has suggested several elements which may be essential in releasing maternal behavior: coat color, quality of movement, vocalizations, and size. Thorough analysis of mother-infant relations will be possible only when more of the physical and social variables in the relationship are better understood. Since several of these factors normally occur together and are confounded, it is essential to investigate them in a laboratory situation to assess the importance of individual factors and to determine the degree to which variations in each affect maternal responses. For example, planned laboratory investigation could assess the importance of coat color by keeping an infant brown or making it white immediately after birth. Natal coat color is present when the infant most needs protection and nourishment from its mother and older monkeys. Change in coat color occurs concomitantly with a decrease in adult interest in the young. The importance of movement is illustrated by one group of langurs which contained three dead, brown-colored young infants. These infants were carried, groomed, and inspected by the mother and other adult females. However, the adults approach a dead infant less frequently than a live infant, and they stay in contact with the dead infant for a shorter time than with moving, vocalizing, live infants.

The young infant's movements are uncoordinated, hesitating, and awkward. When it needs help in steadying itself or in clinging, it grasps its mother's fur or reaches toward her and she immediately supports it or helps it to her body. When the infant touches her, shifts its position, clings tightly, or loses its grasp, she responds immediately. These motions appear to stimulate holding, adjusting, and fondling by the mother. The cries of a newborn may communicate more information about its needs than is suspected by observation alone. Spectographic analysis of vocalizations would determine whether there are important structural differences between these cries and the sounds produced by older infants, cries only slightly distinguishable from each other by the human ear.

The social unit for the protection and nourishment of the newborn langur does not include the adult male. This is a contrast to the baboon newborn whose mother remains with other adult females and young close to the most dominant adult male in the group. Adult male langurs are indifferent to a newborn and are seldom within 15 feet of one. The loudest squeals of a newborn do not draw the attention of an adult male and when an infant needs help, assistance is given by either the mother or another adult female. If an adult male accidentally frightens an infant, the mother instantly threatens, chases, and often slaps the male. Other adult females near the infant may join the mother and chase the male as far as 25 yards.

THE INFANT-ONE LANGUR: FIRST TO THE THIRD MONTH

The second month of life is one of rapidly increasing muscular coordination and greater independence from the mother. The infant is carried, but it is no longer necessary for the mother to pull it under her body when she is about to walk. If she slows her pace after walking for several minutes without stopping to rest, the infant lets its legs drop to the ground. If she does not pause, the infant drags its feet and squeals. Unless the troop is moving rapidly, she sits for several minutes and keeps the infant between her legs (Fig. 4).

At about 2½ months the infant wanders as far as 10 feet from its mother, but makes frequent trips back to nurse for a moment. If the troop is alerted when the infant is away, she immediately runs to it or grunts and pats the ground to draw its attention. The moment the infant is aware of her tension it runs to her.

As the infant goes farther from the mother, it encounters age mates and adult females. Instead of hopping from one place to another without discriminating between monkeys and inanimate objects, it begins to focus its attention on monkeys. The infant's span of attention is short, but it returns again and again to climb on adult females. Infants continue playing by themselves rather than joining others in group play. Adult females are not as interested in an older infant as in a newborn, but frequently seek out infants and groom them. The active infant-one must be restrained to be held for more than a few minutes, and often breaks free and runs to its mother or plays.

THE TRANSITION PERIOD IN LANGUR INFANTS: THIRD TO FIFTH MONTH

The 2 months of color change from dark brown to light gray coincide with important alterations in the social relations of the infant: it depends less on its mother, it attracts less interest from females, and it spends more time with age mates.

By 3 months the infant supplements its milk diet with solid food. The infant samples plants that the mother eats, picks up bits of food she drops, and occasionally takes small pieces from her hands or mouth.

FIG. 4. *Infant-two langur maintains contact with mother while exploring environment.*

She is usually tolerant of this, but does not share or offer food. If the infant gets a bit of food she wants, she takes it from the infant's hands or mouth.

If a small group of females with 3-month-old infant-ones are grooming, several females may walk away, leaving their infants playing around the remaining female. The female tending several infants restrains them from wandering by pulling them back by a tail or leg. Usually infants climb over her or play together nearby. This adult

Mother-Infant Relations in Langurs   293

female-infant relationship is probably based on the tendency for adult females to treat all infants as they do their own.

Adult female interest declines when the infant's color changes from brown to gray. Adult females no longer follow the mother to hold the active infant. If an infant climbs on a female, she tolerates it or moves away. Roughness with an infant, however, provokes threats from nearby females.

The mother is less solicitous, but continues to care for and protect her infant. She lets it clamber up into low branches or onto tree stumps. There is little need of restraint since it returns every few seconds. Until her infant is older, she chases away infant-twos and juveniles which solicit it to play. Differences between males and females are noticeable at about 3 or 4 months; males are rougher and play more actively than do females.

THE INFANT-TWO LANGUR: FIFTH MONTH TO ABOUT ONE YEAR

By 5 months the infant-two runs 20 or 30 feet from its mother. She moves to it whenever the troop is alerted. Because she vocalizes to draw its attention, her protective role is more obvious than when she had to take only a few steps to reach it. When the troop is relaxed, the mother moves away from her infant while she eats and grooms. Short moves of up to 20 feet are not signaled to the playing infant, who must follow if it wants to nurse or to cling. The intervals at which the small infant-two returns to its mother increase until it plays away from its mother for more than 20 minutes at a time.

At approximately 6 months of age the infant-two spends several hours each day playing with male and female age mates. Such a play group is illustrated in Fig. 5. Although the mother no longer chases away infants who encourage the small infant-two to play, she continues to threaten juveniles if they try to wrestle with the infant. Play groups may include as many as sixteen young monkeys, but average two to four, and half of all play groups have fewer than three members. Running, jumping, chasing, wrestling, and tail pulling are supplemented by more complicated forms of play, sometimes oriented toward objects; but play is usually interpersonal and exploratory.

At approximately 8 months, males are larger and stronger than females of the same age, so that play groups of from eight to ten members divide into smaller groups of two and three infants or juveniles of approximate size. Large infants and juveniles play with smaller infants briefly before active wrestling and chasing leave smaller monkeys behind or force them to play by themselves. Since the young mon-

FIG. 5. A play group of infant-twos and juveniles.

key leaves the play group if handled roughly, intervention by mothers or adult females is rare. From a distance of 20 or 25 feet, young monkeys appear to be playing in complete silence, and this is the distance a play group usually stays away from adults. Rough-and-tumble play is frequently accompanied by grunts and quiet squeals, but sharp or loud outcries and continual squealing are rare since these cries draw the attention of adult females which break up the play group. Adult interference in group play activity is more frequent in small troops with few young members where play groups must include infants and juveniles of unequal size and strength.

In a large play group a few monkeys play by themselves for several minutes and then rejoin the group. Solitary play alternates with group play until the infant is about one year old, when group play predominates. By 10 months the infant spends from 4 to 5 hours a day in group play and frequently travels with its age mates when the troop moves.

Adult females occasionally play with infant-twos. If an adult female is forcibly grooming a struggling infant, she often wrestles with it and alternately lets it try to run away and pulls it back by its tail. Infants initiate play with an adult female by jumping on her and racing around her, pulling her fur, and pushing up against her. Infants often swing back and forth on the dangling tail of a female sitting on a low limb, until she moves away.

Mother-Infant Relations in Langurs 295

Until about 10 months of age the male infant has no contact with adult males. At the age of 10 months the infant establishes a relationship with adult males involving a series of special gestures and vocalizations. It runs, squealing tensely, to the moving adult and veers away just before it touches him. Gradually the infant gains confidence and touches the male's hindquarters, and within a week thereafter it approaches and mounts by pulling himself up over the adult's hindquarters. The infant often grasps the adult's ankles with his feet and the long fur on the adult's sides with his hands but there are no pelvic thrusts. Mounting of the adult by the infant appears similar in form to the mounting of a female by a male or dominance mounting between two adults, but when displayed by the infant is probably neither sexual nor dominance behavior. When the infant mounts, the adult stops and stands motionless until the infant dismounts. In the next few weeks another element is added: after the infant dismounts, he runs around to face the adult and both embrace while the infant squeals and tries to push his head against the adult's chest. Touching, mounting, and embracing occur thereafter either as a series or as separate events. One adult male may be mounted and embraced by as many as four infants and juveniles in rapid succession. This approach to the adult male is displayed by the infant until he is 4 years old.

A female infant-two has almost no contact with adult males. Adult females are embraced by female infant-twos on rare occasions when the adult threatens the infant from a short distance. Older infant-two females reciprocate grooming with adult females. A male infant-two usually grooms an adult female to get closer to food, although instances of mutual grooming between male infant-twos and adult females do occur. Grooming is solicited by infants with wounds. One infant-two with a thorn in his foot approached male and female adults in the troop and offered its foot for grooming. Each adult responded by carefully inspecting the foot.

The year-old infant takes an active role in the troop. The bark of a year-old infant can alert the entire troop and rout them from open areas into the safety of trees.

THE WEANING PERIOD OF THE LANGUR: THE ELEVENTH
TO THE FIFTEENTH MONTH

The months during which the infant is weaned are very stressful. In addition to physical rejection, an important part of weaning is the emotional rejection of the infant: the mother, who has been the source of protection and security, now becomes hostile and denying. The infant can no longer run to its mother when it is frightened, and is no longer protected by her when it is hurt by a peer or threatened by an adult. The infant, unaided by a protecting mother, must resolve its conflicts with other troop members. Previously the infant, when threatened or hurt, ran to touch or cling to its mother, and immediately relaxed, its movements becoming less tense and jerky and its squeals and screams stopping soon after.

Because the length of lactation in langurs is unknown, it is not possible to determine whether the 11-month-old infant depends on milk for part of its nourishment. An older infant-two often takes the mother's nipple, but holds it between its lips and does not suck or swallow (Fig. 6). It is possible that the infant nurses during the night when mother and infant sleep together.

It takes about 4 or 5 months before the infant no longer tries to nurse or to cling. Early rejection is mild. At first the mother avoids her infant by moving away, often jumping from one tree to another so the infant must maneuver long distances down to the ground and up into her tree. When the infant catches up with her, she merely turns away, and only after the infant persists in trying to nurse does she hold it off with outstretched arms. The infant immediately squeals and its movements become tense, quick, and jerky. It crouches, peers into her face, and runs around to stay in front as she turns from it.

The mother usually allows her infant to approach after it squeals and climbs over her. She alternates for weeks between temporary rejection and allowing her infant to cling. If the 12-month-old infant persists from 5 to 10 minutes, it usually succeeds in clinging, but after several months of rejection even 30 minutes of following and harassing may not wear down the mother's resistance. Weaning tantrums do not draw the attention of other adults. More irritable females threaten the mother if they are disturbed by the noise and movement, but rather than return the threat, the mother usually moves and is followed by the infant.

Severity of rejection of the infant varies among females and from day to day. A few females make little effort to reject their infant until after they have resumed estrous cycles. At the other extreme, a rare female is very positive in her rejection, and after only a month she strikes her infant whenever it approaches. Rejections are most noticeable when the troop is active, feeding, or moving, and least noticeable early or late in the day when adults rest and groom. Until the last weeks of weaning the infant usually rests beside its mother. The last members of a troop to settle down for the night are older

FIG. 6. Thirteen-month-old infant in close contact with mother.

infant-twos. Long after adults, small infants, and juveniles are quiet, there are cries from large infants whose mothers refuse to let them cling or sleep next to them.

The final stage of weaning begins after several months of partial rejection. Even the most permissive mother persists in her efforts to break the remaining ties of infant dependency. The mother's tension, increasing irritability, and flight from her infant suggest that this final period of rejection is unpleasant and strenuous for her. The daily routine of both the mother and the infant is affected by the intensity of their encounters, and antagonism between mother and infant reaches a peak toward the end of weaning. If she strikes or pushes the infant, keeping it away for several hours, it screams in extreme agitation and becomes aggressive toward her. The infant crouches, springs, throws back its head, twists from side to side, and shakes the branch or jumps up and down. It produces stacatto "ick ick ick" sounds interspersed with a high pitched whine. If it is still denied access to the breast, it slaps and jumps on its mother. Irritable females are usually also more irritable with their infants. Older multiparous females appear to reject their infants with less effort than do younger adult females, but there are exceptions. Grooming is the only conciliatory response of an adult female to her infant in the final stage of weaning. If she begins to groom her infant before it becomes tense and aggressive, this has a calming effect and at least postpones a weaning tantrum. If grooming fails to placate and the infant slaps her, she slaps it in return, grimaces, or slaps the ground. Very few females bite infants and infants are not visibly hurt.

The older infant-two usually travels with age mates when the troop moves and is separated from its mother for long periods during the day. Only if the troop is alerted suddenly does the mother allow her infant to ride. Langur infants never ride on the mother's back, and rapid locomotion on the ground or in trees is nearly impossible with the additional weight of a heavy infant.

A female may resume estrus before her infant is weaned. If estrus overlaps weaning, her rejection of the infant is stronger. Early estrous periods are short and solicitations of adult males less active than normal. The mother's sexual activity is unnoticed by the infant, and it does not try to approach her if it is playing with age mates. If, however, it is sitting nearby or trying to cling as she solicits a male, it may not leave her even while she is mounted. A few infants manage to hold the mother's nipple while she copulates, but most are pushed away. The infant may direct its aggression toward the male and slap or try to bite him, as illustrated in Fig. 7. The male's reaction is indifference unless the infant persists, in which case the male mildly threatens the infant. If the mother forms a temporary consort relationship, she keeps her infant at a distance. Consort pairs do not stay together at night, and the infant usually sleeps near its mother.

At about 14 months the infant no longer receives preferential treatment by adults in the troop and is threatened if it disturbs an adult. The active running, chasing, and wrestling of male infants bring them in contact with adult females more frequently than the relatively sub-

FIG. 7. *Mother being mounted by adult male, while her infant-two slaps the male and a juvenile male grunts and lunges at the copulating pair.*

dued play of the female infants. As a result adults threaten and chase male infants more than twice as often as they do female infants. The mother is less responsive to her infant's cries. If it is hurt or threatened, she does not always come to its rescue.

THE YOUNG JUVENILE LANGUR: THE SECOND YEAR OF LIFE

The 15-month-old juvenile is weaned and independent of its mother. When the juvenile is about 2 years old, its mother gives birth to another infant and any remaining social ties with her are completely severed. Juveniles move freely among adults, and it is no longer possible to determine the mother of any particular juvenile. At night the juvenile sleeps with other juveniles and adult females, and during the day plays, eats, and travels with its peers.

The juvenile leaves the protective group of females with young to assume an independent life. Now its protection is provided by its own alertness and that of the troop. In the next few years the juvenile learns to respond appropriately to the nuances of vocal and gestural communication characteristic of adults. It is no longer under the protection of a mother who signals changing troop tensions. Adults continue to treat the young juvenile with a degree of tolerance and come to its aid when hurt by other juveniles, but the juvenile must learn to protect itself in interactions with peers.

Male juveniles' social relationships are focused almost exclusively on age mates. Other juveniles are important to the female juvenile, but she spends hours a day with adult females and infants. The 2½- to 3-year-old female juvenile spends part of her day grooming adult females. Although she plays several hours each day, it is with other female juveniles and infant-twos rather than with male juveniles. Since female play is less active, aggression within the play group is rare. Although the female juvenile normally has little or no contact with adult males, if a male is being groomed by several adult females, a large female juvenile may hesitatingly approach and touch his fur. Female juveniles seldom approach a male and groom him voluntarily and males solicit grooming from juveniles only if adult females do not respond. When this occurs, the juvenile usually runs away before the male can sit beside her.

Play is the most important activity in the life of the male juvenile, and it is pursued with great abandon for as many as 4 or 5 hours a day. Even the most active and boisterous play is usually silent. The juvenile occasionally squeals or grunts if he falls from a tree or is hit by a play partner but, unless they are prolonged and intense, these sounds do not draw the attention of adults. After the play group is disrupted by adults or by too violent activity, it reassembles within 2 or 3 minutes. Since male play groups cover great distances rapidly, most groups stay on the edge of the troop away from adult females with young infants. Although male and female juveniles often begin to play together, males quickly form all-male groups leaving the female juveniles behind with infant-twos.

Juvenile males mount and embrace adult males approximately four times as frequently as do male infant-twos (Table 1). Unless the adult

TABLE 1

Touching, Mounting, and Embracing of
Adult Males by Male Infant-Twos and Juveniles

Form of Approach	Frequencies by Age Groups		
	Small Infant-Two	Large Infant-Two	Juvenile
Touching the hindquarters	4	19	33
Mounting	0	10	38
Embracing	0	12	61

male looks directly toward the juvenile, a mild form of threat among langurs, the juvenile is not exceptionally tense. Young adult males may prolong the embrace and wrestle with the struggling, squealing juvenile for as long as 2 minutes, but the juvenile is not hurt.

Discussion

Unique experiences occur during the life of every individual to produce a wide range of variation in expression of behavior patterns. In addition to differences among mothers and their treatment of young, the number of age mates varies with the size of the troop. In very small troops there may be only one birth a year, and the infant will be forced to play with older infants and juveniles as it grows rather than with age mates. These young mature in a different social environment from that of the larger troop.

The intense protective mother-infant bond present for the newborn is supplemented by the interest of all adult females. As the infant develops physically its social contacts expand rapidly to include the other members of the troop. By 6 months the infant forms strong ties with its age mates and depends less on its mother for food and comfort. By this time the mother breaks the few bonds the infant has not already shifted to its peers and to other adults—the infant is able to feed by itself and to participate successfully in troop life. Throughout the formative years of an older infant and juvenile's life, the peer group is an extremely important context for the development and practice of behavior essential to adult life. The male juvenile forms a social tie with adult males, whereas the female juvenile is more closely oriented to adult females and to very young infants. Adult males are not included in the social bonds of the female juvenile until she is about 3 years old and approaches to groom them. Although adult females orient themselves as mothers and protectors to all the young in the troop, it is the infant itself who must draw the attention of adult males. The social bonds which result form the basis for future relationships.

Summary

This chapter considers mother-infant relations in the common Indian langur monkey *Presbytis entellus*, the most ground-living of the leaf-eating monkeys of Asia. Although adult langurs are related within a dominance structure, dominance is not as important to langurs as to more ground-living monkeys such as baboons. In general, the daily routine and patterns of interaction within the langur group are more relaxed and less regular than similar patterns in baboons.

Between October 1958 and November 1960, I observed Indian langurs for approximately 750 hours. Observations included all parts of the day and the yearly cycle. Groups of langurs reacted differently, depending on their past experience with people, but the Orcha groups in central India and the Kaukori group in north India became used to me and I walked and sat within the troop. My presence did not noticeably affect their social relations after the first 2 to 4 weeks of observation.

The development of the langur may be divided into six stages.

1. *Newborn langur: Birth to one month.* The brown-colored newborn langur is a focus of attention to all adult and subadult females in a langur troop. Its mother allows several females to hold and carry the newborn the first day of its life. The infant is passed among several females each time it squeals or struggles. Older, multiparous females appear to have the least difficulty keeping the infant quiet and succeed in holding it longer than less experienced subadult and young adult females. The mother quickly retrieves her newborn at the first sign of fighting in the troop or the presence of a predator.

This field study suggests several elements which may serve to release maternal behavior: size, coat color, quality of movement, and vocalizations. The relative importance of any one or a combination of these elements should be assessed in a laboratory or by controlled field experimentation.

The adult male langur is indifferent to the newborn. If he accidentally frightens a newborn, he is chased by the mother and other adult females.

2. *Infant-one langur: First to third month.* The coordination of the infant improves rapidly and by the third month it moves as far as 10 feet from its mother. Adult female interest in the infant-one gradually decreases.

3. *The transition period in langur infants: Third to fifth month.* During the transition period the coat color of the infant changes from brown to light grey. The infant becomes more independent of its mother, adult female interest decreases, and the infant comes in contact with age mates in early group play. One adult female may care for several infants while other mothers are not with their infants.

4. *The infant-two langur: Fifth month to about one year.* The infant-two becomes increasingly independent of its mother. The infant eats by itself and spends several hours each day playing with age mates away from its mother. At approximately 8 months of age noticeable differences between male and female infant-twos appear. The males are more active, stronger, and larger.

The infant-two's relations with adults change. Adult females are not as tolerant of an infant-two and threaten the young monkey when it disturbs the adult. The male infant-two displays a unique mode of approach to adult males, consisting of touching the adult's hindquarters, mounting, and then embracing the adult. The female infant-two has no contact with adult males.

5. *The weaning period of the langur: The eleventh to the fifteenth month.* Weaning is a gradual process lasting from 2 to 5 months. The mother rejects her infant and does not allow it to cling or to nurse. Intensity of weaning varies among adult females but is strongest when the female resumes her estrous cycles before the infant is rejected. By 14 months of age the infant is threatened whenever it disturbs an adult and it can no longer depend on the intervention of a protecting mother for safety.

6. *The young juvenile langur: The second year of life.* In the second year of life the langur is completely independent of its mother. It spends most of the day playing with age mates and at night sleeps with other juveniles and adults. The male juvenile's social relations are focused almost exclusively on age mates, whereas the female juvenile displays interest in newborn infants. She grooms adult and subadult females and is with younger infants more than with males of her age.

References

Harlow, H. F. (1959), Love in infant monkeys. *Sci. Amer.,* **200** (6), 68–74.
Harlow, H. F., and R. R. Zimmerman (1959), Affectional responses in the infant monkey. *Science,* 130, 421–432.
Jay, Phyllis (1963), The Indian langur. In C. H. Southwick (Ed.), *Primate Social Behavior,* Princeton, New Jersey: D. Van Nostrand.
Schaller, G. B. and J. T. Emlen, Jr. (in press), The ecology and social behavior of the mountain gorilla with implications for hominid origins. In F. C. Howell (Ed.), *African Ecology and Human Evolution,* New York: Wenner-Gren Foundation for Anthropological Research; Viking Fund Publications in Anthropology.

10

mother-infant relations in
FREE-RANGING BABOONS

Irven DeVore

The field observations on which this report is based were begun in Kenya in March, 1959. After a month of reconnaissance, systematic observations were begun in the Royal Nairobi National Park on April 1. Between April 1959, and January 1, 1960, I spent more than 800 hours in close observation of baboon troops—most of this time under optimum conditions. In July I was joined by S. L. Washburn, and for the next six months observations were divided between Nairobi Park and the Amboseli Reserve (see Fig. 1). Altogether we spent more than 1200 hours in direct observation of baboons. Throughout the study, photographs were made daily with Leica M-3 cameras equipped with an assortment of lenses from 50 to 400 mm. During the early part of the study, observations were dictated into a "Dictaphone Dictet" portable tape recorder, and these tapes were transcribed each evening. Because many baboon social interactions are exceedingly complex,

The field work on which this report is based was financed by a Ford Foundation grant for the study of the evolution of human behavior. The organization and presentation of the data for this report were supported by a National Science Foundation grant for the analysis of primate behavior while the author was a Fellow of the Miller Institute for Basic Research in Science, University of California, Berkeley. The support of these foundations, and the assistance of Dr. S. L. Washburn, who collaborated in the research, are gratefully acknowledged.

305

occurring rapidly and involving several individuals, some such recording device was considered essential for the accurate collection of behavioral data. When the "Dictet" failed, shorthand notes were taken by Nancy DeVore. These methods permit the observer to record complex behavioral events at the time they occur, and without shifting his eyes from the subjects to a note pad. At the close of the study we directed a professional photographer in taking 5000 feet of 16 mm color film (DeVore and Washburn, 1960; DeVore, 1962).

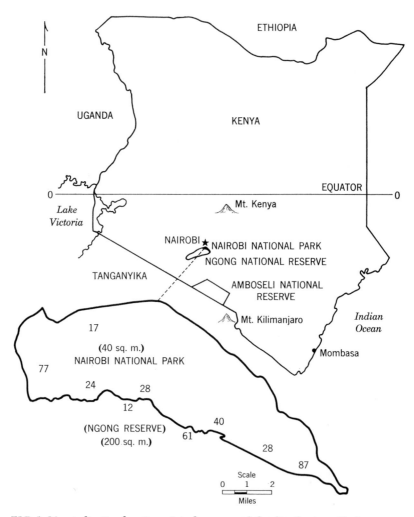

FIG. 1. *Map indicating location of study areas and the distribution of baboon troops in Nairobi Park. Numbers give size and location of troops.*

Descriptions of baboon social behavior and ecology, including troop sizes, home range, diet, sexual behavior, and relations with other animals, have appeared elsewhere (Washburn and DeVore, 1961a; Washburn and DeVore, 1961b; DeVore and Washburn, in press). Because so little was known about the behavior of free-ranging baboons at the time of the study, our aim was to describe the basic features of social life and ecology, and observations on mother-infant relations were only one part of a general program. All troops contain infants, however, and they occupy such an important position in the troop that many observations of infant behavior were recorded. Mother-infant relations described here are a composite of observations on infants in more than twenty-four baboon troops, but are based largely on observations of the nine troops in Nairobi Park, particularly the three troops in which every individual was known. The early life of only one identified infant was studied in detail. This infant, born about June 1, was a member of a troop which was observed continuously from June until mid-September, with additional observations at periodic intervals until late December. (Three additional infants were born in this same troop in early December.) In all, more than 2000 baboons were observed during the study. Age estimates were necessarily approximate; they were based on changes observed in juveniles over a 10-month period as well as on descriptions of the ontogeny of the closely related rhesus macaque.

Reactions of Nairobi Park baboons to humans vary from the very "tame" to the wild and completely unapproachable. The most rewarding observations were made on troops which had become accustomed to the proximity of persons in automobiles, but which were not so tame that the presence of humans disrupted their usual cycle of activities. We gathered most of these data while remaining inside a Land-Rover, staying within a few yards of the troop and moving with it throughout the day. This method permits the observer to keep every animal in the troop under close surveillance with a minimum of disturbance to the troop's normal activities. When these observations were compared with observations made at a distance (through binoculars) both at Amboseli and in Nairobi Park, it was clear that the presence of human observers in an automobile made very little difference in the social behavior of these semitame troops.

Observations were made on both the "olive baboon" of the Nairobi highlands and the "yellow baboon" of the Kenya lowlands and coast. The former were studied primarily in the Royal Nairobi National Park, the latter in the Amboseli Reserve. Both types appear to be only local races of a very widespread genus (Papio) of the African savanna, occurring as far north as the Tibesti Plateau and living in savanna areas all the way to the Cape in the south. Field observations by Washburn in the Rhodesias and others in South Africa (Bolwig, 1959; Hall, 1960; Hall, 1961) indicate that the social behavior of these varieties is strikingly similar over a large area of Africa despite local variation in body size and coat color. Kummer's (1957) description of the behavior of hamadryas baboons shows a basic similarity between this species and the savanna varieties of *Papio*. Together with the macaques, their close relatives in Asia, the terrestrial monkeys of the Old World form a very widespread group with fundamental similarities in morphology, body chemistry, and behavior patterns.

Baboon troops in Kenya

Although maternal care is the central subject of this chapter, the relations between mother and infant are enmeshed in a network of relationships which extends throughout the troop. A brief description of the social organization of a Kenya baboon troop will clarify the relationships described in the following discussion. Baboon troops vary in size from about 10 to 200; the average troop numbered 43 at Nairobi and 80 at Amboseli. Sexual dimorphism is especially marked in baboons: body size, canine teeth, and general robustness are all prominent in the male. As a result, adult males are completely dominant over other troop members. The pattern of dominance relationships among the adult males gives rise to a dominance hierarchy which is conservative and stable. Several of the older males may support each other in dominance interactions, forming a "central hierarchy" against the other adult males. The females and juveniles orient to these central hierarchy males, who, in turn, are the most active males in defending the troop and intervening in intratroop fights.

Dominance relations among adult female baboons are far less stable. Although some females are persistently dominant over others, stages in the reproductive cycle of each female create relative changes in her dominance status. An estrous female assumes a higher relative status when in consort with a male, and a female with a young infant is so protected by adult males that she is virtually immune from agonistic interactions. The remaining pregnant females form a comparatively stable hierarchy during the period of gestation. Although it is true that most social behavior is *ultimately* based on the dominance structure, one would be misled to think of daily life in a baboon troop as wholly or even largely aggressive and dominance oriented. Dominance status is recognized and seldom contested, and most of the day is spent in quiet feeding, resting, and grooming—activities which are only indirectly related to dominance status.

Most of Kenya is subject to seasonal rainfall, with the majority of rain falling between October and May, and the heaviest falling between January and May. In both the Nairobi and Amboseli areas most baboons give birth at the onset of the rainy season. The plants on which baboons depend for food are most abundant in the period from December to May, and probably 80% of the young are born in the months of October, November, and December, that is, just before the food supply reaches its peak. How the baboon's reproductive cycle may be influenced by ecology is not yet known; even in the Nairobi and Amboseli areas some sexual activity occurs throughout the year, and an occasional infant may be born at any time.

Although most rhesus and Japanese macaque females give birth annually, baboon females apparently give birth only every 20 to 24 months. It was not possible to capture and examine females during the study, and this interval of about 2 years is based only on observational data. Estrous swelling and sexual activities do not begin in the female until her infant is about 12 to 15 months old. A gestation period of 6 months indicates that the minimum interval between births is 18 months. In areas where birth peaks are pronounced, this minimum interval may be extended by the effect of seasonal variations on the reproductive cycle.

For whatever reasons they occur, the concentration of births in the rainy season, and the interval of 2 years between infants for each female, have important consequences for the infant baboon. Because most infants are born within a brief period, in a troop of average size these infants will develop in a group of peers. Because of the 2-year interval in births, a newborn has relatively little contact with siblings. Orientation to a peer group, not to uterine kin, is the pattern of baboon life.

Stages of infant development

By a combination of physical and behavioral criteria, the development of young baboons can be divided into six ontogenetic periods, very comparable to the six periods described by Jay for langurs (Chapter 9).

1. The newborn: birth to one month.
2. The infant-one: first to the fourth month.
3. The transition period (color change): fourth to the sixth month.
4. The infant-two: sixth month to one year.
5. The weaning period: eleventh to the fifteenth month.
6. The young juvenile: the second year of life.

The period of color change, when the infant changes from black to light brown, is the only stage marked by an obvious criterion. Other stages involve a somewhat arbitrary division of continuous growth and maturation. In addition, there is variation in the ontogenetic history of different infants, especially during the weaning period.

THE NEWBORN: BIRTH TO ONE MONTH

The newborn and the mother. Although several baboon infants were observed during the first day of life, and many more during the first week, the actual birth of an infant was never seen in the field. Gillman and Gilbert (1946) describe in some detail the birth of an infant in their laboratory colony of *Papio ursinus*. Labor lasted 7 hours and 23 minutes. In the final stages, the mother sat on the edge of a shelf in her cage, the perineum overhanging, and supported the infant's head when it appeared. As more of the body appeared, she pulled gently. Following birth the mother licked the infant clean and ate the placenta. Only 23 minutes after its head appeared, the infant was at the mother's breast.

The relation between mother and infant is constant and intense. The central nervous system of the newborn monkey is approximately the same as that of a 6-month-old human infant, and the monkey develops much faster. As a result, the newborn monkey can cling to its mother within a few hours of birth; when they sleep together at night, when the mother walks with the troop on its daily round, and when they rest during the day, the infant is always in its mother's arms or clinging to her body. A baboon troop travels 3 miles on most days, occasionally twice that far, and it would be impossible for the mother to support the infant with her arm for even a small part of that distance. Because the mother must walk with the troop when it moves, the infant's ability at birth to cling to the hair on its mother's belly is essential for survival. During a long trek, the mother may clasp one hand to the infant on her belly once every 20 or 25 steps, but after the second day this is seldom seen. When the mother rests after a long walk, she usually holds the infant against her with one hand for the first few minutes, especially if she is sitting in a tree or above the ground, allowing the infant to relax its grip and rest.

For the first week or 10 days after birth the infant continues to receive its mother's undivided attention, including constant licking, grooming, and lip-smacking (a gesture of pacification). Grooming is the most important, time-consuming activity in baboon social life, and during the first few days of life, grooming by the mother is especially intensive. Every few minutes she explores the newborn infant's body, parts its fur with her fingers, licks and nuzzles it (Fig. 2). When the infant is not nursing, the mother turns it in every position for minute inspection. During these first days, the infant does not take its mouth from the mother's nipple for more than a few seconds at a time; it is completely dependent on its mother, who devotes her entire attention to the infant.

FIG. 2. Mother grooming an infant 2 or 3 days after birth.

Vocalizations between mother and infant are very few—none, for example, comparable to the wailing of a human infant. Certain gestures by the mother begin early and are modified as the infant matures. Whenever the mother shifts her position she first presses the infant against her with a sweeping motion of her hand. When the infant is 3 weeks old, it frequently sits between the mother's legs without holding on. When the mother is ready to move, she grasps the infant, presses it to her belly, and stands up while still holding the infant against herself with one hand. Dropping her hand, she walks off without giving further support. The infant indicates that it is tired of riding by releasing the grip of its back legs and dangling by its arms beneath the mother. If the mother cannot stop, she scoops it back onto her belly with a sweep of her hand. If the troop is not moving away, however, the infant's action causes the mother to stop and sit with it in her arms for a few minutes. When the infant is still older, it often toddles on the ground under the mother as she walks slowly and eats. By this time the infant is taking almost all the initiative in grasping the mother's belly and riding, and only if the mother is suddenly startled does she clasp the infant to her as she runs farther away. Any of these actions may be accompanied by very soft cries or cooing sounds, usually by the infant. The mother makes almost no sound except that resulting from soft lip-smacking as she grooms her infant. Lip-smacking, initiated at birth by the mother, is one of the most frequent and important of all baboon gestures. For both sexes at all ages this gesture serves to reduce tension and promote tranquility in social interactions.

The newborn and other troop members. The birth of an infant alters its mother's position in the troop entirely. During estrus the female is in consort with the males for short periods only, and during pregnancy she has relatively few contacts with adult males, but during lactation the mother is very closely associated with the adult males. As soon as her infant is born the mother moves to the heart of the troop to be near the oldest and most dominant males of the central hierarchy. Regardless of her former position in the female dominance hierarchy, the mother is now virtually immune from threat by other troop members because she enjoys the complete protection of the dominant males. The males themselves are intent upon protecting the new infant, a protection which necessarily includes the infant's mother. As each new infant is born its mother joins the other new mothers in the troop's center. By December there may be more than 20 mothers with newborn infants in a troop as large as 200. These mothers are a closely knit group, sitting beside adult males, grooming the males and each other when the troop rests, and walking close beside the males when the troop moves. The less dominant males walk at the edge of the troop, providing an extra zone of protection between the mothers in the troop's center and any predators which the troop may encounter (Washburn and DeVore, 1961a).

The birth of a new infant absorbs the attention of the entire troop. From the moment the birth is discovered, the mother is continuously surrounded by the other baboons, who walk beside her and sit as close as possible when she rests. Although they are very persistent, the mother resists all attempts to touch the infant, turning her back or walking away when pressed too closely. After a week or 10 days, older juveniles and females who sit beside the mother and groom her quietly for several minutes may be allowed to reach over and touch the infant lightly. Young juveniles and older infants sit near the mother and watch her newborn intently, but are seldom able to approach the mother because of the older troop members around her. The mother tolerates this interest in her infant very uneasily, and the infant never leaves her arms. Older juvenile or subadult females appear to be most highly motivated toward the newborn infant, and the moment a mother sits one or more of these females is likely to stop whatever she is doing

FIG. 3. An adult female approaches a mother with a particular form of "presenting."

Mother-Infant Relations in Free-Ranging Baboons   313

and join the mother. The mother is approached with extreme gentleness, and, especially if the approaching female is subordinate to the mother in the female hierarchy, the hindquarters are lowered into a cringing form of "presenting" (Fig. 3).

The behavior of the other females around a new mother reflects their dominance status. During a rest period, a young female who begins grooming the mother is soon displaced by a more dominant, fully adult female, who then begins to groom the mother and to try to touch the infant. Since even females normally dominant over the mother usually approach with gestures of pacification and subordination, it is clear that the infant is a very great incentive for them. Occasionally a very dominant female may gently threaten the mother in order to touch the newborn.

Juvenile and young adult males express only perfunctory interest in the infant, but older males in the central hierarchy frequently come and touch the infant. These males are very straightforward, and the mother cringes when a male fondles her infant. (In baboons the direct approach of an adult male is very frightening to other troop members.) She does not try to avoid the males, however, and they often accompany their approach with vigorous lip-smacking. The degree of interest shown by adult males varies considerably. In the Nairobi Park troop observed over the longest period, one of the oldest males invariably joined a mother with a young infant during the daily rest periods (Fig. 4). On several occasions the most dominant males carried young

FIG. 4. The mother, an adult female, and an old adult male (right) watch a young infant closely.

infants on their bellies, as long as 20 minutes in one instance. The older males, especially those in the central hierarchy, show much more interest in infants than do young adult males. All the adult males of the troop, however, are sensitive to the slightest distress cries of a young infant and will viciously attack any human who comes between an infant and the troop. Since infants younger than 6 months are invariably near their mothers, who remove them from any danger, this protective attitude of the adult males is more clearly seen when the infants are older and may have wandered some distance from the mothers. Altmann (1960) found that adult male rhesus macaques also readily attacked him when he captured infant macaques on Santiago Island. These situations occur only when the troop is near human observers, but because of the adult males' generally protective attitude in the presence of predators, it is likely that this same attack would be launched against nonhumans also.

It is scarcely possible to overemphasize the significance of the newborn baboon for the other troop members. Of the many behavior patterns which bind the members of a baboon troop together, the presence of young infants is of foremost importance. Grooming is the most frequent and obvious expression of "friendliness" and well-being, and the grooming clusters in a baboon troop are almost always formed around the mothers with the youngest infants (Fig. 5). The protective presence of the adult males and the attraction of the infants combine to draw the other troop members toward the center of the troop.

FIG. 5. Two adult females and an infant-two form a grooming cluster with a mother (with young infant) and an adult male (background).

Mother-Infant Relations in Free-Ranging Baboons   315

The consequences of these behavior patterns of the other troop members are also very important for the mother and her infant. The protection afforded the mother while her infant is young is unique in baboon adult life and permits her to concentrate on the infant. The development of normal social patterns in the maturing infant depends heavily upon learning. The attractiveness of the young infant assures that it will always be surrounded by attentive troop members and that this learning will take place in a highly protected social environment.

THE INFANT-ONE: FIRST TO THE FOURTH MONTH

Throughout the first month of life the infant rarely leaves its mother's arms. At the end of the first month the infant begins to acknowledge the constant attention of the other troop members, and its motor development now enables it to take a few steps away from the mother. During long rest periods, while the mothers of young infants sit in a cluster, their infants begin to tentatively approach each other. The moment the infants touch, each turns and runs back to its mother, so these first contacts last only a few seconds.

The female birth cycle has important consequences for the infant's socialization. In the first place, the young baboon has no sibling relationship as such. Its mother's previous offspring is 2 years old and has severed virtually all close ties with the mother. In addition, a birth peak assures that most infants will be part of a large group of approximately the same age. Throughout the first year, the infant becomes progressively more attached to this peer group and more independent of the mother. Finally, it is the infants of the previous year, now largely independent of their mothers, who play the major role in enticing the young infants from their mothers and initiating them to group play.

During the first month, the newborn attracts the attention of the older infants (infant-twos) and young juveniles, but they are unable to get near the infant. The interest of the adult females in the young infants begins to wane during the period from 1 to 4 months, and the older infants are able to move in closer to the mothers and to play very carefully with the young infants. This play is very brief; the young infant will not leave its mother for even 2 minutes until it is 9 weeks old, and it will leave then only if it is sitting beside an adult male.

Throughout these early months the mother becomes less and less disturbed by the overtures of the other troop members toward her infant. By 2 months of age the infant is often grasped by other females and clasped to the body, although the infant quickly struggles free and returns to its mother.

Another consequence of the infant's increasing muscular coordination and independence is its first attempts to ride the mother's back. Although there seems to be considerable individual variation, most infants ride briefly on the mother's back at 5 weeks (Fig. 6). Until it is about 2 months old the infant continues to ride underneath the mother more often than on her back, and its position on her back is awkward and insecure. During these first attempts to ride the mother's back, the infant lies across it, at a 90 degree angle to her body. After the age of 2 months the infant often rides the mother's back in this crosswise fashion, but it shifts immediately to the mother's belly if it is frightened or if she is disturbed and runs. If the troop is suddenly startled, or an alarm call is heard, all the infants shift quickly to their mothers' bellies before the troop dashes away.

FIG. 6. A young infant, watching an adult male, rides its mother's back for the first time.

During this period the signals given by the mother become more elaborate. If the infant is sitting or standing beside the mother, the mother may indicate she is ready to walk away by a swift glance over her shoulder at the infant, by a slight lowering of her hindquarters, by a quick step directly away, or by some combination of these. Only if startled does the mother grab the infant and clasp it to herself. On several occasions an infant who had climbed 3 or 4 feet up into a low tree was called down when the mother wanted to move quickly away.

To call the infant, the mother thrust her face toward it, staring intently and lip-smacking loudly. The infant responded by immediately climbing down into the mother's arms.

The 3-month-old infant is mature enough, both physically and socially, to remain away from the mother for longer periods of play and exploration. It still runs back to the mother constantly, but now the time intervals are reversed: the infant is away from the mother for several minutes at a time and in her arms for only a moment. Under ordinary circumstances this time away from the mother is spent tumbling with other black infants of the same age. The infant born in June, outside the birth peak, had no other baboons its own age with which to associate. It spent rest periods crawling all over the adults gathered near its mother. Most of the adult females tolerated or even encouraged the infant's attention, but adult females well below the mother in the hierarchy were very nervous when the infant climbed up on them, and brushed the infant off as quickly and quietly as possible. Adult males, even young adult males, allow black infants to crawl all over them with impunity. Infants of this age were seen climbing over a male's face, leaping repeatedly onto his shoulders from a nearby rock, and sitting upright on a male's back—liberties which no older baboon would dare take.

Interest in the young infant by both adult males and infant-twos reaches its peak in the period from 2½ to 4 months. The infant-twos wait outside the circle of grooming adults, taking every opportunity to draw the young infant a few feet away from the adults and into quiet play. The infant is still black, but is now wandering farther and farther away from the mother, and the older adult males watch it even more

FIG. 7. The stare of an adult male (standing, center) causes a subadult female to release an infant; the infant's mother grooms herself to the left of the male.

closely. Although the infant-twos and young juveniles tumble with the black infant, these adult males are sensitive to the young infant's every sudden move. Any sign of fear or frustration by the black infant causes an adult male to stare toward the play group, sometimes grunting softly, and the offending juvenile releases the infant immediately (Fig. 7). Should the black infant cry out, the adult males leap to their feet and the juveniles scatter in terror while the young infant returns to its mother.

THE TRANSITION PERIOD: FOURTH TO THE SIXTH MONTH

At about the fourth month, baboon infants begin to change from black to brown on the belly and on the sides of the face; by the end of the sixth month, they are predominantly brown and are called "infant-two" in this classification. It is also during this 2-month period that the infant adopts the sitting-up posture while riding the mother (Fig. 8). Although all the infants have adopted this jockey style of riding

FIG. 8. A 5-month-old infant riding jockey style.

Mother-Infant Relations in Free-Ranging Baboons 319

by the sixth month, they lie face down and clutch with both hands and feet when the mothers are forced to run.

Muscular coordination and emotional independence are developing rapidly at this age. Five- and six-month-old infants wander as far as 20 feet from their mothers when the troop is feeding quietly, but run back to the mother and ride her back whenever the entire troop moves to another feeding area. Under normal circumstances the infant takes all the initiative in coming to the mother to ride; the mother merely feeds with the troop, allowing the infant to ride or not as it wishes. But if something alarms the troop, the mother crouches in an easy position for the infant to mount, and looks rapidly around while she waits for the infant to reach her. If the mother sees the infant coming she often runs to meet it, crouching again and then dashing away as the infant leaps onto her back.

During the fifth and sixth months, the infant begins to taste solid foods, although these are probably still a negligible part of its diet. Although much more independent of its mother during the day, the 6-month-old infant draws close to the mother in the late afternoon, always riding her back when the troop moves down to the sleeping trees and sleeping in her arms at night. Interest in the infant by the adult females declines rapidly during this period, and by the time the infant is solid brown, is negligible. Jealous protection by the adult males continues unabated, however, and the older infants and young juveniles increase their efforts to entice the young infants into a play group.

THE INFANT-TWO: SIXTH MONTH TO ONE YEAR

At the beginning of this period the young baboon is still very closely associated with its mother, but by the end, about 6 to 9 months later, the infant is virtually independent. Until it is 7½ months old, the infant rides on its mother's back for a large part of the day. By the end of the eighth month it spends much of the day away from the mother, but still rides its mother to the troop's sleeping trees in the evening and sleeps with her at night. Early in this period the infant tries many vegetable foods, often grasping the seed tassels of grasses as it sits astride its mother. Since the infant continues to take the mother's teats in its mouth, it is impossible to determine the end of her lactation period by observation, but judging by the mother's behavior and the infant's attention to solid foods, the infant is probably receiving little nourishment from the mother by the age of 10 months. If the mother stops to feed in one spot for very long, the infant climbs off her back and forages on its own, staying close by the mother's side during these feeding periods until it is 9 or 10 months old. If the infant finds a particularly choice morsel, this is often taken by the mother for her own consumption.

By its 8th month, the infant has little attraction for the adult females of the troop, and these sometimes threaten or even attack infants of this age. These attacks ordinarily consist of rolling the infant over and either holding it down or giving it a "token bite" on the back or at the nape of the neck. Although no infant is ever visibly wounded by such an attack, it always screeches in terror and its mother comes running to its defense. If the mother is considerably subordinate to the attacking female, her arrival has little effect, but her continued screeches bring an adult male running and all involved scatter. Again it is the oldest males of the central hierarchy, who have been near the infants since birth, who are the most active males in breaking up such squabbles and protecting the infants. The mother continues to intercede for her infant until it is 2 years old, that is, until her next infant is born, but males usually protect infants well into the infants' 3rd year.

Orientation to peer group. As the tie between mother and infant weakens, the infants spend more and more time with their peer group, playing and resting together, and returning to their mothers only at dusk. This group of older infants stays very near the males of the central hierarchy during the day, even though their mothers are staying farther from the center of the troop now and may be separated from their infants by 30 yards. By the end of the 10th month the infant, who until now has depended largely upon its mother for both companionship and protection, looks to its peers for companionship and to the adult males for protection.

The infants play together as the troop walks along, groom each other (as well as their mothers and the adult males) when the troop rests, and join in much more energetic and elaborate play patterns than they did in previous weeks. Running, chasing, tumbling, nipping, and tail-pulling may now last as long as 10 minutes without interruption. Along with this elaboration of social behavior the infants also extend the variety of types of play areas. Until the 8th or 9th month, play is usually confined to flat areas on the plain or under trees. Now the infants seek piles of rocks, low tree limbs, hanging vines, and stream beds, extending their play into a third dimension. Before this age, play is characteristically based on interpersonal contacts; now the physical environment is exploited as well. Young juvenile baboons are no longer kept away from the infants by the adults and frequently join the infant play groups. After a few moments, however, the rougher play of the juveniles usually breaks up the infant play group and the infants withdraw again.

Orientation to adult males. Throughout this description of mother-infant relations in the baboon it has been repeatedly stressed that the relationship of the infant to the adult males is important at every stage of the infant's maturation. A relationship between an infant-two female and an adult male—observed over a 2-month period—illustrates how very close this relationship can become. When first seen, this infant had a disease of the face and scalp which grew steadily worse until the entire top of her skull was exposed. Apparently she was constantly hungry, with the result that she was as bold as an adult male in seeking access to favored feeding spots. When food was offered to the troop, she would run up to the food with the two most dominant males (who together formed the central hierarchy of this troop) and take food from beside them—utterly atypical behavior for a baboon. It soon became

FIG. 9. Female infant takes offered food by the side of beta male (alpha male in foreground and gamma male threatening in background).

clear that she was able to take these liberties only because she enjoyed the complete protection of the older, "beta male", of the dominant pair. The sick infant was beta's constant companion, grooming him through the day, walking in his shadow when the troop moved, and sleeping beside him in the trees at night (Fig. 9). She even stayed beside him while he was in consort with an estrous female. This close association meant virtual ostracism from the other troop members, who rarely came near the infant except to try to threaten her away from her favored position by the adult male. In this respect she was treated much like a subordinate adult female who stays close to her consort during estrus.

When observations were begun on this troop, it contained two very emaciated adult females who disappeared within a few days. One of these females was apparently the sick infant's mother. That the infant was "adopted," not by another adult female, but by the oldest adult male in the troop, illustrates two important facets of the infant-two's relationships in the troop. By the age of 9 months, only an infant's mother, among the adult females, treats the infant in a protective and permissive manner. Instead, adult females begin to set limits on behavior which they will tolerate, and when these limits are exceeded, the infant is frequently rebuffed or chastised by a mild attack. Adult males, on the other hand, remain completely tolerant and protective (Fig. 10). Under these circumstances it is not surprising that an infant of this age became attached to an adult male rather than to another female. This example is a measure of the potential strength of the bond between adult males and infants. This male provided the constant care and protection ordinarily associated with maternal behavior. How frequently such behavior can occur could be checked experimentally. Zuckerman describes what appears to be a very similar relationship between an infant and an adult male hamadryas baboon in the London Zoo colony after the death of the infant's mother (1932, pp. 261-262). Itani (1959, printed in 1962) has described in detail a routinized form of paternal care in Japanese macaques during the birth season. A close tie between individual adult males and individual infants was commonly formed in 3 of the 18 troops being studied. It was rare in 7 more and absent in the remaining 8. Among the monkeys at Takasakiyama, 14 of the 18 dominant males exhibited this behavior. The evidence from baboons and Japanese macaques suggests that social bonds between adult males and infants are very strong in these terrestrial species, in striking contrast to the weak bonds between infants and adult males in more arboreal species (for example, langurs, Chapter 9).

FIG. 10. *Five young juveniles huddle against an adult male (peering over them).*

THE WEANING PERIOD: ELEVENTH TO THE FIFTEENTH MONTH

Shortly after the 9th or 10th month, on the average, the baboon infant undergoes the experience of rejection by the mother—rejection both from taking her nipple and from riding her back. There is wide variation in the time at which rejection occurs, and this period is influenced by many circumstances, including the size of the infant (about this time the infant becomes burdensome to carry) and the temperament of both the mother and her infant. But the most important single cause is the cessation of lactation, which is signaled by a concomitant resumption of turgescence in the mother's sexual skin. Since the female does not go through her normal cycles of sexual skin swelling during pregnancy or lactation, the end of lactation can be crudely estimated by records of the first postpartum swelling in the female. In their laboratory baboon colony, Gilbert and Gillman found that "In the majority of animals, amenorrhoea persists for at least five months; as long as ten months may elapse before the sex skin displays the first signs of renewed turgescence" (1951, p. 118).

The period during which the mother resumes her sexual skin swelling brings about another significant change in her social behavior. For more than a year she has not been receptive to adult males, but as her cycles resume and her swelling increases she becomes receptive, and the males begin to take a sexual interest in her again. Not only is most sexual behavior in baboons incompatible with infant care, but estrus in the female also increases her activity and her irritability. As her sexual skin swelling increases, the mother more actively repulses her infant's attempts to ride or nurse. During her first few monthly cycles these rejections by the mother seem to make the infant more anxious than ever to be in her arms, to hold her nipple in its mouth, and to ride her back to the sleeping trees. When the female is at the peak of her swelling (for about 1 week in a 35-day cycle) she is constantly with adult males and rarely near her infant, but as her swelling subsides she often accepts the infant again (Fig. 11).

FIG. 11. A female is groomed by an adult male while her infant takes her nipple.

During these months of weaning it is the infant who takes the initiative in the mother-infant relationship. The infant follows the mother and grooms her often; the mother seems neutral toward her infant. When the mother forcefully rejects the infant, by brushing it off her back, holding it away from her breast, or by slapping and biting it, the infant gives a cry of fear and frustration which is heard at no other period in baboon life. Although part of this cry was indistinguishable (by the observer) from the distress cry which always brings an adult male to the scene, when given in this context the cry never attracts the attention of the other baboons. When a mother rejects her infant at dusk, the time of day when the infants ordinarily return to their mothers, the infant may go frantically from one adult to another, including the adult males, giving "frustration cries" before each adult. Even during this period the mother will always come to the aid of her infant if it is attacked by another female or juvenile, but if its cries are only from frustration, the mother ignores it.

Effect of mother's status on her infant. Most infants seem to pass through this weaning period rather smoothly, but some definitely do not. Even in the field it is possible to recognize individual differences in the personality of infants by the age of 6 months, and the weaning period emphasizes these differences. There seemed to be a high correlation between the amount of frustration and "insecurity" displayed by an infant and its mother's position in the female dominance hierarchy. Infants whose mothers were near the bottom of the hierarchy gave alarm cries more often and made more frequent demands on their mothers. These infants nursed and tried to ride their mothers' backs many weeks after their peers had ceased doing either. One especially "insecure" infant succeeded in riding its mother's back at the age of

FIG. 12. A frightened older infant riding on mother's back.

Maternal Behavior in Mammals

more than a year, when it was too heavy to be carried any distance by her (Fig. 12).

In general, the year-old infant, even though it is away from the mother's side most of the day, shows that it is still very sensitive to her emotional states. Anything which upsets the mother, such as a serious fight among the females or the flight of the troop from danger, also upsets the infant; it runs to her and stays with her until the crisis is past. Because of this close bond, it is easy to understand that the infant of an especially subordinate female is subjected to repeated emotional shock when its mother must yield continuously before the threats of other females. In addition, mothers who bear the constant brunt of aggressive dominance by the other females seem to be more short-tempered and less responsive to their infants. These experiences of the infant are apparently compounded and intensified by the period of weaning and rejection, giving rise to the observable differences in behavior during this period. Hamburg (in press) has described some of the "endocrine responses to disruption of personally-crucial relationships" in human patients.[1]

By analogy, it is likely that the infants of dominant females are affected by the constant attitude of preeminence displayed by their mothers. In a brief field study it is impossible to link older infants and young juveniles to their mothers with certainty, but observations of an adult female consistently supporting a young juvenile in dominance interactions suggest the remnants of the mother-infant bond. Through stereotyped interactions, in which a juvenile "enlists the support" of an adult female against a third troop member, it is possible for a juvenile to maintain temporary dominance over an otherwise superior animal. For this to be successful, however, the "mother" must herself be dominant over the third party. The dominance status of the mother thus determines the frequency of successful assertions of dominance by the juvenile. Workers at the Japan Monkey Centre, where the life history of many individual monkeys has been kept for nearly a decade, describe the effect of the mother's dominance status on her offspring. Only the

---

[1] In concluding the discussion he says: "Disruption of inter-individual bonds may have profound consequences in carbohydrate, protein, fat, electrolyte and water metabolism, and on crucial functions of the circulation. Such disruption is felt as deeply unpleasant, and an extraordinary variety of coping behavior patterns may be mobilized to restore acceptance, affection and mutual respect. Perhaps serious threat to a key relationship may be as much an emergency in psychophysiologic terms as threat of attack by a predator."

infants of the most dominant females grow up in the troop's center. Here the infants apparently learn, from the adults around them, a domineering attitude toward peripheral troop members, and are more likely to adopt roles of leadership and dominance in adult life (Imanishi, 1960).

This period in the young baboon's development begins with the experience of weaning and ends with the birth of its mother's new infant. Most of this period is spent in the young juvenile play group, away from any adult when the troop is resting (the favorite play period for young baboons), and walking close to the males of the central hierarchy when the troop moves. By the 18th month the young juvenile is so seldom near its mother that it is impossible for an observer to associate the mothers and their offspring unless some crisis arises in the troop. A prolonged fight among the adults or a serious attack upon the juvenile will bring the mother to the juvenile's defense, but both these occurrences are rare. If danger threatens the troop, the juveniles flee to the adult males, not to their mothers. The young juveniles groom the adult males, their mothers, and each other with about equal frequency. The juvenile's mother, now pregnant again, is much more active in the female dominance hierarchy than she has been for many months.

By the time the juvenile is 2 years old its mother has given birth again, and any remaining emotional tie to the mother appears to be severed. It is possible that consistent pairings of adult males and estrous females, or of adult females with each other, are the carryovers from earlier mother-infant relations, but this could not be proved during a brief field study. At 2 years of age the juvenile is with its peer group most of the day. Adult males continue to protect young juveniles, but the juveniles have now learned that they can no longer behave with impunity around adult males. In fact, the adult males are now protecting a new group of newborn infants from the juveniles' rough play.

Patterns of play. Constant peer-group play is the most characteristic activity of this age (2 to 3 years). The young juvenile begins to play at dawn, plays as the troop moves to a feeding place, plays frequently during the feeding periods, and plays almost constantly during rest periods. If a large troop remains in one spot very long, as many as four different play groups may form. Ranging from the cluster of black infants inside the circle formed by their mothers to a boisterous group of older juveniles at the troop's edge, these four play groups represent the infants born during the four preceding annual birth peaks. Harlow and Harlow (1962) have been able to distinguish the play of males from females at about 2 months of age in laboratory rhesus monkeys. This dichotomy is apparent in the play of baboons by the age of 2 years, even in the field. Juvenile male baboons play more roughly and longer; juvenile females groom more frequently and spend more time with the newborn infants in the troop.

Play is even more energetic at this age, but the play remains quiet. Any loud or prolonged noise from the juveniles brings a grunting threat from the adult males and play is interrupted. This same interference in juvenile play by the adult male has been recorded for howling monkeys (Carpenter, 1934), but in langurs (Chapter 9) it is the adult females who thus interfere. In young juvenile baboons the play activity is cyclical: it becomes more and more vigorous until the females drop out. Juvenile males continue until one cries out; adults then break up the play and, after several minutes of quiet, play is resumed.

Demography and socialization. There are demographic variables in normal baboon troops which can considerably affect the socialization experience of the young infant and juvenile. One of the most obvious variables is group size. In a very small troop there may be only one or two infants born each year; in a large troop more than twenty. Play groups tend to build up to a size of at least six or eight individuals, and young infants without a peer group this large will start to play with older infants and young juveniles at an early age. The same is true for infants born outside the annual birth peak, no matter how large the troop. Because these infants are playing with older baboons, they are frightened or hurt more often. This means that adult males will intervene on behalf of these infants much more often than would be necessary if they were playing only with infants of the same age. Whether this frequent contact with the adult male consoles or frightens the infant depends to some extent on the social position of its mother. The offspring of a dominant female is accustomed early in life to the superior position of its mother, and frequent contact with a dominant male would not appear to frighten it as much as it does the offspring of a subordinate female.

Discussion

The history of the maturation of the infant in a baboon troop during its first 30 months of life begins with the intensive mother-infant bond in a very protected social environment, and, through a series of increasing contacts with other baboons, extends outward to a widening circle of troop members. The close companionship and protection of the mother are supplanted by close ties with juvenile peers and by the protection of the adult males. By the time the infant is rejected by the mother it is capable of feeding on its own and is socially mature enough to fit into the pattern of troop life. At about 30 months of age its relations with the adult males shift—no longer the object of very tolerant protection it now enters a relationship of dominance-subordination. By this time it is well-developed enough to keep up easily with the troop on its own, and to sense and flee from danger. At this age it withdraws even more into its peer group and begins to pattern its behavior on the dominance-subordination relationships developing there. In this way the infant passes from the reflexive, dependent period of the neonate, through various combinations of affectional patterns, to a position of independence and individuality within the troop structure.

COMPARISON BETWEEN BABOONS AND LANGURS

The important features of the ontogeny of baboon infants are most clearly seen when contrasted with another monkey species, such as langurs (Chapter 9). A comparison between the two species reveals great similarity in many fundamentals. Both species live in social groups in which adults are organized in dominance hierarchies and whose membership is stable throughout the year. Both the daily round and the annual cycle of activities are very similar. But there are important differences. In baboons the troop is considerably larger, sexual dimorphism is more pronounced, and there are no individuals living outside the troop. These differences are no doubt closely related to the baboon adaptation to life on the ground, where predator pressure is more constant than it is for the more arboreal langur.

Patterns of physical and social development in the infant are also much the same. In both species the infant is very attractive to the other troop members and begins life in a secure, highly protected environment. Other events in the infant's first year—independent locomotion, change in coat color, orientation to a peer group, weaning, and independence from the mother—also occur in the same order and at approximately the same time (Fig. 13). In both species it is the resumption of the mother's sexual activity which terminates the close mother-infant bond. Because births are spaced about 2 years apart, and occur during an annual birth peak, the early experience of both baboon and langur infants is conditioned by a peer group rather than by older siblings.

On the other hand, there are striking differences in the details of

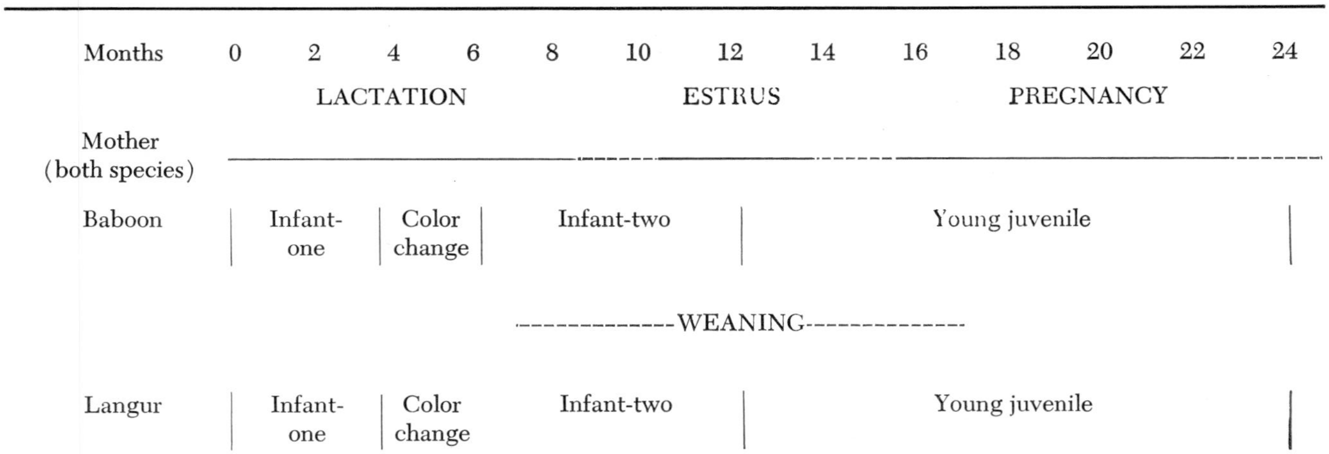

Months 0 2 4 6 8 10 12 14 16 18 20 22 24

Mother (both species) LACTATION ESTRUS PREGNANCY

Baboon Infant-one | Color change Infant-two Young juvenile

Langur Infant-one | Color change Infant-two ------WEANING------ Young juvenile

FIG. 13. The development of baboon and langur infants in relation to stages in the mother's reproductive cycle.

baboon and langur infant life. Perhaps the greatest contrast concerns the relationship between the adult male and the infant. For the baboon this relationship is very close at birth and steadily increases in importance, until by the middle of the second year the young baboon is more closely associated with the adult males of the troop than with its own mother. The infant langur, however, has no contact with adult males at all until it is 8 months old. At this age the infant-two male tensely appoaches adult males for the first time. Although the adult males are tolerant and restrained in these interactions, they are not attentive to the infant langur in any other situation. A female langur has almost no contact with adult males until she is about 3 years old, when she begins to include them among the animals she will groom.

The experience of the newborn infant with the adult females of the troop is also quite different. The newborn baboon does not ordinarily leave its mother's arms during the first month, and the baboon mother will not allow other troop members even to touch her infant for the first week. But the langur newborn is passed from one adult female to another, and may be carried as far as 75 feet from its mother on the day of birth. It is also these adult females who protect the young langur, even chasing adult male langurs who startle the infants. But although it is achieved in different ways, the infant in both species matures in a protected social environment.

Other differences in infant development between baboons and langurs are related to their different locomotor and ecological adaptations. Infant langurs, for example, begin to play in trees at an age when this behavior is still rare in baboons. The abundance of tender, leafy foods available to the infant langur makes it possible for the langur to eat solid food at an earlier age. In these ways morphology, ecological adaptation, and the behavior of the adults combine to mold the maturing infant into a species-specific way of life.

It is also clear, however, that within the spectrum of behavior patterns appropriate for the adult of either species there is wide latitude for individual expression. Unique influences and experiences occur during the life of every infant. Variations in the mother's reproductive physiology, her temperament, and her experience with previous offspring all affect the infant's early life. The dominance status of the mother may strongly influence the development and direction of the infant's social relationships. In baboons, the troop itself may be one in which dominance relations are unstable and there are frequent fights, or one in which fighting is rare. The troop may be small and the infant may never experience the social relations of a large peer group. These different life experiences must have a profound effect on the maturation of the infant, with resulting variations in adult behavior. It is not possible to more than suggest the nature of these social and environmental influences on socialization from observations made during a brief field study. To understand them will require the close coordination of detailed field observations with laboratory experiments.

Summary

This report is based on a 10-month field study of baboons in Kenya during 1959. Although more than 2000 baboons were observed, the description of mother-infant relations is based largely on three troops in which every individual was known. These troops were accustomed to persons in automobiles and observations could be made at close range.

The development of the infant baboon is divided into six periods.

The newborn: Birth to one month. The mother of a newborn infant avoids direct contact with other troop members but stays near the protective adult males of the central hierarchy. The intense relationship between the mother and her newborn includes many behavior patterns, such as grooming and lip-smacking, which are important tranquilizing gestures in adult life. The mother and infant are under the constant protection of the adult males both from danger outside the troop and from aggression within the troop. As a result, the mother is not subject to most dominance interactions and is free to satisfy the needs of her infant. Young infants are an attractive stimulus to other troop members, and their presence in the troop has an integrating effect.

The infant-one: First to the fourth month. An annual birth peak provides most infants with a large peer group. Older infants and young juveniles draw the infant-one into play, but most of the infant's time is spent with other infants its own age. The gathering of mothers in the troop's center provides a context for play among these infant-ones. Interest by other troop members reaches its peak during this period.

The transition period: Fourth to the sixth month. During this period the infant's fur changes from black to brown and it begins to ride its mother's back in a sitting-up posture. The infant may wander as far as 20 feet from its mother and begins to eat some solid food.

The infant-two: Sixth month to one year. This is a period of increasing independence from the mother. Adult females (except the mother) begin to rebuff the infant, but the permissive attitude of the adult males continues. By the end of the tenth month, the infant spends more time in a play group of peers than with its mother. This play group stays near the dominant, central hierarchy males, and special circumstances can produce a very close association between an infant and an adult male.

The weaning period: Eleventh to the fifteenth month. With the cessation of lactation and the resumption of estrous cycles, the mother more vigorously prevents the infant from taking her nipple and from riding her back. Some infants pass through this stage more easily than others; the infants of mothers of low status appear to have the most difficulty. There is evidence that the status of the mother may affect the status of her offspring as adults.

The young juvenile: The second year of life. By the end of this period almost all ties to the mother have been broken, and the mother is caring for a newborn. In a crisis young juveniles are more likely to seek out adult males than their mothers. Constant play with peers is characteristic of this age. Demographic factors influence the experience of the juvenile during this formative age. By about 30 months of age, the juvenile is part of the troop dominance hierarchy and gets little preferential treatment from adult males.

A comparison of the development of baboon and langur infants reveals behavior patterns which are broadly similar but which contrast in detail. The treatment of the neonate by adult females and the relationship between the maturing infant and the adult males differ markedly in the two species. Many of these differences are related to ecological adaptations, reflecting the contrast between a terrestrial and a more arboreal species. In addition, unique experiences during the maturation of infants of both species contribute to the individuality of adult behavior.

References

Altmann, S. A. (1960), A field study of the sociobiology of rhesus monkeys, *Macaca mulatta.* Unpublished doctoral dissertation, Harvard University.
Bolwig, N. (1959), A study of the behaviour of the Chacma baboon, *Papio ursinus. Behaviour,* **14,** 136–163.
Carpenter, C. R. (1934), A field study of the behavior and social relations of howling monkeys. *Comp. Psychol. Monogr.,* **10** No. 2 (whole No. 48).
DeVore, I. (1962), Baboon ecology, 16 mm sound, color film, University of California at Berkeley.
DeVore, I., and S. L. Washburn (1960), Baboon behavior, 16 mm sound, color film, University of California at Berkeley.

DeVore, I., and S. L. Washburn (in press), Baboon ecology and human evolution. In F. C. Howell (Ed.), *African Ecology and Human Evolution,* New York: Wenner-Gren Foundation for Anthropological Research; Viking Fund Publications in Anthropology.

Gilbert, Christine, and J. Gillman (1951), Pregnancy in the baboon *Papio ursinus. S. Afr. J. Med. Sci.,* **16,** 115–124.

Gillman, J., and Christine Gilbert (1946), The reproductive cycle of the Chacma baboon (*Papio ursinus*) with special reference to the problems of menstrual irregularities as assessed by the behaviour of the sex skin. *S. Afr. J. med. Sci.,* **11,** (Biol. Suppl.) 1–54.

Hall, K. R. L. (1960), Social vigilance behaviour of the Chacma baboon, *Papio ursinus. Behaviour,* **16,** 261–294.

Hall, K. R. L. (1961), Feeding habits of the Chacma baboon. *Advanc. Sci.,* **17,** 559–567.

Hamburg, D. A. (in press), Emotions in perspective of human evolution. In P. Knapp (Ed.), *Expression of Emotions in Man,* New York: International Universities Press.

Harlow, H. F., and Margaret K. Harlow (1962), Social deprivation in monkeys. *Sci. Amer.,* **207** (5), 136-146.

Imanishi, Kinji (1960), Social organization of subhuman primates in their natural habitat. *Curr. Anthrop.,* **1,** 393–407.

Itani, J. (1959, printed in 1962), Paternal care in the wild Japanese monkey, *Macaca fuscata fuscata. Primates, the Journal of Primatology,* **2** (1) 61–93.

Kummer, H. (1957), Soziales Verhalten einer Mantelpavian-Gruppe. *Schweiz. Z. Psychol.,* **33,** 1–91.

Washburn, S. L., and I. DeVore (1961a), The social life of baboons. *Sci. Amer.,* **204** (6) 62–71.

Washburn, S. L., and I. DeVore (1961b), Social behavior of baboons and early Man. In S. L. Washburn (Ed.), *Social Life of Early Man,* New York: Wenner-Gren Foundation for Anthropological Research; Viking Fund Publications in Anthropology, **31.**

Zuckerman, S. (1932), *The Social Life of Monkeys and Apes,* London: Kegan Paul, Trench, Trubner and Co.

author index

The page numbers in italics indicate that the author is listed in the References at the end of the chapter.

Collias, N. E., 209, 212, 213, 217, 218, 229
Conley, D., 243
Connon, Helen, 62, 92
Cook, R. C., 207, 230
Coomans, H. E., 48
Cooper, J. B., 123, 125, 126, 127, 131, 137, 141, 143, 165
Cowie, A. T., 46, 50, 55, 175, 202
Crary, D. D., 98, 99, 101, 102, 103, 116, 120, 121
Cross, B. A., 47, 49, 55, 202
Cross, H. A., 271, 281
Cupps, P. T., 165, 166
Curran, R. H., 99, 100, 104, 120

Daniels, T. W., 249, 253
Darling, F. F., 2, 4, 6, 251, 253
Davis, R. B., 3, 6
Davis, W. B., 206, 219, 230
Dawson, W. M., 207, 231
Denenberg, V. H., 67, 91, 93, 98, 99, 102, 103, 104, 105, 106, 108, 115, 118, 120, 121, 216, 230
Denniston, R. H., II., 249, 253
Dethier, V. G., 10, 55
DeVore, I., 6, 306, 307, 313, 334, 335
de Vos, A., 237, 253
Dice, L. R., 63, 64, 66, 80, 85, 91
Dieterlen, F., 4, 7
Dilger, W. C., 227, 230
Drake, J. D., 63, 91
Dubois, Edna, 202
Dunn, Alta B., 223, 230
Dutt, R. H., 205, 230

Eckert, J. F., 47, 56
Eckstein, P., 125, 165
Ederstrom, H. E., 172, 192, 202
Edwards, R. L., 63, 91
Eibl-Eibesfeldt, I., 2, 7, 9, 25, 47, 49, 55
Eleftheriou, B. E., 67, 87, 92
Emlen, J. T., Jr., 282, 304
Evans, F. C., 64, 91
Ewer, R. F., 143, 144, 151, 165, 178, 199, 202

Failla, M. L., 122, 168
Farber, M., 56
Farooq, A., 98, 109, 111, 121
Fitch, H. S., 63, 91
Folley, S. J., 46, 49, 50, 55, 202
Foss, B. M., 167
Foster, Dorothy D., 86, 87, 91
Frank, A. H., 205, 231
Fraps, R. N., 205, 231
Fraser, A., 211, 230
Fredericson, E., 190, 202
Frisch, O. v., 3, 7, 203, 230
Frommer, G. P., 99, 120, 216, 230
Fuchs, Stephanie S., 52, 56

Gantt, W. H., 231
Garrigus, U. S., 204, 232
Gault, W. T., 66, 91
Gibson, E. J., 209, 212, 230
Gilbert, Christine, 310, 324, 335
Gill, J. C., 176, 202
Gillman, J., 310, 324, 335
Goodnight, C. J., 4, 7
Goodpaster, W. W., 63, 92
Goodwin, R. F. W., 47, 55
Gordon, M., 11, 55
Grassé, P. P., 55, 166, 167
Gregory, D. W., 207, 232
Günther, S., 123, 166
Gurney, Nancy, 202

Hafez, E. S. E., 121, 167
Hafter, E., 108, 120
Hain, Annie M., 123, 166
Hall, E. R., 61, 63, 73, 92
Hall, K. R. L., 308, 335
Hall, Kathleen, 123, 166
Hamburg, D. A., 327, 335
Hammond, J., 205, 230
Hansen, E. W., 256, 257, 281
Hansen, R. M., 66, 73, 92
Harlow, H. F., 6, 165, 204, 230, 256, 259, 271, 278, 281, 282, 329, 304, 335
Harlow, Margaret K., 329, 335
Harris, G. W., 49, 55, 123, 166, 202
Harrop, A. E., 170, 202
Hartman, C. G., 2, 7
Hayne, D. W., 62, 92

Ottinger, D. R., *91*

Parkes, A. S., *165*
Peixoto, A. M., 205, *230*
Petropolus, S. F., 104, *120*
Pfaffmann, C., 145, *166*
Phillips, R. W., 205, 207, *231*
Pitts, W. H., 63, *91*
Pournelle, G. H., 66, 67, *93*
Prechtl, H., 144, *166*
Pruitt, W. O., Jr., 245, *253*

Quast, J. C., 63, *93*
Quilligan, E. J., 49, *56*

Racadot, J., 123, *167*
Rainey, D. G., 63, *93*
Rasmussen, K., 207, *231*
Rawson, K. S., 71, *93*
Ressler, R. H., 87, *93*
Rethlingshafer, D. A., *92*
Richardson, K. C., *202*
Richmond, J. B., 211, 213, 214, 217, 223, 229, *230,*
Richter, C. P., 46, 47, *54, 56,* 124, *165*
Riddle, O., 123, *167*
Riess, B. F., 89, *93*
Robson, J. M., 113, *120*
Rosenblatt, J. S., 9, 15, 21, 44, *56,* 122, 124, 141, 144, 145, 146, 150, 153, 156, *167, 168*
Ross, S., 89, *93,* 98, 99, 101, 104, 106, 108, 114, 115, 116, 117, *120, 121,* 216, *230*
Rothchild, I., 38, 49, *56,* 123, *167*
Rowell, Thelma E., 6, 7, 43, *56*
Ryser, F. A., 62, *93*

Sawin, P. B., *93,* 98, 99, 100, 101, 102, 103, 104, 106, 108, 110, 115, 116, *120, 121,* 216, *230*
Schaffner, B., *229*
Schaller, G. B., 282, *304*
Schleidt, W. M., 114, *166*
Schloeth, R., 243, *253*
Schneirla, T. C., 9, 15, 21, 44, *56,* 122, 124, 141, 144, 145, 146, 150, 153, 154, 156, *167, 168*

Schofield, Brenda M., 113, *120*
Schorger, A. W., 63, *93*
Scott, J. P., 89, *93,* 171, 178, 186, 190, 202, 213, 217, 218, 221, 223, *231,* 233, *253*
Scott, Patricia P., 124, 125, *168*
Seay, B., 256, 270, 272, 273, *281*
Seitz, P. F. D., 89, *93*
Sellars, R. W., *56*
Selye, H., 49, *57*
Senn, M. J. E., *167*
Sgouris, J. T., 107, *120*
Sheard, Norah M., 1, 7, 9, 28, 41, 45, 48, *57,* 204, *232*
Sheldon, W. G., 219, *231*
Short, H. L., 3, *6*
Siegel, S., 172, *202*
Silveira, S., 205, *230*
Silver, I. A., 47, *55*
Simpson, E. C., 205, *230*
Slijper, E. J., 46, *57*
Smith, W. P., 73, *93*
Southwick, C. H., *304*
Spencer, C. C., 204, 206, 207, 219, *231*
Spencer, C. J., 219, *232*
Steinberg, June, 47, *57*
Stephens, M. W., *91*
Stevens, S. S., *54, 229*
Steyn, T. J., 143, *168*
Stone, C. P., 1, 7, 9, 25, 47, *57*
Sturman-Hulbe, Mary, 1, 7, 9, 25, *57*
Sumner, F. B., 62, *93*
Svihla, A., 67, 83, *93*
Sykes, J. F., 205, *232*

Talwalker, P. K., 123, *166*
Terman, C. R., 66
Thomson, W., 176, *202*
Thorne, O., 64, *93*
Tietz, Esther G., 108, *121*
Tinklepaugh, O. L., 1, 7
Tobach, Ethel, 15, 122, 127, 141, *168*
Tomilin, M. I., 2, 7
Tribe, D. E., 206, *232*
Turkewitz, G., 9, 21, *56,* 122, 141, 145, 146, 150, 156, *167, 168*
Turner, C. W., 49, 50, *56*

Uyldert, Ina, 53, *57*

Villegas, V., 207, *232*

Wallace, L. R., 207, 208, 209, 227, *232*
Warden, C. J., 1, 7
Warwick, E. J., 205, *232*
Washburn, S. L., 305, 306, 307, 308, 313, *334, 335*
Waters, R. H., *92*, 146, *165*
Wells, E. F. V., 125, 148, *168*
Welker, W. I., 195, *202*
Weston, E., 148, 153, *168*
Wiesner, B. P., 1, 7, 9, 28, 41, 45, 48, 57, 204, *232*
Williams, S. M., 204, *232*
Williams, W. L., 49, *55*
Willman, J. P., 205, 223, *232*
Wilson, Charis, 148, 153, *168*
Wilson, E. D., 98, *121*
Wilson, J. F., 207, *232*

Wilson, P. N., 205, 219, *232*
Wislocki, G. B., 137, *168*
Withrow, R. B., *93*
Wodinsky, J., 146, 150, 156, *167, 168*
Woolsey, C. N., *165*
Worden, A. H., 98, 99, *121*
Wortis, J., *231*
Wortis, R. P., 89, *92*

Yeates, N. T. M., 207, *232*
Yerkes, R. M., 2, 7
Young, W. C., 7, 9, *55, 57, 92, 166,* 205, *232*

Zarrow, M. X., 49, *57*, 98, 99, 106, 108, 112, 115, *120, 121*
Zimmerman, R. R., 282, *304*
Zuckerman, S., 125, *165*, 323, *335*

subject index

Goat, 99, 203–232
Gorilla, 282, 304
Grooming, 19, 258, 260, 263, 264, 270,
    285–288, 292, 296, 299, 302,
    304, 310–315, 321, 325, 333
  in female juveniles, 304
  of mother by other animals, 288, 313–
    314
  of observer by langurs, 285
  by young, 296, 302, 321
  of young by other animals, 292, 296
    by mother, 258, 260, 263, 264,
    286–287, 310, 311, 312, 333
Guinea pig, 3

Hair loosening in rabbit, 98, 107–111,
    119
Hair plucking in rabbit, 98, 102, 107,
    116
Hamster, 2, 6, 7, 43
Hare, 60
Heeling response in moose and elk, 238–
    240, 244–245, 250–252
Hen, 243
Herding in the dog, 189, 199, 201
Holding of infant by mother, 264, 286,
    287, 289, 291, 310, 312
Home site of kittens, 143–146
Hormonal processes in maternal be-
    havior, 47, 49, 51–54, 99, 106–
    114, 119, 123–124, 126, 161,
    205, 278–279
  neurohormonal control, 54, 123, 124,
    126, 161
Horse, 243
Human infant, 59, 217, 310

Imprinting, 217, 238, 239, 245
Inspection of infants by mother, 286,
    287, 290, 310, 311
Interspecies rearing, see Separation,
    adoption or fostering
Isolation studies in the cat, see Separa-
    tion

Japanese macaque, 267, 309, 323

Lactation, 47, 49–51, 53, 99, 106–108,
    119, 123, 124, 126, 260, 269,
    297, 320, 331, 334

Lactation, duration, 99, 260, 297, 320
  effect of contact, 269
  of nipple stimulation, 49
  hormonal control, 49, 106–107
  see also Nursing
Langur, 6, 266, 282–304, 309, 323,
    329, 330, 332, 334
Licking, of fetal membranes by mother,
    12, 18, 124, 130, 212
  of mother by young, 242–243
  of young by mother, 12, 13–14, 17,
    18–19, 21, 48, 51, 54, 67, 123,
    124, 128, 130, 131, 135–138,
    141–143, 145, 148, 158, 162,
    172, 179–182, 189, 197, 199, 201,
    207, 209, 211, 228, 236, 242,
    245, 248, 252, 286, 310–311
    decrease in frequency, 179
    duration, 17, 142
    effect of observer, 197
    effects, 14, 143, 145, 148, 180, 181,
    209, 242, 252
    measure, 179
    during parturition, 128, 131, 135–
    138, 141–142, 236
    protests of young, 180
    regions licked, 12, 14, 48, 182
Licking self by mother, 10–13, 46, 48,
    51, 54, 123, 126, 130, 134, 136–
    138, 141–142, 145, 161
  during parturition, 11–13, 46, 134
  hormonal control, 46
  order of licking, 10
  shift to newborn, 54
Lion, 122, 125, 127, 141, 143, 148, 153
Lip-smacking, 310, 312, 314, 318, 333
  by adult males to mother, 314
  by mother to infant, 310, 312, 318,
    333
Location of mothers and young, 192–
    193, 252, 283, 312, 321, 333

Males, response to infants, see Young's
    attractiveness
Manipulation of infants, (including
    nudging, stroking, touching),
    242, 245, 252, 263–264, 286,
    288–290, 313, 314

Nursing, 19, 20, 21–22, 28–43, 48, 61, 123, 135, 143, 146, 148, 150–152, 173, 175–179, 186–187, 189, 197, 201, 211, 214, 215, 236, 242–243, 248–249, 252, 258, 270, 297
  development, 21
  duration, 146, 177, 211, 215, 236, 297
  effect of Caesarian section, 48
  initiation by mother, 21, 148, 150, 151
  measures, 175
  see also Lactation, Suckling

Orangutan, 283
Overdependence, infantile, 273, 274
Overprotection, maternal, 273, 274
Ovulation, 95, 205

Parity, effect on maternal behavior, 52, 102–104, 114–115, 119, 141, 214, 226–227, 258, 267, 268, 269, 271–275, 281, 290, 299, 303
Parturition, 15–17, 19, 46, 48, 51, 54, 66, 124, 126–127, 128–129, 130–131, 134–138, 141–143, 161–165, 206, 208, 228, 234–236, 242, 252, 310, 312
  behavior preceding, 126–127, 162, 206, 234–236, 242, 252
  duration of labor, 128–129, 161, 310
  effect of parity, 141, 143
  gross body movements, 130, 131, 135–136, 141–142
  intervals: contraction, emergence, placental, delivery, 128, 130–131, 138, 163, 165
  order of events, 15, 128–129, 142
  patterning of activities, 128, 137, 141
  phases, 15–17, 19
  physiological changes, 46, 48, 51, 54
  response to fetus, 130–131, 134
  signs of, 15, 206
  variability, 66, 137, 141–142, 206, 208
  see also Afterbirth, Amnion, Birth fluids, Cord, Fetal membranes, Placenta

Peer group, 200, 255, 261, 292, 294–295, 299, 300, 302, 303, 304, 309, 316, 321, 330, 333
Peromyscus, 58–93
Pig, 176, 227
Placenta, 18, 67, 103, 124, 128, 130, 136, 140, 161, 208, 209, 310
  expulsion, 18, 136, 208
  ingestion, 18, 67, 103, 130, 136, 140, 161, 209, 310
Play of young, 152, 182–183, 186, 196–197, 199, 200–201, 238, 245, 248, 250, 252, 260, 285, 290, 292–295, 301–304, 316, 318, 320–321, 328–329, 333–334
  duration, 294–295, 301, 321
  in groups, 196, 201, 294–295, 303, 304, 316, 321, 328, 333–334
  with adult animals, 295, 302, 318, 329
  by mothers with young, 152, 182–183, 199, 201, 248
  with observer, 197, 285
  with self, 197, 292, 295
  types, 196, 238, 260, 294–295, 321, 328–329
Positive responses of mothers, 263–266
Postpartum resting period, 143–145
Posture of mothers, 148, 179, 194, 199, 211
  adjusting of posture for young, 148, 179, 199, 211
Posture signals between mother and young, 239, 245, 248, 249, 250, 252
Precocial young, 3, 123, 211
Pregnancy, see Gestation
Presenting, 262, 313–314
  "affectional present," 262
  to mothers, 313–314
Primiparous mothers, see Parity
Protection of young, see Defense of young
Punishing of young by mothers, 172–173, 187–189, 199, 201, 250, 258, 264–266, 279–280, 299, 321, 323, 333
  acts preceding, 187, 266
  inconsistency, 188

Suckling by young, 187, 211, 228, 238, 242, 243, 286–289, 292, 294, 304
  duration, 99, 172
  latency, 158, 160
  see also Nursing

Tail wagging in newborn sheep, 211
Temperature regulation in the newborn, 20, 62, 172, 209
Territoriality, 80, 244, 245
Threats, 235, 250, 257, 263, 266, 289, 294, 299, 304, 312, 314, 319 321, 329
Tiger, 122, 125, 146, 148
Tonic immobility, 220
Transport of young by mother, 73–74, 90, 146, 286
Tuition of young by mother, 86–88, 90, 147, 245
Twitching in pups, 190–192

Urinating and defecating in the young, 14, 180–181, 155, 242
  see also Licking by mother

Vicuña, 2
Viewing of infant by mother, 271–273, 318
Vision in young, 123, 174, 194
Vocalizations, 78–81, 90, 145–147, 151–152, 158, 179, 181, 195, 199, 209, 218, 237, 238–239, 245, 249, 252, 288, 289, 291, 292, 294, 295, 296, 300, 301, 312, 315, 321, 325, 326
  of mother in response to young's vocalizations, 78, 145, 179, 181, 199, 209, 300, 321
  sonographic analysis, 78–81

Vocalizations, spectrographic analysis, 291
  of young, 78–81, 90, 145–147, 151–152, 158, 179, 181, 195, 209, 218, 237, 238, 249, 252, 288, 289, 291, 292, 295, 296, 300, 301, 312, 315, 321, 325, 326
  to young by mother, 199, 238–239, 245, 252, 288, 294, 312

Weaning, 22, 46, 61, 83–85, 90, 153–154, 162, 219, 229, 240, 244, 249, 252, 296–299, 304, 324–326, 331, 334
  effect, on infant, 325
  of litter size, 154
  inconsistency in mothers, 297
  related to resumption of estrous cycle, 324
  tantrums of young, 297, 299
  variability in mothers, 297, 299, 304, 324
  weight loss as measure, 84–85
  see also Rejection, Separation

Young's attractiveness, 6, 52, 66, 143, 161, 210–211, 213, 237, 241–242, 288–289, 291–292, 301, 302–304, 310, 311, 313, 314, 315, 316, 320, 321, 322–323, 328, 329, 333
  to adult females, 52, 210–211, 213, 237, 288–289, 302–304, 313, 316, 320, 321, 323
  to adult males, 66, 241–242, 291, 292, 301, 303, 304, 314, 315, 322–323, 328, 329, 333
  to group, 6, 303, 313, 315, 333
  to juveniles, 301, 313, 320
  to mother, 6, 143, 161, 310, 311